Pure Mathematics for Advanced Level

Part A

Pure Mathematics for Advanced Level
is available either as a single volume or in two parts:

Part A: Chapters 1–15
Part B: Chapters 16–28
Complete Volume: Chapters 1–28

Pure Mathematics for Advanced Level

Part A

J. A. H. Shepperd
Department of Mathematics, University of Manchester
Institute of Science and Technology

C. J. Shepperd
Head of Mathematics, Hinchingbrooke School, Huntingdon

HODDER AND STOUGHTON
LONDON   SYDNEY   AUCKLAND   TORONTO

British Library Cataloguing in Publication Data

Shepperd, J. A. H.
   Pure mathematics for Advanced level.
   [Part A]
   1. Mathematics—1961–
   I. Title   II. Shepperd, C. J.
   510   QA39.2

   ISBN 0 340 32476 7

First printed 1983
Copyright © 1983

Typeset in Times New Roman (Monophoto) by Macmillan India Ltd., Bangalore

Printed in Great Britain for
Hodder and Stoughton Educational,
a division of Hodder and Stoughton Ltd.,
Mill Road, Dunton Green, Sevenoaks, Kent TN13 2YD,
by Clark Constable (1982) Ltd., Edinburgh

Contents

7   Polynomials   97

Definitions, algebra of polynomials, rational functions, division of a polynomial by a linear polynomial, factors of a polynomial, the sign of a polynomial function.

8   Composition of functions and applications to graphs   107

Composition of mappings, composition of real functions, translation of a graph, one-way stretches of a graph, reflections of a graph, composition of a function with a linear function, symmetries of a graph, inverse functions, conditions for an inverse function to exist.

9   Indices and logarithms   125

Powers of a number, rules of indices, extension to negative indices, extension to rational numbers, diversion, the power function 2^x and the logarithmic function $\log_2 x$, the logarithmic function $\log_a x$, rules for manipulating logarithms, change of base.

10   Linear laws   138

Linear relations (revision), mathematical models and linear laws, conversion of a law to a linear form, summary of substitutions.

11   Sketch graphs   148

Revision, the graph of a cubic function, useful ideas for graph sketching, the graph with equation $y = x^n$, $n \in \mathbb{N}$, the graph of $(x - h)^n$, scale change and the graph of $y = a(x - h)^n$, $n \in \mathbb{N}$, negative powers of x, rational powers of x.

12   Vectors II   160

Column vectors in the plane, linear combinations of vectors, Cartesian coordinates in three dimensions, the equation of a line in two dimensions, the vector equation of a line in three dimensions, scalar products, planes through the origin, the vector equation of a general plane, parametric equation of a plane, angles between lines and planes, distance of a point from a plane.

13   Inequalities   207

Ordering the real numbers, use of the modulus sign, solution of inequalities involving linear quotients, quadratic inequalities, inequalities using the modulus sign.

14   Numerical methods for solving equations   220

Graphical methods, decimal search, the midpoint method (interval bisection), linear interpolation the chord method, the use of tangents.

15 Complex numbers 232

Extensions of number systems, solution of polynomial equations, representation of complex numbers, polar coordinates, the triangle inequalities, complex conjugates, loci in the complex plane.

Answers to Part A 263

Index

Preface

The two volumes, *Pure Mathematics for Advanced Level*, *Part A* and *Part B*, provide the pure mathematics half of an Advanced level G.C.E. course in mathematics, in which the other half may be applied mathematics (either mechanics or statistics, or a mixture of these) or further pure mathematics. The material has been selected and organised to provide the necessary pure mathematics required in the applied mathematics. It includes all the 'common core' in mathematics which has been accepted by all the G.C.E. Boards. This core forms about 70 per cent of the material in the two volumes. We have attempted to plot a path midway between the extremes of the 'traditional' and 'modern' versions of sixth-form mathematics, which have existed for nearly twenty years. The books, therefore, match the new A-level mathematics syllabuses introduced by the University of London Board and the Joint Matriculation Board, which have removed the undesirable dichotomy between 'trad.' and 'mod.'. We have used the best of modern teaching ideas but have kept in mind the traditional skills. We believe that it is through the practice of mathematical skills that the desired understanding of fundamental concepts will be achieved.

The material is arranged for linear use by a student working alone, but a teacher will find it straightforward to vary the order of study. Many chapters begin with revision material and practice exercises. New work is illustrated by many worked examples and the exercises in the sections are carefully graded to lead the student towards an understanding in depth. It is intended that all these exercises should be completed. Miscellaneous exercises, at the end of the chapters, contain more practice material, which is not graded in difficulty and which may contain applications of work from any previous chapters. Many exercises are from the past papers of the Associated Examining Board (AEB), the University of Cambridge Local Examinations Syndicate (C), the Joint Matriculation Board (JMB), the University of London University Entrance and School Examinations Council (L), the Oxford and Cambridge Schools Examination Board School's Mathematics Project (SMP). We gratefully acknowledge these Board's permission to reproduce their questions. We give our own brief answers for which the Boards bear no responsibility.

The teacher, who is changing from a traditional mathematics course to one of the new courses, will find that all the new material required is contained in *Part A*. As a result, *Part B* contains mostly traditional material, although the approach may give it a new look. Calculus is introduced in *Part A* in a practical manner and then is dealt with more formally in *Part B*. Other topics, such as vectors, numerical solution of equations and complex numbers, are dealt with in depth in *Volume A*. Some of these topics have been introduced in two 'bites' in order to aid the digestion.

We express our grateful thanks to many who have helped us in this work, to a number of colleagues, and in particular to Miss Joyce Batty and to the editors. Above all, we give tribute to the forbearance of Jenny and Beryl without whose support this work would never have been completed.

C. J. Shepperd
J. A. H. Shepperd

Pure Mathematics for Advanced Level is available either as a single volume or in two parts.

Part A: Chapters 1–15
Part B: Chapters 16–28
Complete Volume: Chapters 1–28

Notation

$=$	is equal to
$\approx$	is approximately equal to
$\neq$	is not equal to
$<$	is less than
$\leqslant$	is less than or equal to
$>$	is greater than
$\geqslant$	is greater than or equal to
$\nless$	is not less than
$\ngtr$	is not greater than
$\sqrt{}$	the positive square root
$\Rightarrow$	implies that
$\Leftarrow$	is implied by
$\Leftrightarrow$	implies and is implied by
$\{a, b, c, \ldots\}$	the set with elements a, b, c, $\ldots$
$\in$	is an element of
$\notin$	is not an element of
$:$	such that
$\{x: a < x < b\}$	the set of x such that a is less than x and also x is less than b
$n(A)$	the number of elements in the set A
$\mathscr{E}$	the universal set
ϕ	the empty set, null set
S'	the complement of the set S
$\cup$	the union of
$\cap$	the intersection of
$\subseteq, \subset$	is a subset of, is a proper subset of, respectively
$\backslash$	the set difference, $A \backslash B = A \cap B'$
$\mathbb{N}$	the set of positive integers and zero $\{0, 1, 2, \ldots\}$
$\mathbb{Z}$	the set of integers $\{0, \pm 1, \pm 2, \ldots\}$
$\mathbb{Z}^+$	the set of positive integers
$\mathbb{Q}$	the set of rational numbers
$\mathbb{Q}^+$	the set of positive rational numbers
$\mathbb{R}$	the set of real numbers
$\mathbb{R}^+$	the set of positive real numbers
$\mathbb{C}$	the set of complex numbers
$f: A \rightarrow B$	the function f maps the set A into the set B
$f(x)$	the function value for x
$f: x \mapsto y$	f is the function under which x is mapped into y

f^{-1}	the inverse function of f

For functions f and g where domains and ranges are subsets of $\mathbb{R}$

$f+g$	is defined by $(f+g)(x) = f(x)+g(x)$
$f.g$	is defined by $(f.g)(x) = f(x)g(x)$
fg	is defined by $(fg)(x) = f(g(x))$
$\rightarrow$	approaches, tends to (in the context of a limit)
∞	infinity
$\mid\ \mid$	the unsigned part of a signed number, the modulus
$[x]$	the integer part of the number x
Σ	the sum of (precise limits may be given)
$n!$	n factorial
$\begin{pmatrix} n \\ r \end{pmatrix}$	the binomial coefficient $n(n-1)(n-2)\ldots(n-r+1)/r!$
δx	a small increment of x
$f', f'', f^{(3)}, \ldots f^{(n)}$	the first, second, third, ... nth derivatives, respectively, of f
$\dfrac{dy}{dx}$	the derivative of y with respect to x
$\int y\,dx$	the indefinite integral of y with respect to x
$\displaystyle\int_a^b y\,dx$	the definite integral of y with respect to x between the limits $x=a$ and $x=b$
$\ln x$	the natural logarithm of x
e^x	the exponential function of x
$\mid\mathbf{r}\mid, r$	the magnitude of the vector $\mathbf{r}$
$\mathbf{i}, \mathbf{j}, \mathbf{k}$	unit vectors in the mutually perpendicular directions Ox, Oy, Oz
$\mathbf{a}.\mathbf{b}$	the scalar product of the vectors $\mathbf{a}$ and $\mathbf{b}$
i	square root of -1
$\mid z \mid$	the modulus of the complex number z
$\arg z$	the argument of the complex number z
z^*	the conjugate of the complex number z
$\mathrm{Re}(z)$	the real part of the complex number z
$\mathrm{Im}(z)$	the imaginary part of the complex number z

1 The Algebra of Functions

1.1 Sets

In mathematics, we are concerned with collections of objects of various kinds, which form sets. In particular, we are concerned with sets of numbers, which are subsets of the set $\mathbb{R}$ of *real* numbers. We remind the reader of some definitions and state the set theory notation that we shall use.

Definitions and notation A *set* is a clearly defined collection of distinct objects, which are called the *members* or *elements* of the set. When x is a member of the set A, we write $x \in A$ meaning x belongs to A. If x is not a member of A, then we write $x \notin A$ meaning x does not belong to A. When we wish to list the members of a set, we write $A = \{a, b, c, d\}$ meaning that A is the set whose members are a, b, c and d; for example, $2 \in \{1, 2, 3\}$ and $3 \notin \{2, 4, 6\}$. These ideas may be shown in a *Venn diagram*, in which a set is indicated by a closed curve encircling all of its members. In Fig. 1.1, the elements a and d belong to both sets A and B, while b and c belong to A but not to B, and e and f belong to B and not to A.

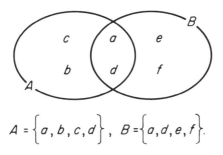

$$A = \{a, b, c, d\}, \quad B = \{a, d, e, f\}.$$

Fig. 1.1 Venn diagram of 2 sets.

Equality of sets

Two sets are *equal* when they consist of the same collection of elements, that is, when each member of one set belongs to the other set and conversely. Thus, $A = B$ means that $x \in A$ if and only if $x \in B$. When listing the members of a set, the order of the list is unimportant and so are any repetitions. For example,

$$\{1, 2, 3\} = \{2, 3, 1\} = \{3, 3, 1, 2, 1, 2\},$$

because each of these three sets contains just the three elements 1, 2 and 3, and hence they are equal sets.

Braces are also used when a set is described by means of some defining property. Thus

$$\{1, -1\} = \{x : x^2 = 1\},$$

where the colon means 'such that'. In this notation, the symbol x can be replaced by any other symbol, so

$$\{x : x^2 = 1\} = \{y : y^2 = 1\} = \{a : a^2 = 1\}.$$

Such a symbol is called a *dummy* variable.

Sets of numbers

We shall use the following notation for certain sets of numbers, which are all contained in the set $\mathbb{R}$ of real numbers.

$\mathbb{N}$ is the set of *natural* numbers, where $\mathbb{N} = \{0, 1, 2, 3, \ldots\}$;
$\mathbb{Z}$ is the set of *integers*, where

$$\mathbb{Z} = \{0, 1, -1, 2, -2, \ldots\} = \{\ldots, -2, -1, 0, 1, 2, \ldots\};$$

$\mathbb{Z}^+$ is the set of positive integers, where $\mathbb{Z}^+ = \{1, 2, 3, \ldots\}$;
$\mathbb{Q}$ is the set of *rational* numbers, where $\mathbb{Q} = \{p/q : q \neq 0 \text{ and } p, q \in \mathbb{Z}\}$;
$\mathbb{Q}^+$ is the set of positive rational numbers, where $\mathbb{Q}^+ = \{p/q : p, q \in \mathbb{Z}^+\}$;
$\mathbb{R}^+$ is the set of positive real numbers, where $\mathbb{R}^+ = \{x : x \in \mathbb{R} \text{ and } x > 0\}$.

Implications

When a statement Q can be deduced, by means of a mathematical argument, from another statement P, we say that Q is *implied* by P, or P implies Q, which is written $P \Rightarrow Q$. When both $P \Rightarrow Q$ and $Q \Rightarrow P$, then we say that P is *equivalent* to Q, or P if and only if Q, which is written $P \Leftrightarrow Q$. For example,

$$x \in \mathbb{N} \Rightarrow x \in \mathbb{Z}, \quad \text{and} \quad x^2 = 1 \Leftrightarrow x \in \{1, -1\}.$$

When Q cannot be deduced from P, then we say that P does not imply Q, which is written $P \nRightarrow Q$. Such a result would be proved by constructing a *counter-example*. For example, $x \in \mathbb{Z} \nRightarrow x \in \mathbb{N}$ because $-1 \in \mathbb{Z}$ but $-1 \notin \mathbb{N}$.

Subsets

We say that the set A is a *subset* of the set B when each element of A is also an element of B, and we use the notation $A \subseteq B$, meaning that

$$x \in A \Rightarrow x \in B.$$

From this definition, it will be seen that, for any set B, $B \subseteq B$, and we define a proper subset A of a set B to be a subset of B, not equal to B. We then use the notation $A \subset B$ meaning that

$$x \in A \Rightarrow x \in B \text{ and for some } b, b \notin A \text{ and } b \in B.$$

So $A \subset B$ means that $A \subseteq B$ and $A \neq B$.
A subset is indicated on a Venn diagram by marking part of that area which represents the whole set. An example is shown in Fig. 1.2(a).

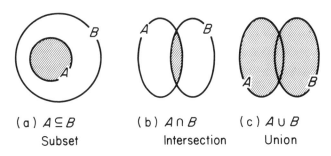

| (a) $A \subseteq B$ | (b) $A \cap B$ | (c) $A \cup B$ |
| Subset | Intersection | Union |

Fig. 1.2

Intersection

The *intersection* of two sets A and B is the set of all elements which belong to both the sets A and B, with the notation

$$A \cap B = \{x : x \in A \text{ and } x \in B\}.$$

Union

The *union* of two sets A and B is the set of all elements which belong to either the set A or to the set B or to both A and B, with the notation

$$A \cup B = \{x : x \in A \text{ or } x \in B\}.$$

Given two sets A and B, represented on a Venn diagram, their intersection, $A \cap B$, and their union, $A \cup B$, may be indicated by shading the appropriate area, as is shown in Fig. 1.2(b) and (c).

The universal set and the empty set

The set of all possible elements under consideration in a given piece of work is called the *universal* set and is denoted by $\mathscr{E}$. In many cases, we are concerned with the set of all real numbers and so $\mathscr{E} = \mathbb{R}$, but we might use $\mathscr{E} = \mathbb{Z}$ if, in some piece of work, we wished to restrict the argument to the integers.

On a Venn diagram, the universal set is usually represented by a large rectangle, inside which all the other sets occur. In Fig. 1.3(a), we show the universal set $\mathscr{E} = \mathbb{R}$, with subsets $\mathbb{Q}$ and $\mathbb{Z}$.

(a) Universal set $\mathbb{R}$ (b) Disjoint sets   (c) Complement A'
    $\mathbb{Z} \subseteq \mathbb{Q} \subseteq \mathbb{R}$ $A \cap B = \phi$ of A shaded.

Fig. 1.3

If two sets have no elements in common, then their intersection will be a set containing no elements. This set, with no members, is called the *empty set*, or the *null set*, and is denoted by the symbol ϕ.

Two sets A and B such that $A \cap B = \phi$ are called *disjoint* sets. For example, the set $A = \{2n : n \in \mathbb{Z}\}$ of even integers and the set $B = \{2n + 1 : n \in \mathbb{Z}\}$ of odd integers are disjoint, since no integer is both even and odd, hence $A \cap B = \phi$. Disjoint sets are shown in a Venn diagram in Fig. 1.3(b).

The *complement* of a set A is the set of all elements in the universal set $\mathscr{E}$ which are not members of A. The complement of A is denoted by A'. Thus

$$A' = \{x : x \in \mathscr{E} \text{ and } x \notin A\}.$$

It follows that $\phi = A \cap A'$ and $\mathscr{E} = A \cup A'$. See Fig. 1.3(c).

Note: For every set A, $\phi \subseteq A$ and $A \subseteq \mathscr{E}$. Such a pair of subset relations can be written together as $\phi \subseteq A \subseteq \mathscr{E}$.

Set difference

It is useful to have a notation for the set of elements which belong to one set A and do not belong to another set B, and we shall call this the *difference* of the sets A and B with the notation $A \backslash B$. This means that

$$A \backslash B = \{x : x \in A \text{ and } x \notin B\} = A \cap B'.$$

For example, $\mathbb{R} \backslash \mathbb{Q}$ is the set of *irrational* real numbers.
With this notation, there is no need for the set B to be a subset of A; for example,

$$\{1, 2, 3, 4, 5\} \backslash \{4, 5, 6, 7, 8\} = \{1, 2, 3\}$$

and $\mathbb{Q} \backslash \mathbb{R} = \phi.$

EXAMPLE

Given two sets A and B, prove that

(i) $A \cap B \subseteq A \subseteq A \cup B$,
(ii) if $A \cup B \subseteq A \cap B$ then $A = B$,
(iii) $A \cap B = A \Leftrightarrow A \subseteq B$.

(i) Let $x \in A \cap B$, then $x \in A$ and $x \in B$ so $x \in A$. Hence $A \cap B \subseteq A$. Let $y \in A$, then $y \in A$ or $y \in B$ and so $y \in A \cup B$. Hence $A \subseteq A \cup B$.
(ii) If $A \cup B \subseteq A \cap B$, let $x \in A$, then $x \in A \cup B$ by (i), so $x \in A \cap B$ and thus $x \in B$. Hence $A \subseteq B$. Similarly, if $y \in B$ then $y \in A$. Therefore $A = B$.
(iii) First suppose that $A \cap B = A$. If $x \in A$, then $x \in A \cap B$ and so $x \in B$. Hence $A \subseteq B$. Conversely, suppose that $A \subseteq B$. Then, if $x \in A$, $x \in B$ so $x \in A \cap B$ and thus $A \subseteq A \cap B$. Also, by (i), $A \cap B \subseteq A$, and, therefore, $A = A \cap B$.

EXERCISE 1.1A

1   Given the sets $A = \{a, b, c, d\}$, $B = \{a, c, e, f\}$, $C = \{b, e, d\}$, list the elements of the sets: (i) $A \cup B$, (ii) $A \cap B$, (iii) $A \cap (B \cap C)$, (iv) $(A \cap B) \cap C$, (v) $A \cap (B \cup C)$, (vi) $(A \cap B) \cup C$, (vii) $A \backslash B$, (viii) $A \backslash C$, (ix) $(A \backslash B) \cup (A \backslash C)$, (x) $(A \backslash B) \cap (A \backslash C)$.
2   Using the sets given in question 1, describe all the subsets of $A \cup C$, which contain three elements, by listing their elements.
3   State whether the following statements are true, false, or invalid:
(i) $0 \in \mathbb{Z}$, (ii) $\{0, 1\} \subseteq \mathbb{Z}$, (iii) $0 \subseteq \mathbb{Z}$, (iv) $\phi \in \mathbb{Z}$, (v) $0 \in \phi$, (vi) $\phi \subseteq \mathbb{Z}$, (vii) $\mathbb{N} \subseteq \mathbb{Z}$, (viii) $\mathbb{Z} \subset \mathbb{N}$, (ix) $\mathbb{Z} \subset \mathbb{Q}$, (x) $1 \notin \mathbb{N}$.
4   List the members of the following subsets of the set $\mathbb{Z}$ of integers:
(i) $\{x : x^2 = 4\}$, (ii) $\{x : x^2 = -1\}$, (iii) $\{x : x^3 = -1\}$, (iv) $\mathbb{N} \cap \{x : x \leqslant 5\}$, (v) $\mathbb{Z} \cap \{x : 10 < x^2 < 50\}$.
5   List all the subsets of the set: (i) $\{1, 2\}$, (ii) $\{a, b, c, d\}$.
6   Given that the universal set is $\mathbb{R}$, $A = \{2n : n \in \mathbb{N}\}$, $B = \{x : x < 3\}$, and $C = \{x : x \in \mathbb{Z}, \ 2 \leqslant x\}$, describe the set: (i) $A \cap B$, (ii) $A \cap C$, (iii) B', (iv) $B \cap C'$, (v) $A \cap B \cap C$, (vi) $A \cap (B \backslash C)$, (vii) $(A \cap B) \backslash C$, (viii) $B \cup C \cup A$.
7   Prove that $A \cap (B \cup C) = (A \cap B) \cup (A \cap C)$, for any sets A, B and C.
Check your answers to these exercises (page 267). If you require more practice, work through the Exercise 1.1B below.

EXERCISE 1.1B

1   The set A is the set of all positive real numbers less than 1.5. Mark the following true, false or invalid:
(i) $1 \in A$, (ii) $1 \subseteq A$, (iii) $\frac{1}{2} \in A$, (iv) $0 \notin A$, (v) $\phi \in A$, (vi) $\{\frac{1}{2}, \frac{3}{8}, \frac{7}{8}\} \subset A$, (vii) $3/2 \in A$, (viii) $2 \in A$.
2   B is the set of plane quadrilaterals. State whether it is true or false that $x \in B$ when: (i) x is a square, (ii) x is a triangle, (iii) x is a trapezium, (iv) x is a hexagon, (v) x is a circle, (vi) x is a parallelogram, (vii) x is a rhombus, (viii) x is a pentagon, (ix) x is a rectangle.
3   Describe the following sets in the form $(x : P(x)\}$, where $P(x)$ is a defining statement:
(i) $\{1, 3, 5, 7\}$, (ii) $\{1, 8, 27, 64\}$, (iii) $\{-2, 0, 2\}$.
4   List the subset of $\mathbb{Z}$ of integers whose squares are less than 30.
5   State if each of the following statements is true or false for x, y, $z \in \mathbb{Z}$. If it is false, determine the largest subset of $\mathbb{Z}$ for which the statement is true:
(i) $x + y = y + x$, (ii) $(x + y) + z = x + (y + z)$, (iii) $x - y = y - x$, (iv) $(xy)/y = x$, (v) $y = 1/x \Rightarrow x = 1/y$, (vi) $(x + y)^2 = x^2 + y^2$,

(vii) $x^2 - y^2 = (x - y)(x + y)$, (viii) $x(yz) = (xy)z$, (ix) $x^2 x^3 = x^5$,
(x) $x^2 = y \Rightarrow y^2 = x$, (xi) $(x - 2)(x + 1) = 0$, (xii) $2(x - 1) = 2x - 2$,
(xiii) $x - 1 = 1 - x$, (xiv) $2x^2 - 5x + 2 = 0$, (xv) $2x \leqslant x + 1$.

6   Does every set contain at least two distinct subsets? If so, prove it. If not, list all the sets which contain less than two distinct subsets.

7   Given that $X = \{a, b, c, d\}$, find all possible sets Y and Z such that
(i) $\{a\} \subseteq Y \subseteq X$, (ii) $\{a, b\} \subseteq Z \subseteq X$.

8   Given real numbers a and b, with $a < b$, define the interval (a, b) by $(a, b) = \{x : a < x < b\}$. State whether the following statements are true or false: (i) $(1, 2) \subseteq (0, 3)$, (ii) $(2, 5) \subseteq (3, 8)$, (iii) $(2, 5) \subset (1, 10)$,
(iv) $(-1, 1) \subseteq (-1, 1)$, (v) $6 \in (5, 7)$, (vi) $(1, 2) \cap (2, 3) = \phi$,
(vii) $(1, 3) \cap (2, 4) = (2, 3)$, (viii) $(1, 3) \backslash (2, 4) = (2, 3)$,
(ix) $((2, 4) \cap (3, 5)) \cup (1, 3) = (2, 4) \cap ((3, 5) \cup (1, 3))$.
Find three intervals, which are all different, and call them A, B, C, such that $(A \cap B) \cup C = A \cap (B \cup C)$.

9   Determine, for each of the statements P, Q, S, T, whether it implies, is implied by, or is equivalent to, the statement 'R: one member of the set A is also a member of the set B':
(i) $P : A \subseteq B$, (ii) $Q : A = B$, (iii) $S : A \cap B \neq \phi$, (iv) $T : A \cup B \neq \phi$.

10   Given that $A \subseteq B, B \subseteq C, C \subseteq A$, prove that $A = B = C$. Hence, prove that if E is the set of even positive integers, S is the set of sums of two odd positive integers and Q is the set of positive integers whose squares are even, then $E = S = Q$.

1.2 Functions

A *function* is a mapping from one set A to another set B; that is, given any member a of the set A, the function determines one and only one member b of the set B. Functions may be defined in which the sets A and B are of any types, but we shall be concerned with sets of numbers.

Definitions and notation
f: $A \rightarrow B$ means that f is a function mapping the set A to the set B;
f: $a \mapsto f(a)$ means that, for $a \in A$, the function f assigns just one $f(a)$ in B;
the set A is called the *domain* of the function f;
the set B is called the *codomain* of the function f;
$f(a)$ is called the *image* of a under the function f, or
$f(a)$ is called the *value* of the function f at the point a of its domain A.

    The function is only defined when we know (i) the domain A of f, and (ii) the value f (a) of f for every point a in A. For example, if $A = B = \mathbb{Z}$ and the function f maps x to $2x$, then f: $\mathbb{Z} \rightarrow \mathbb{Z}$, f is defined by $f(x) = 2x$ for all $x \in \mathbb{Z}$. Thus $f(0) = 0$, $f(1) = 2$, $f(-3) = -6$, and so on.

    The function g: $\mathbb{N} \rightarrow \mathbb{N}$, defined by $g(x) = 2x$ for all $x \in \mathbb{N}$, takes the same values as does f for all points of $\mathbb{N}$. However, the functions f and g are not the same function since they have different domains.

Real functions

A *real function* is a function whose domain is a subset of the set $\mathbb{R}$ of real numbers and whose codomain is $\mathbb{R}$, so that the values of the function are also real numbers. When the domain of a real function is not stated, and the value of the function is given by some formula or formulae, then the domain of the function is assumed to be the *largest* subset of $\mathbb{R}$ for which the value of the function is defined. For example:

the function f with $f(x) = 1/x$ has domain $\mathbb{R}\backslash\{0\}$;

the function g with $g(x) = \sqrt{x}$ (the non-negative square root of x) has domain $\{x : x \in \mathbb{R}, 0 \leqslant x\}$, the set of non-negative real numbers.

The range of a function

Consider a real function $f : A \to \mathbb{R}$, with domain $A \subseteq \mathbb{R}$. For any subset C of A, the set of all the images of all the points in C is called the *image* of C under f and is denoted by

$$f(C) = \{f(x) : x \in C\}.$$

The image under f of the domain A of f is called the *range* of f, and so the range of f is

$$f(A) = \{f(x) : x \in A\},$$

a subset of $\mathbb{R}$, (Fig. 1.4).

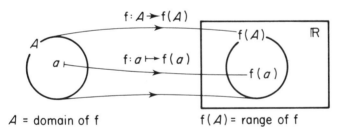

$$f : A \to f(A)$$
$$f : a \mapsto f(a)$$

A = domain of f $f(A)$ = range of f

Fig. 1.4

EXAMPLE 1
Find the domain and range of the function f given by
(i) $f(x) = 1/(1-x)$, (ii) $f(x) = \sqrt{(1-x^2)}$.

(i) $f(x)$ is defined for all real values of x except $x = 1$, so the domain of f is the set $\mathbb{R}\backslash\{1\}$. Putting $y = f(x) = 1/(1-x)$, we find $y - yx = 1$ and so $x = (y-1)/y$. All possible values of y can occur except 0, so the range of the function f is $\mathbb{R}\backslash\{0\}$.
(ii) $f(x)$ is defined for non-negative values of $1-x^2$ so the domain of f is $\{x : -1 \leqslant x \leqslant 1\}$. Clearly, the range of f is $\{x : 0 \leqslant x \leqslant 1\}$.

EXAMPLE 2
Determine whether the given equation defines a function f such that $y = f(x)$ and, if so, state the domain and range of f: (i) $2y + 1 = x$, (ii) $x^2 - 2y^2 = 4x$.

(i) The equation is equivalent to $y = \frac{1}{2}(x-1)$ and so this defines the function f with $f(x) = \frac{1}{2}(x-1)$; the domain and range of f are both $\mathbb{R}$.

(ii) The equation may be rewritten $y^2 = \frac{1}{2}(x^2 - 4x)$ and this does not define $y = f(x)$ uniquely, since if $x = 8$, y can be either 4 or -4. Therefore, the equation **does not define a function**.

The Cartesian graph of a function

The function f with domain A is completely defined by the set of ordered pairs $\{(x, f(x)) \colon x \in A\}$. For a real function f, these pairs may be plotted in the x–y plane by putting $y = f(x)$, and this gives the Cartesian graph of the function f. For example, we illustrate, in Fig. 1.5, the Cartesian graphs of the functions f, g, h, with a common domain $\mathbb{R}$, which are given by $f(x) = 4$, $g(x) = 3 - \frac{3}{2}x$, $h(x) = \frac{1}{2}x^2 - 4$.

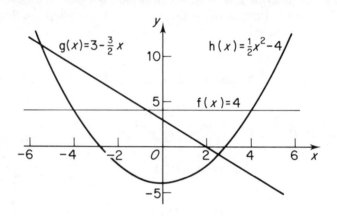

Fig. 1.5

Sums and products of functions

We often form new functions from given functions by using the usual processes of arithmetic on the values of the functions, which may be added, multiplied, and so on. As an example, consider the four functions:

f, with domain $\mathbb{R}$, given by $f(x) = 1 + x$;
g, with domain $\mathbb{R}$, given by $g(x) = x^3$;
h, with domain A, given by $h(x) = \sqrt{x}$, where $A = \{x \colon 0 \leqslant x\}$;
k, with domain B, given by $k(x) = 1/(x-1)$, where $B = \mathbb{R}\setminus\{1\}$.

For any $x \in \mathbb{R}$,

$$f(x) + g(x) = 1 + x + x^3$$

and this may be considered to be the value of a new function $(f+g)$, with the same domain $\mathbb{R}$, that is,

$$(f+g)(x) = 1 + x + x^3.$$

We may also form a new function as a sum of constant multiples of f and g, for example,

$$2f(x) - g(x) = 2 + 2x - x^3 = F(x),$$

where $F = 2f - g$ defines the new function F with domain $\mathbb{R}$.

If we form a similar combination of functions which have different domains, then the new function will have a domain which is the intersection of the domains of the original functions, since this is where it will be defined.

Thus,

$$3h(x) - 2k(x) = 3\sqrt{x} - \frac{2}{x-1} = G(x),$$

where $G = 3h - 2k$ with domain $A \cap B$.

We may also multiply functions by multiplying their values at common points of their domains, for example,

$$f(x) . k(x) = (1 + x)/(x - 1) = H(x),$$

and $H = f.k$ with domain $\mathbb{R} \cap B(= B)$. The quotient of two functions may also be formed provided that we also exclude from the new domain all points where the denominator vanishes, for example,

$$\frac{f(x)}{h(x)} = \frac{1 + x}{\sqrt{x}} = K(x),$$

where $K = f/h$, with domain $(\mathbb{R} \cap A) \setminus \{0\}$, that is, $\mathbb{R}^+$.

Arithmetic of functions

We use the above ideas to define arithmetical operations on real functions and, provided that we are careful to note the correct domains of the functions, all the usual rules of arithmetic will be satisfied.

Definitions Let f and g be real functions with domains A and B respectively, let $C = \{x : g(x) = 0\}$ be the set of zeros of the function g, and let a and b be real numbers. Then we define the function:

$h = f + g$	by $h(x) = f(x) + g(x)$	with domain $A \cap B$;
$h = f - g$	by $h(x) = f(x) - g(x)$	with domain $A \cap B$;
$h = af$	by $h(x) = af(x)$	with domain A;
$h = af + bg$	by $h(x) = af(x) + bg(x)$	with domain $A \cap B$;
$h = f.g$	by $h(x) = f(x).g(x)$	with domain $A \cap B$;
$h = f/g$	by $h(x) = f(x)/g(x)$	with domain $A \cap B \setminus C$.

Note that the set $A \cap B \setminus C$ is unambiguous without the insertion of brackets because

$$A \cap (B \setminus C) = (A \cap B) \setminus C = A \cap B \cap C'.$$

EXAMPLE 3

Let f and g be the real functions defined by $f(x) = 2x$ *and* $g(x) = \sqrt{x}$. *Find the domain and the range of each of f and g.*

In each of the following cases, write down $h(x)$ *and the domain and range of h:*
(*i*) $h = f + 3g$, (*ii*) $h = f \cdot g$, (*iii*) $h = g \cdot g$, (*iv*) $h = f/g$.

The domain of f is $\mathbb{R}$ and its range is also $\mathbb{R}$. The domain of g is $\mathbb{R}_0^+$, where $\mathbb{R}_0^+ = \{x : x \geq 0\}$, and its range is also $\mathbb{R}_0^+$.
(i) $h(x) = f(x) + 3g(x) = \mathbf{2x + 3\sqrt{x}}$. The domain of h is $\mathbb{R} \cap \mathbb{R}_0^+$, which is $\mathbb{R}_0^+$. For $x \in A$, $f(x) \geq 0$ and $g(x) \geq 0$, so $h(x) \geq 0$, and the range of h is $\mathbb{R}_0^+$.
(ii) $h(x) = f(x) \cdot g(x) = \mathbf{2x\sqrt{x}}$. Again the domain and the range of h is $\mathbb{R}_0^+$.
(iii) $h(x) = g(x) \cdot g(x) = \sqrt{x}\sqrt{x} = \mathbf{x}$. Thus h is the identity function on the domain $\mathbb{R}_0^+ \cap \mathbb{R}_0^+$, which is $\mathbb{R}_0^+$. The range of h is also $\mathbb{R}_0^+$.
(iv) $h(x) = f(x)/g(x) = 2x/\sqrt{x} = \mathbf{2\sqrt{x}}$. The domain of h is $\mathbb{R} \cap (\mathbb{R}_0^+ \setminus \{0\})$, which is $\mathbb{R}^+$, and the range of h is also $\mathbb{R}^+$.

EXERCISE 1.2

1 The domain of the function f is $\{1, 2, 3, 4\}$. Find the range of f if:
   (i) $f(x) = 2x$, (ii) $f(x) = 5 - x$, (iii) $f(x) = x^2 - 4$, (iv) $f(x) = \sqrt{x}$.
2 State what is wrong with the following statements;
   (i) $f(x) = x^2 - 1$, f has domain $\mathbb{Z}$ and range $\mathbb{N}$;
   (ii) the function f has domain $\{1, 2, 3, 4\}$ and range $\{5, 6, 7, 8, 9\}$;
   (iii) the function f has domain $\mathbb{N}$ and $f(x)$ is the solution of the equation $f(x)^2 = x$;
   (iv) the function f has domain $\mathbb{Z}$ and $f(x) = \sqrt{(x^2 - 1)}$.
3 Determine whether the given equation defines a real function f such that $f(x) = y$ and, if it does, state the domain and range of f:
   (i) $y = 3x$, (ii) $3y + 4x = 5$, (iii) $2y = x^2$, (iv) $y^2 = 4x$, (v) $y^3 = 4x$,
   (vi) $x^2 + y^2 = 9$, (vii) $x^2 + y^2 = 0$, (viii) $\sqrt{y} = x$.
4 State the domain and the range of the real function f given by:
   (i) $f(x) = 5x$, (ii) $f(x) = x^2$, (iii) $f(x) = 2x - 1$, (iv) $f(x) = \sqrt{x}$,
   (v) $f(x) = 2x^2 - 1$, (vi) $f(x) = 1/(x - 2)$, (vii) $f(x) = \log_{10} x$,
   (viii) $f(x) = 2^x$, (ix) $f(x) = \sqrt{(x^2 - 4)}$, (x) $f(x) = \sqrt{(9 - x^2)}$.
5 Given the functions f and g, where $f(x) = x^2$ and $g(x) = \sqrt{(-x)}$, find $h(x)$ and the domain and the range of the function h, if:
   (i) $h = f$, (ii) $h = g$, (iii) $h = 2f + g$, (iv) $h = 3f \cdot g$,
   (v) $h = g \cdot g$, (vi) $h = f/g$, (vii) $h = g/f$.
6 How many different functions can be defined:
   (i) with domain $\{a, b\}$ and range $\{x, y\}$,
   (ii) with domain $\{a, b, c\}$ and range $\{x, y\}$,
   (iii) with domain $\{a, b\}$ and range $\{x, y, z\}$?
7 Which of the Cartesian graphs in Fig. 1.6 represent a function?
8 The *identity function* f is defined by $f(x) = x$, with domain $\mathbb{R}$. The *modulus function* g is defined by $g(x) = |x| = x$ if $x \geq 0$, $|x| = -x$ if $x < 0$, with domain $\mathbb{R}$. The *integer-part function* h is defined by $h(x) = [x] = $ the largest integer which is less than or equal to x, with domain $\mathbb{R}$. Find the ranges of the following functions and sketch their Cartesian graphs:
   (i) g, (ii) h, (iii) $f + g$, (iv) $f - g$, (v) $f \cdot g$, (vi) f/g, (vii) $f - h$.

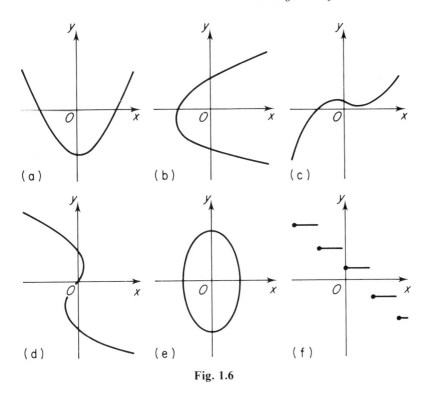

Fig. 1.6

1.3 Linear functions (revision)

We summarise some results concerning linear functions and their graphs.

The constant function

The constant function f has domain $\mathbb{R}$ and, for some fixed $c \in \mathbb{R}$, $f(x) = c$. The graph of the constant function is a line parallel to the axis Ox (Fig. 1.7(a)).

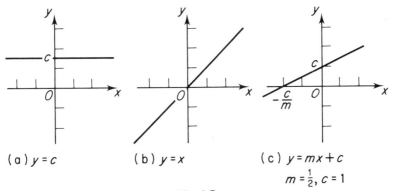

(a) $y = c$ (b) $y = x$ (c) $y = mx + c$
$m = \frac{1}{2}, c = 1$

Fig. 1.7

The identity function

The identity function f has domain $\mathbb{R}$ and $f(x) = x$. Its graph is the line $y = x$, through the origin O, with gradient 1, that is, $\tan 45°$ (Fig. 1.7(b)).

The general linear function

The linear function f has domain $\mathbb{R}$ and, for some fixed $m, c \in \mathbb{R}$,

$$f(x) = mx + c.$$

The graph of f is the straight line through $(0, c)$ with gradient m. If $m = \tan \theta$, the line makes an angle θ with the positive x-axis, provided that the scales on the two axes are the same. If $m \neq 0$, the graph meets the x-axis at the point $(-c/m, 0)$, (Fig. 1.7(c)). The constant function and the identity function are special cases of a linear function.

The equation of the graph of the linear function f is

$$y = f(x) = mx + c.$$

The general linear equation in one variable x is of the form $mx + c = 0$, with $m, c \in \mathbb{R}$. This equation has a unique solution $x = -c/m$ if $m \neq 0$, and has no solution if $m = 0$. This corresponds to the fact that the graph of the function f meets the x-axis at $(-c/m, 0)$ if $m \neq 0$, and is parallel to the x-axis if $m = 0$.

The straight line with gradient m, passing through the point (a, b), has equation $y - b = m(x - a)$ and is the graph of the function f, with domain $\mathbb{R}$, given by $f(x) = m(x - a) + b$. This is, of course, the same as the function f with $f(x) = mx + c$, where $c = b - ma$.

EXERCISE 1.3

1 Write down the form of $f(x)$ for the linear function f whose graph passes through the origin and has gradient: (i) 3, (ii) $-\frac{1}{2}$, (iii) m.

2 Find the form of $f(x)$ and hence write down the gradient of the graph of f, when the equation of this graph is: (i) $3y = x$, (ii) $3x + 5y = 0$, (iii) $\frac{1}{2}x = \frac{3}{4}y$, (iv) $3x - 2y = 0$,   (v) $ax = by$,   (vi) $2x + 3y = 4$,   (vii) $5x = y - 3$, (viii) $3y + 5 = 0$,   (ix) $ax + by + c = 0$.

3 For what point in their common domain $\mathbb{R}$ do the functions f and g have the same value, where $f(x) = 3x - 2$ and $g(x) = 6 - x$? Interpret this result in terms of the graphs of the functions f and g.

4 Given that $3x + 4y = 5$, find functions f and g such that $y = f(x)$ and $x = g(y)$. By interchanging x and y in this last equation, write down the linear expression $g(x)$, which defines the function g. Draw the graphs of $y = f(x)$ and $y = g(x)$ and show that they are reflections of one another in the line $y = x$.

5 The function f is linear and $f(1) = 2$, $f(-1) = 4$. Find the gradient of the graph of f and hence find $f(x)$. Solve the equation $f(x) = 0$. Show that the points $(1, 2)$, $(-1, 4)$, $(2, 1)$ are collinear.

6 Plot the points $A(2, 3)$, $B(4, 0)$ and $C(-4, -1)$, on a graph. Find the three linear functions whose graphs form the three sides of the triangle ABC.

Measure the angle BAC and calculate the product of the gradients of AB and AC. State what you expect to be the product of the gradients of any two perpendicular lines.

7 The graphs of the linear functions f and g are respectively the lines having equations $2x + 3y = 4$ and $y = 2x + 8$. Find the coordinates of the point P where these two lines intersect. Show that the graph of the function h, where $h = 2f - g$, is also a straight line through P.

8 Given linear functions f and g and real numbers a and b, with $a + b = 1$, prove that h, where $h = af + bg$, is also a linear function and that the graphs of f, g and h either meet at a point or are parallel.

2 Quadratic Equations and Quadratic Functions

2.1 Algebraic manipulation

Before proceeding further in the study of algebra, the reader is recommended to perform a self-test on some of the following exercises on algebraic manipulation. If it is found that practice is necessary, then all the exercises should be completed. First, we work through some examples.

EXAMPLE 1   *Simplify* (i) $(a+b)(a^2-ab+b^2)$, (ii) $\dfrac{x}{y}+\dfrac{y}{x}-\dfrac{(x+y)^2}{xy}$.

(i) $(a+b)(a^2-ab+b^2) = a^3 - a^2b + ab^2 + a^2b - ab^2 + b^3 = \boldsymbol{a^3 + b^3}$.

(ii) $\dfrac{x}{y}+\dfrac{y}{x}-\dfrac{(x+y)^2}{xy} = \dfrac{x^2}{xy}+\dfrac{y^2}{xy}-\dfrac{x^2+2xy+y^2}{xy} = \dfrac{x^2+y^2-x^2-2xy-y^2}{xy}$

$$= \dfrac{-2xy}{xy} = \boldsymbol{-2}.$$

EXAMPLE 2   *Factorise* (i) a^2-b^2, (ii) $\dfrac{x}{y^2}+\dfrac{y}{x^2}$.

(i) $a^2-b^2 = \boldsymbol{(a+b)(a-b)}$.

(ii) $\dfrac{x}{y^2}+\dfrac{y}{x^2} = \dfrac{x^3+y^3}{x^2y^2} = \dfrac{1}{x^2}\dfrac{1}{y^2}\boldsymbol{(x+y)(x^2-xy+y^2)}$.   (cf. Example 1).

EXAMPLE 3   *Simplify:* (i) $\sqrt{(12)} \times \sqrt{2}$, (ii) $\sqrt{3}(2-\sqrt{2})+\sqrt{2}(3-\sqrt{3})$,
(iii) $\dfrac{\sqrt{3}}{1+\sqrt{2}}$, (iv) $(\sqrt{2}+\sqrt{3})(2\sqrt{3}-\sqrt{2})$, (v) $\dfrac{\sqrt{3}+\sqrt{5}}{\sqrt{6}-\sqrt{5}}$.

(i) $\sqrt{(12)} \times \sqrt{2} = 2\sqrt{3} \times \sqrt{2} = \boldsymbol{2\sqrt{6}}$.

(ii) $\sqrt{3}(2-\sqrt{2})+\sqrt{2}(3-\sqrt{3}) = 2\sqrt{3}-\sqrt{6}+3\sqrt{2}-\sqrt{6}$
$$= \boldsymbol{2\sqrt{3}+3\sqrt{2}-2\sqrt{6}}.$$

(iii) $\dfrac{\sqrt{3}}{1+\sqrt{2}} = \dfrac{\sqrt{3}(1-\sqrt{2})}{(1+\sqrt{2})(1-\sqrt{2})} = \dfrac{\sqrt{3}-\sqrt{6}}{1-2} = \boldsymbol{\sqrt{6}-\sqrt{3}}$.

(iv) $(\sqrt{2}+\sqrt{3})(2\sqrt{3}-\sqrt{2}) = 2\sqrt{6}-2+6-\sqrt{6} = \boldsymbol{4+\sqrt{6}}$.

(v) $\dfrac{\sqrt{3}+\sqrt{5}}{\sqrt{6}-\sqrt{5}} = \dfrac{(\sqrt{3}+\sqrt{5})(\sqrt{6}+\sqrt{5})}{(\sqrt{6}-\sqrt{5})(\sqrt{6}+\sqrt{5})} = \dfrac{\sqrt{3}\sqrt{2}\sqrt{3}+\sqrt{3}\sqrt{5}+\sqrt{5}\sqrt{6}+5}{6-5}$

$$= 3\sqrt{2}+\sqrt{(15)}+\sqrt{(30)}+5.$$

Note some useful factorisations:
$$p^2 - q^2 = (p-q)(p+q),$$
$$p^3 - q^3 = (p-q)(p^2+pq+q^2),$$
$$p^3 + q^3 = (p+q)(p^2-pq+q^2).$$

EXERCISE 2.1

1 In the following expressions, remove the brackets and collect together like terms:

(i) $x - (2x - y)$
(ii) $x^2 - x(x - 2)$
(iii) $3(a - 2b) - 2(a - 3b)$
(iv) $2(x + y) - y(3 - x)$
(v) $x(x - 2) + 2(x + 2)$
(vi) $5(x^2 - 4) + 3(2x + 7)$
(vii) $(a + 2b)(3a - 6b)$
(viii) $(x - 2)(x + 3) - x(x + 1)$
(ix) $2(a + 2b - 3c) + 3(c - 2a + 3b)$
(x) $(r + s - t)(r - s + t)$
(xi) $(a + b)(a - b) - (a - b)^2$
(xii) $(x + y)^3$
(xiii) $(2x - 3)^3$
(xiv) $(a - b)(a^2 + ab + b^2)$
(xv) $(x - 2y + 3z)^2$
(xvi) $(x - 1)^2(x + 1)^2$
(xvii) $(x^2 + 1)(x^4 - x^2 + 1)$
(xviii) $(a - b)(b - c)(c + a)$.

2 Simplify the following expressions:

(i) $\dfrac{1}{x} + \dfrac{1}{y} - \dfrac{1}{xy}$
(ii) $\dfrac{a}{b} - \dfrac{b}{a}$
(iii) $\dfrac{2x - 3}{4} - \dfrac{2(x - 3)}{3}$

(iv) $\dfrac{2}{x} - \dfrac{3}{x} + \dfrac{4}{x}$
(v) $\dfrac{1}{2x} - \dfrac{1}{3x} + \dfrac{1}{4x}$
(vi) $\dfrac{2y}{x} - \dfrac{y}{2x}$

(vii) $\dfrac{2x}{y} - \dfrac{3y}{x}$
(viii) $\dfrac{3}{xy^2} - \dfrac{2}{x^2 y}$
(ix) $\dfrac{x + 1}{x - 1} - \dfrac{x - 1}{x + 1}$

(x) $x + \dfrac{x^2 + xy}{x - y}$
(xi) $\dfrac{x}{x + y} + \dfrac{y}{x - y} + \dfrac{1}{x}$
(xii) $\dfrac{3xy}{x^2 - y^2} - \dfrac{y}{x + y}$.

3 Factorise the following expressions:

(i) $2a + 2b$
(ii) $x^2 + 3x$
(iii) $x^3 - x^2$
(iv) $ab + bc$
(v) $a^2 - b^2$
(vi) $x^2 - 4y^2$
(vii) $36t^2 - 4$
(viii) $a^2 b - bc^2$
(ix) $2x^2 + 3x - 2$
(x) $2t^2 + 7t - 30$
(xi) $(x + y)^2 - z^2$
(xii) $2x^3 + 2x^2 - x - 1$
(xiii) $a^3 - b^3$
(xiv) $8x^3 - 27y^3$
(xv) $r^3 - s^3 t^3$
(xvi) $2x^3 + 2y^3$
(xvii) $a^4 - b^4$
(xviii) $y^6 - 1$.

4 Simplify the following expressions:

(i) $\dfrac{1}{a + b} - \dfrac{1}{a - b}$
(ii) $\dfrac{2a - 2b}{a^3 - b^3}$

(iii) $\dfrac{x^2 - x - 6}{9 - x^2}$
(iv) $\dfrac{1}{x + y} - \dfrac{x}{x^2 - y^2}$

(v) $\dfrac{p^2-q^2}{p^2+pq} \times \dfrac{pq}{p-q}$　　　　　(vi) $\dfrac{4}{x-2}+\dfrac{2x}{2-x}$

(vii) $\dfrac{2x+1}{12}-\dfrac{3x+2}{18}$　　　　　(viii) $\dfrac{2}{x^2-2x+1}+\dfrac{3}{x^2-3x+2}$

(ix) $\dfrac{3}{2a+4}+\dfrac{a-1}{a^2-4}$　　　　　(x) $\dfrac{2a}{a+b}+\dfrac{2b}{a-b}+\dfrac{a^2+b^2}{b^2-a^2}$

(xi) $\dfrac{1}{1-x}-\dfrac{1}{1+x}+\dfrac{2x}{1+x^2}$　　　　　(xii) $\dfrac{x+y}{y}-\dfrac{2x}{x+y}+\dfrac{x^2y-x^3}{y(x^2-y^2)}.$

5　Simplify the following:

(i) $2\sqrt{3}+3\sqrt{3}-4\sqrt{3}$　　　　　(ii) $\sqrt{(12)}-\sqrt{3}+4$

(iii) $\sqrt{2}(3-2\sqrt{2})+2(3-\sqrt{2})$　　　　　(iv) $3\sqrt{2}+\sqrt{6}-\sqrt{(18)}$

(v) $2\sqrt{(18)}+\sqrt{(50)}-2\sqrt{2}$　　　　　(vi) $\sqrt{3}(\sqrt{2}+\sqrt{6})-\sqrt{6}(\sqrt{2}+\sqrt{3})$

(vii) $(\sqrt{2})^3$　　　　　(viii) $3\sqrt{5}+\sqrt{5}(\sqrt{(10)}-\sqrt{2})$

(ix) $3\sqrt{2}\times 2\sqrt{3}$　　　　　(x) $\sqrt{(18)}\div\sqrt{2}$

(xi) $2\sqrt{2}\times 3\sqrt{2}$　　　　　(xii) $\sqrt{5}\div\sqrt{(20)}$

(xiii) $(1+\sqrt{2})^2$　　　　　(xiv) $(\sqrt{2}-\sqrt{3})^2$

(xv) $(3\sqrt{2}+\sqrt{3})(2\sqrt{3}-\sqrt{2})$　　　　　(xvi) $(\sqrt{2}+\sqrt{3})(\sqrt{2}-\sqrt{3})$

(xvii) $(\sqrt{a}+\sqrt{b})(\sqrt{a}-\sqrt{b})$　　　　　(xviii) $(2+\sqrt{3})^3.$

6　Express in a form with a rational denominator:

(i) $\dfrac{1}{\sqrt{3}}$　　　(ii) $\dfrac{2}{\sqrt{5}}$　　　(iii) $\dfrac{\sqrt{3}}{\sqrt{2}}$　　　(iv) $\dfrac{1}{3\sqrt{2}}$

(v) $\dfrac{1}{\sqrt{2}-1}$　　　(vi) $\dfrac{1}{\sqrt{5}+\sqrt{2}}$　　　(vii) $\dfrac{\sqrt{2}}{\sqrt{3}+1}$　　　(viii) $\dfrac{2}{5+\sqrt{2}}$

(ix) $\dfrac{\sqrt{2}-1}{\sqrt{2}+1}$　　　(x) $\dfrac{\sqrt{2}-1}{\sqrt{6}}$　　　(xi) $\dfrac{(1+\sqrt{2})^2}{\sqrt{2}-1}$　　　(xii) $\dfrac{\sqrt{5}-2\sqrt{3}}{\sqrt{6}-\sqrt{5}}.$

7　Given that $x=1+\sqrt{2}$ and $y=2-\sqrt{3}$, express in a form that has a rational denominator:

(i) x^2　　　　　(ii) xy　　　　　(iii) x/y

(iv) $x+\dfrac{1}{y}$　　　　　(v) $\dfrac{x-1}{y+1}$　　　　　(vi) $\dfrac{1}{x}+\dfrac{1}{y}$

(vii) $\dfrac{x}{y}-\dfrac{y}{x}$　　　　　(viii) $\dfrac{xy}{x+y}$　　　　　(ix) $\dfrac{x^2+y^2}{xy}.$

2.2 Solution of quadratic equations (revision)

For a real function f, a real number α such that $f(\alpha)=0$ is called a solution of the equation $f(x)=0$ or, alternatively, a *zero* of the function f. Thus the solution of the equation $f(x) = 0$ is the set $\{\alpha \in \mathbb{R}: f(\alpha) = 0\}$, called the *solution set* of the equation $f(x) = 0$, and also called the set of zeros of the function f.

In the case of a quadratic equation $ax^2 + bx + c = 0$, the solution may be obtained by *factorisation* or by *completing the square*.

EXAMPLE 1   *Solve the equation* $x^2 + 5x + 6 = 0$.

$$x^2 + 5x + 6 = 0 \Leftrightarrow (x+2)(x+3) = 0 \qquad \text{(factorise by inspection)}$$
$$\Leftrightarrow x + 2 = 0 \text{ or } x + 3 = 0 \; (uv = 0 \Leftrightarrow u = 0 \text{ or } v = 0)$$
$$\Leftrightarrow x = -2 \text{ or } x = -3,$$

so the solution set of the equation is $\{-2, -3\}$.

EXAMPLE 2   *Solve the equation* $2x^2 + 5x - 12 = 0$.

Method I (by factorisation)

$$2x^2 + 5x - 12 = (2x - 3)(x + 4) \text{ and so}$$
$$2x^2 + 5x - 12 = 0 \Leftrightarrow 2x - 3 = 0 \quad \text{or} \quad x + 4 = 0$$
$$\Leftrightarrow x = \tfrac{3}{2} \quad \text{or} \quad x = -4$$
$$\Leftrightarrow x \in \{\tfrac{3}{2}, -4\}.$$

Method II (by completing the square) We use the identity

$$(x + k)^2 = x^2 + 2kx + k^2$$

so that we may make the expression into a square by adding k^2. The first step is to obtain a coefficient of x^2 equal to 1, thus

$$2x^2 + 5x - 12 = 2(x^2 + \tfrac{5}{2}x) - 12 \quad (\text{so } k = \tfrac{5}{4})$$
$$= 2(x^2 + 2\tfrac{5}{4}x + (\tfrac{5}{4})^2) - 12 - 2(\tfrac{5}{4})^2$$
$$= 2(x + \tfrac{5}{4})^2 - \tfrac{121}{8}$$
$$= 2[(x + \tfrac{5}{4})^2 - \tfrac{121}{16}].$$

Hence $\qquad 2x^2 + 5x - 12 = 0 \Leftrightarrow (x + \tfrac{5}{4})^2 = \tfrac{121}{16}$
$$\Leftrightarrow x + \tfrac{5}{4} = \tfrac{11}{4} \quad \text{or} \quad x + \tfrac{5}{4} = -\tfrac{11}{4}$$
$$\Leftrightarrow x = \tfrac{6}{4} = \tfrac{3}{2} \quad \text{or} \quad x = -\tfrac{16}{4} = -4.$$
$$\Leftrightarrow x \in \{\tfrac{3}{2}, -4\}.$$

EXERCISE 2.2

1   Determine whether or not the given number is a solution of the given equation, by means of substitution in the equation:

(i) $\alpha = -3$, $x^2 - 2x - 15 = 0$
(ii) $\alpha = \sqrt{2}$, $x^2 + 2 = 0$
(iii) $\alpha = -\sqrt{5}$, $x^2 = 4x + 1$
(iv) $\alpha = 1 + \sqrt{2}$, $x^2 + 4x + 3 = 0$
(v) $\alpha = 2 + \sqrt{5}$, $x^2 = 4x + 1$
(vi) $\alpha = \sqrt{3} - 1$, $2x^2 + 4x = 4$.

2   Solve the following equations, by inspection:
  (i) $(x-1)(x+2) = 0$ (ii) $(y+4)(y+5) = 0$ (iii) $(2x-1)(x+3) = 0$
  (iv) $x(3x+2) = 0$ (v) $(t-4)^2 = 0$ (vi) $(3x-5)^2 = 0$
  (vii) $(2x-3)(3x+2) = 0$ (viii) $(x-a)(x-b) = 0$ (ix) $(x-1)^2 = 4$
  (x) $(2x-1)^2 = 25$ (xi) $(5-3x)^2 = 36$ (xii) $(ax-b)^2 = c^2$.

3   Solve the following equations, by factorisation:
  (i) $x^2 - 2x - 15 = 0$ (ii) $x^2 - x - 12 = 0$ (iii) $x^2 + 3x - 54 = 0$
  (iv) $x^2 + 13x + 42 = 0$ (v) $x^2 + 11x - 312 = 0$ (vi) $3x^2 - 4x + 1 = 0$
  (vii) $2x^2 - 5x - 12 = 0$ (viii) $5x^2 - 18x - 8 = 0$ (ix) $8x^2 + 24x + 10 = 0$
  (x) $28x^2 - 2x - 6 = 0$ (xi) $9x^2 - 27x + 20 = 0$ (xii) $x^2 - 33x + 272 = 0$
  (xiii) $12x^2 - 58x - 10 = 0$ (xiv) $6x^2 + 7x = 3$ (xv) $2x^2 = 3x + 14$
  (xvi) $x^2 + 4 = 4x$ (xvii) $(x-3)(x+2) = (x+2)(x-1)$
  (xviii) $(2x-1)(x-2) = 5$ (xix) $(2-x)(1-2x) = 5$ (xx) $x^2 - 1 = (x-1)^2$.

4   Complete the following:
  (i) $x^2 + 4x + \ldots = (x + \ldots)^2$ (ii) $x^2 - 10x + \ldots = (x - \ldots)^2$
  (iii) $s^2 - 3s + \ldots = (s - \ldots)^2$ (iv) $x^2 + 2ax + \ldots = (x + \ldots)^2$
  (v) $x^2 + x + \ldots = (x + \ldots)^2$ (vi) $x^2 + 4xy + \ldots = (x + \ldots)^2$.

5   What must be added to complete the square?
  (i) $x^2 + 12x$ (ii) $x^2 - 6x$ (iii) $t^2 + 2at$
  (iv) $y^2 - 3y$ (v) $z^2 + 4z$ (vi) $4x^2 + 4x$
  (vii) $2x^2 - 2x$ (viii) $3x^2 + 5x$ (ix) $ax^2 + bx$.

6   Solve the following equations, by completing the square:
  (i) $x^2 - 4x + 1 = 0$ (ii) $x^2 - 2x - 4 = 0$ (iii) $x^2 - 6x + 7 = 0$
  (iv) $x^2 - 3x + 1 = 0$ (v) $4x^2 - 12x + 7 = 0$ (vi) $9x^2 - 6x - 4 = 0$
  (vii) $x^2 - 2ax + b = 0$ (viii) $a^2x^2 - 2ax - 2 = 0$ (ix) $ax^2 + bx + c = 0$.

2.3 The graph of a quadratic function

The graph of the function f, given by $f(x) = x^2 - 3x$, may be drawn by plotting points (x, y) and joining them by a smooth curve, using a table of calculated values:

$$x: \quad -1 \quad 0 \quad 1 \quad 2 \quad 3 \quad 4$$
$$y: \quad 4 \quad 0 \quad -2 \quad -2 \quad 0 \quad 4$$

This graph is shown in Fig. 2.1(a). The graph of any quadratic function is called a *parabola*. On completing the square for the function f,

$$f(x) = x^2 - 3x = x^2 - 2.\tfrac{3}{2}x + \tfrac{9}{4} - \tfrac{9}{4} = (x - \tfrac{3}{2})^2 - \tfrac{9}{4}.$$

Since, for all x, $(x - \tfrac{3}{2})^2 \geqslant 0$, $f(x) \geqslant -\tfrac{9}{4}$ and the least value of $f(x)$ is $-\tfrac{9}{4} = f(\tfrac{3}{2})$. Also

$$f(\tfrac{3}{2} + d) = d^2 - \tfrac{9}{4} = f(\tfrac{3}{2} - d),$$

for any d, and the function takes equal values at points equidistant on either side of the line $x = \tfrac{3}{2}$. Therefore the graph is *symmetrical* about the line $x = \tfrac{3}{2}$, reflection in this line being a symmetry of the graph.

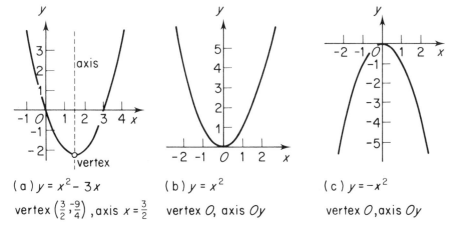

(a) $y = x^2 - 3x$

vertex $\left(\frac{3}{2}, \frac{-9}{4}\right)$, axis $x = \frac{3}{2}$

(b) $y = x^2$

vertex O, axis Oy

(c) $y = -x^2$

vertex O, axis Oy

Fig. 2.1 Parabolas.

The line of symmetry, $x = \frac{3}{2}$, is called the *axis* of the parabola. The lowest point $(\frac{3}{2}, -\frac{9}{4})$ is called the *vertex* of the parabola. For large values of x, both positive and negative, $f(x)$ becomes large and positive. We can express this fact, which tells us something about the shape of the graph at large distances from the origin, by saying that:

as x tends to positive infinity, $f(x)$ tends to positive infinity;

as x tends to negative infinity, $f(x)$ tends to positive infinity.

For these statements, we use the notation:

$$\text{as } x \to +\infty, \text{ } f(x) \to +\infty; \quad \text{as } x \to -\infty, \text{ } f(x) \to +\infty.$$

It must be understood that, in these statements, there is no suggestion that there is such a number as infinity; there is not. All that is implied is that $f(x)$ behaves in a certain way for large values of x.

The process of completing the square standardises a quadratic. From the standard form, the vertex and the axis of the parabola which is the graph of the function, may be found. Another approach is to start with a standard form. The parabola with equation $y = ax^2$ is symmetrical about the line $x = 0$, so the y-axis is the axis of this parabola, which touches the x-axis at the origin, O. If $a > 0$, O is the lowest point on the graph, so the origin is the vertex of this parabola, the parabola is $\cup$ shaped, with its vertex downwards. For $a < 0$, the vertex O is the highest point of the graph, which is $\cap$ shaped, with its vertex upwards (see Fig. 2.1(b), (c)).

If we translate the plane so that the origin moves to the point (p, q), the parabola $y = ax^2$ will be translated to become the curve with equation $y - q = a(x - p)^2$, since we have to replace x by $x - p$ and y by $y - q$. This new parabola has a vertex at (p, q) and has axis $x = p$, and its equation is

$$y = a(x - p)^2 + q = ax^2 - 2apx + ap^2 + q.$$

Sketching the graph of a quadratic function

The graph of the function f, where $f(x) = ax^2 + bx + c$, is a parabola with equation $y = f(x)$. In order to sketch this parabola, we may note a number of key facts:

the graph crosses the y-axis at $(0, c)$;

if $f(x)$ can be factorised and its zeros found, the graph crosses the x-axis at points where x takes the values of these zeros (the *roots* of $f(x) = 0$);

by completion of the square for $f(x)$, the vertex and axis of the parabola may be found;

the parabola is ∪ shaped, with vertex downwards, if $a > 0$;

the parabola is ∩ shaped, with vertex upwards, if $a < 0$.

EXAMPLE   *Sketch the parabola with equation:*
(*i*) $y = x^2 + 2x - 3$; (*ii*) $y = -2x^2 + 3x + 4$.

(i) $x^2 + 2x - 3 = (x + 1)^2 - 4 = (x + 3)(x - 1)$, and so the parabola has vertex at the point $(-1, -4)$ and axis given by $x = -1$. It crosses the y-axis at $(0, -3)$ and the x-axis at $(-3, 0)$ and $(1, 0)$. The coefficient of x^2 is positive so y tends to positive infinity as x tends to positive infinity and to negative infinity. Thus the graph is ∪ shaped, with its vertex downwards. From this information, the graph is drawn in Fig. 2.2(a).

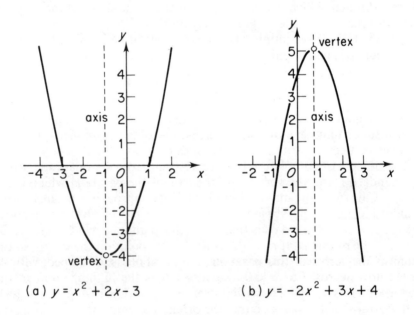

(a) $y = x^2 + 2x - 3$ (b) $y = -2x^2 + 3x + 4$

Fig. 2.2

(ii) Again we use the process of completing the square in order to change the equation into standard form and then to factorise it.

$$-2x^2 + 3x + 4 = -2\left(x^2 - \frac{3}{2}x\right) + 4 = -2\left\{x^2 - 2\left(\frac{3}{4}\right)x + \left(\frac{3}{4}\right)^2\right\} + 2\left(\frac{3}{4}\right)^2 + 4$$

$$= -2\left(x - \frac{3}{4}\right)^2 + \frac{41}{8} = -2\left\{\left(x - \frac{3}{4}\right)^2 - \frac{41}{16}\right\}$$

$$= -2\left(x - \frac{3}{4} - \frac{\sqrt{(41)}}{4}\right)\left(x - \frac{3}{4} + \frac{\sqrt{(41)}}{4}\right),$$

on factorising the difference of two squares. Thus the parabola has axis $x = \frac{3}{4}$, vertex $(\frac{3}{4}, \frac{41}{8})$ and meets the axes at $(0, 4)$, $(\{3 + \sqrt{(41)}\}/4, 0)$ and $(\{3 - \sqrt{(41)}\}/4, 0)$. Since the coefficient of x^2 is negative, the vertex is upwards, and the graph is shown in Fig. 2.2(b).

EXERCISE 2.3

1 Find the vertex and the axis of the parabola with the given equation and sketch the parabola: (i) $y = (x + 1)^2$, (ii) $y = (x - 1)^2 - 4$, (iii) $y = x^2 + x - 2$, (iv) $y = -2x^2 + 3x + 14$, (v) $y = 2x - 3x^2$, (vi) $y = (2 - x)(1 + 2x)$.
2 Write down the equation of a parabola: (i) with vertex $(2, 3)$ and passing through $(0, 7)$, (ii) with axis $x = -3$ and passing through $(-1, 0)$ and $(0, -5)$. In each case, state whether the parabola has its vertex upwards or downwards.

2.4 A formula for the solution of a quadratic equation

The process of completing the square, used in §2.2 and §2.3, can be applied to the general quadratic function f, where $f(x) = ax^2 + bx + c$, with $a \neq 0$.

$$f(x) = ax^2 + bx + c = a\left(x^2 + \frac{b}{a}x\right) + c$$

$$= a\left\{x^2 + 2\frac{b}{2a}x + \left(\frac{b}{2a}\right)^2\right\} - a\left(\frac{b}{2a}\right)^2 + c$$

$$= a\left(x + \frac{b}{2a}\right)^2 - \frac{b^2 - 4ac}{4a} = a\left(x + \frac{b}{2a}\right)^2 - \frac{\Delta}{4a},$$

where $\Delta = b^2 - 4ac$. The number Δ is called the *discriminant* of the quadratic function f. This leads to a formula for the solution of a quadratic equation.

$$ax^2 + bx + c = 0 \Leftrightarrow \left(x + \frac{b}{2a}\right)^2 = \frac{\Delta}{4a^2}$$

$$\Leftrightarrow x + \frac{b}{2a} = \pm\frac{\sqrt{\Delta}}{2a}$$

on taking square roots. Therefore, given the equation $ax^2 + bx + c = 0$,
if $\Delta < 0$, there are no solutions,
if $\Delta = 0$, there is just one solution, $x = -b/2a$,
if $\Delta > 0$, there are two solutions, $x = (-b + \sqrt{\Delta})/2a$ and
$x = (-b - \sqrt{\Delta})/2a$.

EXAMPLE   *Solve the equations (i) $3x^2 + 7x + 3 = 0$; (ii) $3x^2 + 7x + 5 = 0$.*

(i) Let $f(x) = 3x^2 + 7x + 3$,   then $\Delta = 7^2 - 4 \times 3 \times 3 = 13 > 0$,   so   there
are two solutions to the equation $f(x) = 0$, namely $x = (-7 + \sqrt{13})/6$ and
$x = (-7 - \sqrt{13})/6$.
(ii) Let $f(x) = 3x^2 + 7x + 5$, then $\Delta = 7^2 - 4 \times 3 \times 5 = -11 < 0$, so the equation
$f(x) = 0$ has no solutions; its solution set is the empty set ϕ.

EXERCISE 2.4

1   Use the formula method to solve the equation:

(i) $x^2 - 2x - 15 = 0$	(ii) $x^2 - x - 12 = 0$
(iii) $x^2 + 3x - 54 = 0$	(iv) $x^2 + 13x + 42 = 0$
(v) $x^2 + 11x - 312 = 0$	(vi) $3x^2 - 4x + 1 = 0$
(vii) $2x^2 - 5x - 12 = 0$	(viii) $5x^2 - 18x - 8 = 0$
(ix) $8x^2 + 24x + 10 = 0$	(x) $28x^2 - 2x - 6 = 0$
(xi) $9x^2 - 27x + 20 = 0$	(xii) $x^2 - 33x + 272 = 0$
(xiii) $12x^2 - 58x - 10 = 0$	(xiv) $6x^2 + 7x = 3$
(xv) $2x^2 = 3x + 14$	(xvi) $x^2 + 4 = 4x$
(xvii) $(x - 3)(x + 2) = (x + 2)(x - 1)$	(xviii) $(2x - 1)(x - 2) = 5$
(xix) $(2 - x)(1 - 2x) = 5$	(xx) $x^2 - 1 = (x - 1)^2$.

Check your answers by comparison with your answers to question **3** of
Exercise 2.2.

2.5 The discriminant and the location of the graph

The sign of the discriminant, $\Delta = b^2 - 4ac$, provides information about
the graph of the quadratic function f, where $f(x) = ax^2 + bx + c$.
If $\Delta < 0$, $f(x) = 0$ has no solutions, so the graph does not meet the x-axis;
if $\Delta > 0$, $f(x) = 0$ has two solutions, so the graph crosses the x-axis at
2 points;
if $\Delta = 0$, $f(x) = 0$ has one solution, so the graph touches the x-axis at
1 point.
For each of these three cases, the constant a, which is the coefficient of x^2,
may be positive or negative, corresponding to the graph having vertex
downwards or upwards. This gives a total of six possible cases, which are
illustrated in Fig. 2.3.

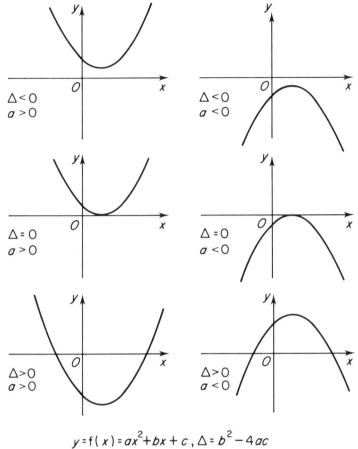

$$y = f(x) = ax^2 + bx + c, \Delta = b^2 - 4ac$$

Fig. 2.3

Range of the quadratic function

For the quadratic function f, given by $f(x) = ax^2 + bx + c$, the sign of a determines whether the vertex $(-b/2a, -\Delta/4a)$ is a minimum or a maximum point on the graph of f and so we see that

if $a > 0$, the range of f is $\{x : x \geqslant -\Delta/4a\}$,
if $a < 0$, the range of f is $\{x : x \leqslant -\Delta/4a\}$.

EXAMPLE *Find the range and the set of zeros of the function f given by:*
(i) $f(x) = x^2 - 4x + 3$,   (ii) $f(x) = -x^2 + 2x - 2$,   (iii) $f(x) = x^2 - 4x + 5$,
(iv) $f(x) = -x^2 + 2x - 2$.

(i) $f(x) = x^2 - 4x + 3 = (x-2)^2 - 1 = (x-3)(x-1), \Delta = 4, a = 1$, so the range of f is $\{x : x \geqslant -1\}$ and the set of zeros of f is $\{1, 3\}$.
(ii) $f(x) = x^2 - 4x + 4 = (x-2)^2$, $\Delta = 0, a = 1$, so the range of f is $\{x : x \geqslant 0\}$ and the set of zeros of f is $\{2\}$.

(iii) $f(x) = x^2 - 4x + 5 = (x-2)^2 + 1, \Delta = -4, a = 1$, so the range of f is $\{x : x \geq 1\}$ and the set of zeros of f is ϕ.
(iv) $f(x) = -x^2 + 2x - 2 = -(x-1)^2 - 1, \Delta = -4, a = -1$, so the range of f is $\{x : x \leq -1\}$ and the set of zeros of f is ϕ.

EXERCISE 2.5

1   Write down the value of the discriminant Δ of the function f and state the number of zeros of f, when: (i) $f(x) = x^2 + 4x + 4$,   (ii) $f(x) = 2x^2 + 1$, (iii) $f(x) = 9x^2 - 6x + 1$,   (iv) $f(x) = -2x^2 + 5x - 3$.

2   State the number of solutions, in the set of real numbers, of the equation:
(i) $x^2 + 3x - 2 = 0$,   (ii) $x^2 - 9 = 0$,   (iii) $x^2 + 4x + 8 = 0$,
(iv) $2x^2 = 4x - 2$,   (v) $a^2 x^2 - 3ax + 2 = 0, 0 \neq a \in \mathbb{R}$,
(vi) $x^2 - 4ax + 4a^2 = 0, a \in \mathbb{R}$.

3   By completing the square, or otherwise, find the range of the real function f given by $f(x) = x^2 - 6x + 12$. Sketch the graph of f.

4   For the quadratic function f as given, find the range of f and state at how many points the graph of f meets the x-axis:
(i) $f(x) = x^2 - 4x + 12$ (ii) $f(x) = 3x^2 - 7x + 2$ (iii) $f(x) = 2 - 3x + 4x^2$
(iv) $f(x) = 1 - 4x - 2x^2$ (v) $f(x) = (x-2)(3-x)$
(vi) $f(x) = (x-2)(3-x) - 1$.

5   For the curve given by the following equation, state in how many points the curve meets the y-axis and in how many points it meets the x-axis, and find the set of values of y for which there are points on the curve:
(i) $y = \frac{1}{2}x^2 + 5x + 6$ (ii) $y = 4x^2 - 30x + 25$ (iii) $y = 5 - 8x - 3x^2$
(iv) $y = 10x - x^2 - 25$ (v) $y = (x-2)(x-4)$ (vi) $y = (x-3)(5-x)$.

6   Find $f(x)$ for the quadratic function f, whose graph:
(i) passes through the points $(0, 2)$, $(4, 0)$, $(5, 0)$,
(ii) passes through the points $(0, -7)$, $(-2, 0)$, $(3, 0)$,
(iii) has vertex $(2, -1)$ and passes through $(0, 3)$,
(iv) has axis $x = 1$ and passes through $(0, 2)$, $(3, -7)$.

7   The expression $ax^2 + bx + c$ takes the value 2 when $x = -2$ and when $x = 4$, and its minimum value is -7. Find the values of x for which the value of the expression is 9.   (L)

8   Express $3x^2 - 12x + 14$ in the form $a(x-p)^2 + q$. Show how the graph of $y = 3x^2 - 12x + 14$ may be obtained from the graph of $y = x^2$ by appropriate translations and stretches.

9   Prove that, for all real values of x, the expression $-x^2 + 4x - 5$ is negative.   (L)

10   Given that $f(x) \equiv 3x^2 + 2x - 8$, find $f(0)$, the values of x for which $f(x) = 0$, and the set of values of x for which $f(x) > 0$.   (L)

2.6 Symmetric properties of the roots of a quadratic equation

Let α and β be the solutions of the quadratic equation $ax^2 + bx + c = 0$; α and β are also called the *roots* of the equation. Then

$$\alpha + \beta = -b/a \quad \text{and} \quad \alpha\beta = c/a.$$

This follows from §2.4, since

$$\alpha + \beta = (-b + \sqrt{\Delta} - b - \sqrt{\Delta})/2a = -b/a,$$
$$\alpha\beta = (b^2 - \Delta)/4a^2 = (b^2 - b^2 + 4ac)/4a^2 = c/a.$$

Alternatively, the same result may be obtained by factorisation,

$$ax^2 + bx + c = a(x - \alpha)(x - \beta) = a(x^2 - (\alpha + \beta)x + \alpha\beta).$$

The results are still true when $\alpha = \beta$ and $\Delta = 0$.

Summary: If the quadratic equation $ax^2 + bx + c = 0$ has one or two real roots, (i.e. $\Delta \geqslant 0$) then the *sum* of the roots is $-b/a$ and the *product* of the roots is c/a. Conversely, we may write down a quadratic equation whose roots have sum s and product p, namely $x^2 - sx + p = 0$.

Using these results, it is possible to find a quadratic equation whose roots are symmetric functions of the roots of a given quadratic equation, without actually solving this equation. This is illustrated by some examples.

EXAMPLE   *Show that the quadratic equation $2x^2 + 5x + 1 = 0$ has two roots. If these roots are α and β, find quadratic equations with roots:*

(i) α^2 *and* β^2, (ii) $\dfrac{1}{\alpha}$ *and* $\dfrac{1}{\beta}$, (iii) α^3 *and* β^3.

The discriminant $\Delta = 25 - 8 = 17 > 0$, so the equation has two distinct real roots, α and β and $\alpha + \beta = -\frac{5}{2}$, $\alpha\beta = \frac{1}{2}$. We use these results to calculate the sum and the product of the roots of the new equation.

(i) $\alpha^2 + \beta^2 = \alpha^2 + 2\alpha\beta + \beta^2 - 2\alpha\beta = (\alpha + \beta)^2 - 2\alpha\beta = 25/4 - 1 = 21/4,$
$\alpha^2\beta^2 = (\alpha\beta)^2 = \frac{1}{4}$, so the required equation is $x^2 - 21x/4 + \frac{1}{4} = 0$ or
$4x^2 - 21x + 1 = 0$.

(ii) $\dfrac{1}{\alpha} + \dfrac{1}{\beta} = \dfrac{\alpha + \beta}{\alpha\beta} = -5$ and $\dfrac{1}{\alpha}\dfrac{1}{\beta} = \dfrac{1}{\alpha\beta} = 2$, so the required equation is

$x^2 + 5x + 2 = 0$. Alternatively, replace x by $\dfrac{1}{x}$ in the original equation.

(iii) $\qquad \alpha^3 + \beta^3 \doteq (\alpha + \beta)(\alpha^2 - \alpha\beta + \beta^2) = (\alpha + \beta)(\alpha^2 + 2\alpha\beta + \beta^2 - 3\alpha\beta)$

$$= (\alpha + \beta)\{(\alpha + \beta)^2 - 3\alpha\beta\} = -\tfrac{5}{2}(\tfrac{25}{4} - \tfrac{3}{2}) = -\tfrac{95}{8},$$

and $\alpha^3\beta^3 = (\alpha\beta)^3 = \frac{1}{8}$. Thus, the equation is $8x^2 + 95x + 1 = 0$.

EXERCISE 2.6

1   Without finding the roots, show that the following equations have two real roots and write down their sum and their product:

(i) $x^2 + 3x - 5 = 0$, (ii) $3x^2 - 2x - 2 = 0$, (iii) $4x^2 + 10x + 3 = 0$,

(iv) $x^2 + 4dx - d^2 = 0, d \in \mathbb{R}$, (v) $x + \dfrac{1}{x} = 4$, (vi) $2r^2 - 3r - 4 = 0$.

2 For equations (i), (iii) and (v) in question **1**, if the roots are α and β, write down the values of (a) $3(\alpha+\beta)$, (b) $(\alpha+\beta)^2$, (c) $(\alpha-\beta)^2$, (d) $\alpha^2\beta^2$, (e) $\dfrac{1}{\alpha}+\dfrac{1}{\beta}$,
(f) $2\alpha^2+2\beta^2+5\alpha\beta$, (g) $(\alpha+\beta)^3$, (h) $3\alpha\beta(\alpha+\beta)$, (i) $\alpha^3+\beta^3$.

3 Using the above results, in each of the 3 cases, write down a quadratic equation whose roots are: α^2, β^2; $\dfrac{1}{\alpha},\dfrac{1}{\beta}$; $2\alpha+\beta, \alpha+2\beta; \alpha-\beta, \beta-\alpha; \alpha+\dfrac{1}{\beta}, \beta+\dfrac{1}{\alpha}$; α^3, β^3.

4 The function

$$f(x) = x^2 + px + 1,$$

where p is a constant, is zero when $x = \alpha$ and $x = \beta$; and the function

$$g(x) = x^2 - 9x + q,$$

where q is a constant, is zero when $x = \alpha + 2\beta$ and $x = \beta + 2\alpha$. Find p and q, and show that $f(3) = g(3)$. (*JMB*)

5 The equation $ax^2 + bx + c = 0$ has roots α, β. Express $(\alpha+1)(\beta+1)$ in terms of a, b and c. (*L*)

MISCELLANEOUS EXERCISE 2

1 Given that the roots of the equation $ax^2 + bx + c = 0$ are β and $n\beta$, show that $(n+1)^2 ac = nb^2$. (*L*)

2 Given that α and β are the roots of the equation $x^2 - px + q = 0$ obtain the quadratic equation whose roots are $1/\alpha^2$ and $1/\beta^2$. (*JMB*)

3 The equations $ax^2 + bx + c = 0$ and $bx^2 + ax + c = 0$, where $a \neq b$, $c \neq 0$, have a common root. Prove that $a + b + c = 0$. (*L*)

4 Given that b and c are non-zero constants and that the equations $x^2 + bx + c = 0$ and $7x^2 + 2bx - 3c = 0$ have a common root, prove that $b^2 = 4c$. (*L*)

5 If a, b, c are constants and $a < 0$, derive the condition under which $ax^2 + bx + c$ will be negative for all real values of x. Given that

$$f(x) = px^2 - 2x + 3p + 2,$$

(a) find the two values of p for which the equation $f(x) = 0$ has equal roots,
(b) find the set of values of p for which $f(x)$ is negative for all real values of x.
Sketch the graph of $y = f(x)$ for each of the cases $p = -2, p = 1$. (*L*)

6 If the two roots of the quadratic equation

$$ax^2 + 2bx + c = 0$$

differ by 4, show that $8a = -c \pm \sqrt{(c^2 + 16b^2)}$. Find the two values of a for which the equation $ax^2 + 2x + 3 = 0$ has roots differing by 4. (*L*)

7 The real roots of the equation $x^2 + 6x + c = 0$ differ by $2n$, where n is real and non-zero. Show that $n^2 = 9 - c$. Given that the roots also have opposite signs, find the set of possible values of n. (*JMB*)

8 The roots of the equation $9x^2 + 6x + 1 = 4kx$, where k is a real constant, are denoted by α and β.
(a) Show that the equation whose roots are $1/\alpha$ and $1/\beta$ is

$$x^2 + 6x + 9 = 4kx.$$

(b) Find the set of values of k for which α and β are real.

(c) Find also the set of values of k for which α and β are real and positive. *(L)*

9 If a, b, c are constants and $a > 0$, derive the condition that $ax^2 + bx + c$ should be positive for all real values of x. Prove that the equation

$$x - 1 = k(x - 2)(x + 1)$$

has real roots for all non-zero values of k. *(L)*

10 Given that α and β are the roots of the equation

$$x^2 - px + q = 0,$$

prove that $\alpha + \beta = p$ and $\alpha\beta = q$.

Prove also that

(a) $\alpha^{2n} + \beta^{2n} = (\alpha^n + \beta^n)^2 - 2q^n$,

(b) $\alpha^4 + \beta^4 = p^4 - 4p^2 q + 2q^2$.

Hence, or otherwise, form the quadratic equation whose roots are the fourth powers of those of the equation $x^2 - 3x + 1 = 0$. *(L)*

11 Given that α, β are the roots of the equation

$$2x^2 - 7x - 17 = 0,$$

show that an equation with roots $(\alpha - 4)$, $(\beta - 4)$ is

$$2x^2 + 9x - 13 = 0.$$

Find the coordinates of the point of intersection of the curves whose equations are

$$y = 2x^2 - 7x - 17$$

and

$$y = 2x^2 + 9x - 13.$$

Calculate the coordinates of the vertex of each curve and sketch both curves on the same diagram, labelling each curve clearly. *(L)*

12 Find the ranges of values of k for which the equation

$$(x - 5)(x + 1) = k(x - 7)$$

has real roots.

Deduce the range of the function

$$g : x \mapsto \frac{(x - 5)(x + 1)}{(x - 7)},$$

(for all real $x \neq 7$). *(JMB)*

13 Given that the roots of the equation $x^2 + px + q = 0$ are α and β, express $(\alpha - 2\beta)(\beta - 2\alpha)$ in terms of p and q. Hence, or otherwise, show that the condition for one root of the equation to be double the other is $2p^2 = 9q$. *(JMB)*

14 Given that the equation $x^2 + px + q = 0$ has roots α and β, express p and q in terms of α and β. Find the equation, with coefficients expressed in terms of p and q, whose roots are $3\alpha - \beta$ and $3\beta - \alpha$. *(JMB)*

15 Given that one root of the equation $x^2 + px + q = 0$ is twice the other root,

show that $2p^2 = 9q$. The roots of the equation

$$x^2 + (2k+4)x + (k^2 + 3k + 2) = 0$$

are non-zero and one root is twice the other root. Calculate the value of k.
(*JMB*)

16 If α and β are the roots of the equation $x^2 + bx + c = 0$, express $(\alpha - \beta^2)(\alpha^2 - \beta)$ in terms of b and c. Hence, or otherwise, show that, if one root of the equation is the square of the other, then $b^3 + c^2 + c = 3bc$.
(*JMB*)

17 The roots of the equation

$$x^2 + px + q = 0$$

are α, β. Show that the equation whose roots are α^2, β^2 is

$$x^2 + (2q - p^2)x + q^2 = 0.$$

Without finding the roots of either equation, determine all possible pairs of values of p, q for which the two equations have the same roots.   (*JMB*)

3 Trigonometry I

3.1 O-level revision

For acute angles, the trigonometric ratios are defined in terms of the ratios of the sides of a right-angled triangle. Let the triangle ABC have a right-angle at B and let angle $BAC = \theta°$, see Fig. 3.1(a). Then $\cos \theta° = AB/AC$, $\sin \theta° = BC/AC$, $\tan \theta° = BC/AB$, where we use the usual abbreviations cos, sin, tan, for cosine, sine, tangent.

(a) Right-angled triangle

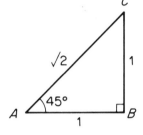

(b) Isosceles right-angled triangle

Fig. 3.1

Pythagoras' theorem, $AB^2 + BC^2 = AC^2$, then gives the result

$$\cos^2 \theta° + \sin^2 \theta° = 1.$$

For some particular angles, the trigonometric ratios can be found exactly, in terms of rational numbers or surds, otherwise we have to approximate to them using tables or calculators. For example, consider the right-angled isosceles triangle ABC, with $AB = 1 = BC$, of Fig. 3.1(b). The angle $BAC = 45°$ and $AC = \sqrt{2}$. Thus

$$\cos 45° = 1/\sqrt{2} = \sin 45°, \quad \tan 45° = 1.$$

Next, consider the equilateral triangle ACD with an altitude CB and sides AC, AD, CD each of length 2, as shown in Fig. 3.2(a). Then $AB = 1$, $BC = \sqrt{3}$ and angle BAC is $60°$, angle ACB is $30°$, and so

$$\cos 60° = \frac{1}{2}, \quad \sin 60° = \frac{\sqrt{3}}{2}, \quad \tan 60° = \sqrt{3},$$

$$\cos 30° = \frac{\sqrt{3}}{2}, \quad \sin 30° = \frac{1}{2}, \quad \tan 30° = \frac{1}{\sqrt{3}}.$$

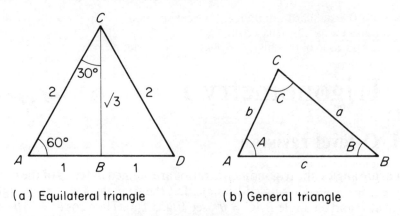

(a) Equilateral triangle   (b) General triangle

Fig. 3.2

Notation   For a general triangle ABC, not necessarily right-angled, we denote the three angles by A, B and C and the lengths of the sides by $a = BC$, $b = CA$ and $c = AB$, as shown in Fig. 3.2(b).

EXERCISE 3.1

1   Verify that $\cos^2\theta + \sin^2\theta = 1$, for $\theta = 0°$, $30°$, $45°$, $60°$, $90°$.
2   Let the triangle ABC be right-angled at B.
    (a) Given that $AB = 3$, $BC = 4$, find the angles A and C;
    (b) Given that $AC = 6$, $A = 40°$, find AB, BC and angle C;
    (c) Given that $AB = 5$, $A = 20°$, find BC and AC.
3   A ship sails on a triangular route, 100 km on a bearing 010° E. of N., then 200 km on a bearing 020° E. of N., and finally returning to its starting point. Find the bearing on which the ship must sail for the return leg, and the total distance travelled.
4   (a) Find the height of a tree if the elevation of the top of the tree from a point on horizontal ground, at a distance 10 m from the tree, is 60°.
    (b) Find the height of the tree if the ground slopes at 10° down from the base of the tree to the point of observation. Assume that this point is still at a distance 10 m from the base of the tree, measured along the ground, and that the observed elevation of the top of the tree is still 60°.
5   Find the radius of a circle which has a chord of length 0.1 m subtending an angle 120° at the centre.
6   Given that the radius of the Earth is R and that the angle of depression (below the horizontal) of the horizon, as seen from the top of a cliff at a height h above sea-level, is $\theta°$, prove that $\cos\theta° = R/(R + h)$.
7   A pendulum bob P is suspended from a point O by a string of length 0·8 m, and the point O is 1 m above the floor. If the pendulum swings through a total angle 2θ find, in terms of θ, the greatest height of P above the floor.
8   Given a triangle ABC, not necessarily right-angled, where the lengths of BC and AC are a and b respectively and the acute angle ACB is C, prove that the area of the triangle is $\frac{1}{2}ab\sin C$. Prove that the same formula gives the area when the angle C is obtuse.

9 With the standard notation for a general triangle ABC, use the result of question **8** to show that $a/\sin A = b/\sin B = c/\sin C$.

10 Find the ratio of the lengths of the sides of a rectangle whose diagonals cross at an angle θ.

11 The base of a right circular cone has radius r and the height of the cone is h. Find, in terms of r and h,
(i) the slant height k of the cone;
(ii) $\sin \phi$, where ϕ is the angle between a line on the curved surface of the cone and its base;
(iii) $\sin \theta$, where θ is the angle at the top of the cone between the axis and a line on the curved surface;
(iv) the area of the curved surface of the cone.

3.2 Trigonometric ratios of angles of any magnitude

On a Cartesian graph $O(x, y)$, draw a circle of unit radius, centre O, meeting the axis Ox at the point $A(1,0)$, as shown in Fig. 3.3. An angle $\theta°$, of any magnitude, can be represented on this graph by a rotation of Ox through $\theta°$ measured positively towards Oy. If, after such a rotation $\theta°$, the new position of Ox meets the circle at $P(x, y)$, then the angle AOP is $\theta°$, and the point P corresponds to the angle $\theta°$. A positive angle $\theta°$ is represented by an anticlockwise rotation of OA about O through $\theta°$.

A negative angle $-\theta°$ is represented by a clockwise rotation of OA about O through the angle $+\theta°$. Thus in Fig. 3.3, the points $P_1(-\frac{1}{2}, \sqrt{3}/2)$, $P_2(\frac{1}{2}, -\sqrt{3}/2)$, $P_3(-1, 0)$, $P_4(-\sqrt{3}/2, -\frac{1}{2})$ correspond to angles of $120°$, $-60°$, $180°$, $570°$, respectively.

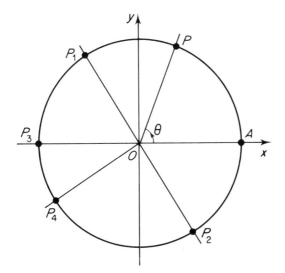

Fig. 3.3

EXERCISE 3.2A

1 Draw a unit circle with centre O and axes $O(x, y)$ and, on the circle mark the points $P_1, P_2, \ldots, P_6$, which correspond to angles $40°$, $230°$, $-20°$, $-200°$, $400°$, $1000°$. Without calculating the coordinates of these six points, state the signs of each of their x and y coordinates.

When $P(x, y)$ is the point on the unit circle corresponding to the angle $\theta°$, so that angle AOP is $\theta°$ measured positively in an anticlockwise sense, then we define the circular functions:

$$\cos \theta° = x \qquad\qquad \sin \theta° = y \qquad\qquad \tan \theta° = y/x, \text{ if } x \neq 0$$
$$\sec \theta° = 1/x, (x \neq 0) \quad \operatorname{cosec} \theta° = 1/y, (y \neq 0) \quad \cot \theta° = x/y, (y \neq 0).$$

Thus the cosine and sine of $\theta°$ are respectively the projections of OP on to the axes Ox and Oy, with the sign taken into account. Referring to Fig. 3.3, for example, we see that

$$\cos 120° = -\tfrac{1}{2} \quad \cos(-60°) = \tfrac{1}{2} \qquad \cos 180° = -1 \quad \cos 570° = -\sqrt{3}/2,$$
$$\sin 120° = \sqrt{3}/2 \quad \sin(-60°) = -\sqrt{3}/2 \quad \sin 180° = 0. \qquad \sin 570° = -\tfrac{1}{2}.$$

If $P(x, y)$ corresponds to the positive rotation $\theta°$ and Q corresponds to the corresponding negative rotation $-\theta°$, then clearly Q is the reflection of P in the axis Ox, so that Q is the point $(x, -y)$. Hence

$$\cos(-\theta°) = \quad x \quad = \cos \theta°,$$
$$\sin(-\theta°) = -y \quad = -\sin \theta°,$$
$$\tan(-\theta°) = -y/x = -\tan \theta°.$$

The addition of any integer multiple of $360°$ to $\theta°$ (positive or negative) will not change the position of the corresponding point P and so leaves all the trigonometric functions unaltered. Thus for $n \in \mathbb{Z}$,

$$\cos(\theta + n360)° = \cos \theta°,$$
$$\sin(\theta + n360)° = \sin \theta°,$$
$$\tan(\theta + n360)° = \tan \theta°.$$

This result may be described by saying that $\cos \theta°$ and $\sin \theta°$ are *periodic* functions with period 360. So the value of one of these functions may be found from the value for θ lying between 0 and 360. The graphs of $\cos \theta°$ and $\sin \theta°$, with domain $\{\theta : 0 \leqslant \theta \leqslant 360\}$ are shown in Fig. 3.4.

The following transformations of the Cartesian plane are equivalent:

(i) an enlargement with scale factor -1;
(ii) a reflection in the origin O;
(iii) a rotation about the origin O through $180°$.

Such a transformation transforms a point $P(x, y)$ into the point Q $(-x, -y)$, and if P corresponds to the angle $\theta°$ then Q corresponds to the

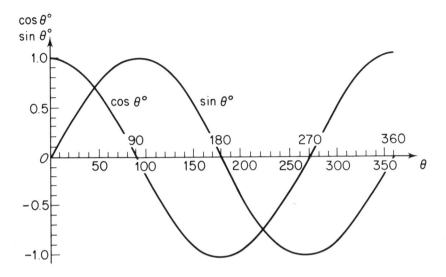

Fig. 3.4 Graphs of cos $\theta°$ and sin $\theta°$, $0 \leqslant \theta \leqslant 360$.

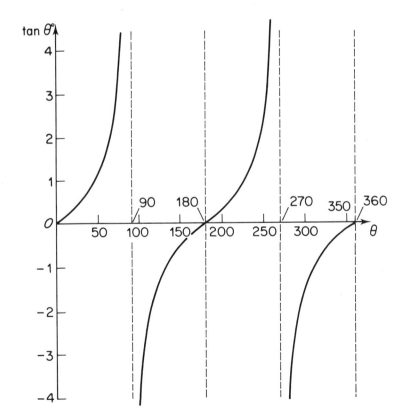

Fig. 3.5 Graph of tan $\theta°$, $0 \leqslant \theta \leqslant 360$.

angle $(\theta + 180)°$. Thus

$$\cos (\theta + 180)° = -x = -\cos \theta°,$$
$$\sin (\theta + 180)° = -y = -\sin \theta°,$$

but
$$\tan (\theta + 180)° = \frac{-y}{-x} = \frac{y}{x} = \tan \theta°.$$

Hence $\tan \theta°$ is periodic with period 180, which is half the period of $\cos \theta°$ and $\sin \theta°$. When θ is an odd multiple of 90, the corresponding point P has coordinates $x = 0 = \cos \theta°$, and $y = \pm 1 = \sin \theta°$. In such cases, $\tan \theta° = y/x$ is not defined since $y/0$ does not make sense. For angles slightly smaller than these critical angles $\tan \theta°$ is very large and positive while for angles slightly larger than the critical ones $\tan \theta°$ is very large and negative. These properties of $\tan \theta°$ are illustrated in its graph, shown in Fig. 3.5. Note that the vertical scale for the graph of $\tan \theta°$ is double that for the graphs of $\cos \theta°$ and $\sin \theta°$ in Fig. 3.4.

For any angle $\theta°$, corresponding to a point P on the unit circle, there is an angle $\phi°$ lying between $0°$ and $360°$, with $\phi = \theta + 360n$, for some $n \in \mathbb{Z}$, and P also corresponds to the angle $\phi°$. We can then classify angles into four sets, according to the signs of their cosines and sines. The results are summarised in Table 3.2 and in Fig. 3.6.

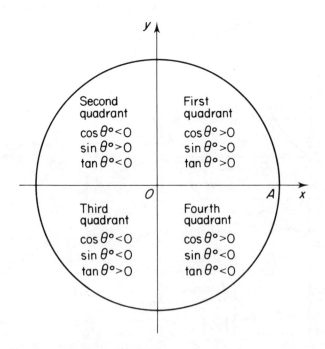

Fig. 3.6 Signs of the circular functions.

Table 3.2 The signs of the circular functions

First quadrant	Second quadrant	Third quadrant	Fourth quadrant
$0 < \phi < 90$	$90 < \phi < 180$	$180 < \phi < 270$	$270 < \phi < 360$
$x = \cos \theta° > 0$	$x = \cos \theta° < 0$	$x = \cos \theta° < 0$	$x = \cos \theta° > 0$
$y = \sin \theta° > 0$	$y = \sin \theta° > 0$	$y = \sin \theta° < 0$	$y = \sin \theta° < 0$
$\dfrac{y}{x} = \tan \theta° > 0$	$\dfrac{y}{x} = \tan \theta° < 0$	$\dfrac{y}{x} = \tan \theta° > 0$	$\dfrac{y}{x} = \tan \theta° < 0$

EXAMPLE *Find in terms of* $\cos \theta°$ *and* $\sin \theta°$: (a) $\cos (180 + \theta)°$,
(b) $\sin (180 - \theta)°$, (c) $\cos (90 + \theta)°$, (d) $\sin (90 - \theta)°$.

Let $P(x, y)$ be the point on the unit circle which corresponds to the angle $\theta°$.
(a) The point corresponding to $(180 + \theta)°$ is $(-x, -y)$ so $\cos (180 + \theta)° = -x$
$= -\cos \theta°$.
(b) The point corresponding to $-\theta°$ is $(x, -y)$ so the point corresponding to
$(180 - \theta)°$ is $(-x, y)$ and $\sin (180 - \theta)° = y = \sin \theta°$.
(c) The point corresponding to $(90 + \theta)°$ lies in the next quadrant to P and has
coordinates $(-y, x)$ so $\cos (90 + \theta)° = -y = -\sin \theta°$.
(d) Since $90 - \theta = 180 - (90 + \theta)$, the point corresponding to $(90 - \theta)°$ has
coordinates (y, x), on using (b) and (c), so $\sin (90 - \theta)° = x = \cos \theta°$.
Note that the method of proof used here is independent of the quadrant in which
the angle $\theta°$ lies. The same result will always be obtained by assuming that $\theta°$ lies
in the first quadrant. Thus in (b) if $\theta°$ lies in the first quadrant, x and y are positive,
$-\theta°$ lies in the fourth quadrant and so $(180 - \theta)°$ lies in the second quadrant, with
corresponding point $(-x, y)$.

EXERCISE 3.2B

1 Complete the following table of quadrants in which the angles lie:

Angle	$\theta°$	$-\theta°$	$(180 + \theta)°$	$(180 - \theta)°$	$(90 + \theta)°$	$(90 - \theta)°$
Quadrant	1	4				1
	2	3		1		
	3		1			
	4				1	

2 Find, in terms of $\cos \theta°$ and $\sin \theta°$, the following:
   (i) $\cos (-\theta)°$ (ii) $\sin (-\theta)°$ (iii) $\tan (-\theta)°$
   (iv) $\cos (180 + \theta)°$ (v) $\sin (180 + \theta)°$ (vi) $\tan (180 + \theta)°$
   (vii) $\cos (180 - \theta)°$ (viii) $\sin (180 - \theta)°$ (ix) $\tan (180 - \theta)°$
   (x) $\cos (90 + \theta)°$ (xi) $\sin (90 + \theta)°$ (xii) $\tan (90 + \theta)°$
   (xiii) $\cos (90 - \theta)°$ (xiv) $\sin (90 - \theta)°$ (xv) $\tan (90 - \theta)°$.

3 State whether the equation is true or false in general:
   (i) $\cos (-\theta)° = \cos (180 + \theta)°$ (ii) $\cos (\theta - 270)° = -\sin \theta°$,
   (iii) $\tan (\theta - 180)° = -\tan \theta°$ (iv) $\sin (270 + \theta)° = \sin \theta°$,
   (v) $\sin (\theta - 90)° = \cos \theta°$ (vi) $\sin (\theta + 45)° = \cos (45 - \theta)°$.

4   (a) Given that $\sin\theta° = 4/5$, find the possible values of the other two trigonometric ratios for $\theta°$;
   (b) Given that $\tan\theta° = -5/12$, find the possible values of $\cos\theta°$ and $\sin\theta°$.

Other trigonometrical ratios

You will have found, in question **2** of Exercise **3.2B** that $\tan(90+\theta)° = -1/\tan\theta°$ and $\tan(90-\theta)° = 1/\tan\theta°$. The function $1/\tan$ and the reciprocals of the sine and cosine functions are of sufficient importance to be given their own names:
the reciprocal of cosine is secant and is written sec,
the reciprocal of sine is cosecant and is written cosec,
the reciprocal of tangent is cotangent and is written cot.
Thus we have three more circular functions:

$$\sec\theta° = \frac{1}{\cos\theta°}, \text{ with domain } \mathbb{R}\setminus\{(2n+1)90:n\in\mathbb{Z}\},$$

$$\operatorname{cosec}\theta° = \frac{1}{\sin\theta°}, \text{ with domain } \mathbb{R}\setminus\{180n:n\in\mathbb{Z}\},$$

$$\cot\theta° = \frac{1}{\tan\theta°}, \text{ with domain } \mathbb{R}\setminus\{180n:n\in\mathbb{Z}\}.$$

Note that, since $\tan\theta° = \dfrac{\sin\theta°}{\cos\theta°}$, $\cot\theta° = \dfrac{\cos\theta°}{\sin\theta°}$.

Consequences of Pythagoras' theorem

$$\cos^2\theta° + \sin^2\theta° = 1,$$
$$1 + \tan^2\theta° = \sec^2\theta°, \text{ when } \cos\theta° \neq 0,$$
$$\cot^2\theta° + 1 = \operatorname{cosec}^2\theta°, \text{ when } \sin\theta° \neq 0.$$

Proof Since $\cos\theta° = \pm x$ and $\sin\theta° = \pm y$, $\cos^2\theta° = x^2$ and $\sin^2\theta° = y^2$. Now, for every point $P(x, y)$ on the unit circle, $x^2 + y^2 = 1$, so, for all values of θ, $\cos^2\theta° + \sin^2\theta° = 1$. The other results are obtained by dividing by $\cos^2\theta°$ and $\sin^2\theta°$ respectively, for values of θ in their domains.

EXERCISE 3.2C

1   For each of the functions (a) $\sec\theta°$, (b) $\operatorname{cosec}\theta°$, (c) $\cot\theta°$, state the domain, the range and the period of the function.
2   Using the graphs of $\cos\theta°$, $\sin\theta°$ and $\tan\theta°$, of Figs 3.4 and 3.5, sketch the corresponding graphs of $\sec\theta°$, $\operatorname{cosec}\theta°$ and $\cot\theta°$.
3   Prove that (i) $\sin^3\theta + \sin\theta\cos^2\theta = \sin\theta$, (ii) $\dfrac{\cos^2\theta}{1-\sin\theta} = 1 + \sin\theta$.

4 Simplify: (i) $\sec\theta - \sec\theta\sin^2\theta$, (ii) $\cos\theta\,\mathrm{cosec}\,\theta\tan\theta$,
(iii) $\cos^2\theta(1 + \tan^2\theta)$, (iv) $(\sin\theta + \cos\theta)^2 + (\sin\theta - \cos\theta)^2$,
(v) $\tan\theta + \dfrac{\cos\theta}{1 + \sin\theta}$, (vi) $\dfrac{\sin\theta - \cos\theta + 1}{\sin\theta + \cos\theta - 1}$.

3.3 Solution of trigonometric equations

Because of the periodic nature of the circular functions, there is generally an infinite number of solutions to a trigonometric equation, unless the domain is restricted and solutions are limited to some fixed set of values.

EXAMPLE 1 *Solve the equation* $\sin 2\theta^\circ = 0$:
(a) for $0 \leqslant \theta < 360$, *(b) for general values of* θ.

(a) Since $\sin\phi^\circ = 0$ for $\phi \in \{0, 180, 360, 540\}$, on putting $\theta = \frac{1}{2}\phi$ we see that the solution set of $\sin 2\theta^\circ = 0$ is **{0, 90, 180, 270}**.
(b) Using the same argument as in (a) the solution of $\sin 2\theta^\circ = 0$ for general values of θ is the set **$\{90n : n \in \mathbb{Z}\}$**.

EXAMPLE 2 *Solve the equation; for* $0 \leqslant \theta \leqslant 360$:
(i) $\cos\theta^\circ = \cos\alpha^\circ$; *(ii)* $\sin\theta^\circ = \sin\alpha^\circ$; *(iii)* $\tan\theta^\circ = \tan\alpha^\circ$, *where* $0 < \alpha < 90$.

We use the symmetries of the graphs of the circular functions, as indicated in Fig. 3.7, to solve these equations.

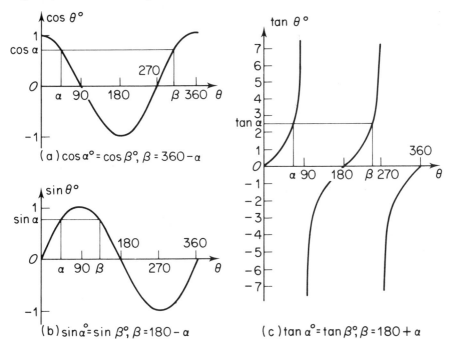

(a) $\cos\alpha^\circ = \cos\beta^\circ$, $\beta = 360 - \alpha$

(b) $\sin\alpha^\circ = \sin\beta^\circ$, $\beta = 180 - \alpha$

(c) $\tan\alpha^\circ = \tan\beta^\circ$, $\beta = 180 + \alpha$

Fig. 3.7

(i) In (a) we see that $\cos \alpha° = \cos(360 - \alpha)°$ and so the solution set of the equation $\cos \theta° = \cos \alpha°$ is $\{\alpha, \mathbf{360-\alpha}\}$.
(ii) In (b) we see that $\sin \alpha° = \sin(180 - \alpha)°$ giving the solution set $\{\alpha, \mathbf{180-\alpha}\}$.
(iii) Similarly from (c) $\tan \alpha° = \tan(180 + \alpha)°$ and the solution of the equation is $\theta = \alpha$ **or** $\theta = \mathbf{180 + \alpha}$.

As in other equations, the method of factorising may be used to solve trigonometric equations, using the fact that a product is zero when one of the factors is zero.

EXAMPLE 3   *Solve* $\sin \theta° + 2 \cos \theta° \sin \theta° = 0, 0 \leqslant \theta \leqslant 360$.

Since $\sin \theta° + 2 \cos \theta° \sin \theta° = \sin \theta° (1 + 2 \cos \theta°)$, the equation is satisfied when either $\sin \theta° = 0$ or when $\cos \theta° = -\frac{1}{2}$. In the required range of values of θ, the graphs of Fig. 3.7 indicate that these equations require that $\theta = 0$ or 180 or that $\theta = 120$ or 240. Each of these values satisfies the equation, so the solution set is $\{\mathbf{0, 120, 180, 240}\}$.

When more than one circular function appears in the equation, one strategy for the solution is to eliminate one of the functions, and this may be done by using the consequences of Pythagoras' theorem.

EXAMPLE 4   *Solve the equation* $3 \tan^2 \theta° - 2 \sec^2 \theta° = 1, -180 < \theta < 180$.

Obtain an equation in $\tan \theta°$ by using the relation $\sec^2 \theta° = 1 + \tan^2 \theta°$. $3 \tan^2 \theta° - 2(1 + \tan^2 \theta°) = 1$, so $\tan^2 \theta° = 3$, an $\tan \theta° = \pm \sqrt{3}$. This gives the solution set $\{\mathbf{60, 120, -60, -120}\}$, since each of these values satisfies the equation.

EXAMPLE 5   *Solve the equation* $\tan \theta° = \sec \theta°, 0 \leqslant \theta \leqslant 360$.

Multiplying by $\cos \theta°$, we find that $\sin \theta° = 1$, which is only satisfied by $\theta = 90$, in the given range. However, this does not satisfy the equation since 90 is not in the domain of $\tan \theta°$ nor of $\sec \theta°$, and so the **solution set is empty**.

It should be noted that, in the solutions above, the procedure was to find a set of values in which θ must lie and then to check that each of the values satisfies the equation. The procedure used to find the set of values may give rise to values which do not satisfy the equation, as happened in Example 5. It is necessary to be on one's guard against obtaining such false roots of an equation, as is seen in the next example.

EXAMPLE 6   *Solve the equation* $\cos \theta° - \sin \theta° = 1, 0 \leqslant \theta < 360$.

To obtain an equation in $\cos \theta°$, by eliminating $\sin \theta°$, rewrite the equation as $\cos \theta° - 1 = \sin \theta°$, square and use Pythagoras' theorem.

Then $\qquad \cos^2 \theta° - 2 \cos \theta° + 1 = \sin^2 \theta° = 1 - \cos^2 \theta°$,

so $\qquad 2 \cos^2 \theta° - 2 \cos \theta° = 0$ or $\cos \theta° (\cos \theta° - 1) = 0$.

Thus either $\cos \theta° = 0$ and $\theta = 90$ or 270,

or $\cos \theta° = 1$ and $\theta = 0$.

On testing these values of θ in the original equation,

$$\cos 0° - \sin 0° \quad = 1 - 0 = 1,$$
$$\cos 90° - \sin 90° \quad = 0 - 1 = -1,$$
$$\cos 270° - \sin 270° = 0 - (-1) = 1,$$

so the solution set is $\{0, 270\}$, and the 'false solution', $\theta = 90$, is discarded. It arose from the process of squaring.

EXAMPLE 7   *Find the general solution of the equation* $\cos \theta° = \sin \alpha°$*; for a given number* α.

We have to satisfy the equations

$$\cos \theta° = \sin \alpha° = \cos (90 - \alpha)°$$

and, on using the results of Example 2, either $\theta = 90 - \alpha + 360n$ or $\theta = -(90 - \alpha) + 360n$, where n is an integer. All these values satisfy the equation and so the solution set is $\{360n + 90 - \alpha, \ 360n - 90 + \alpha : n \in \mathbb{Z}\}$.

EXERCISE 3.3

1   Solve the following equations for $0 \leqslant \theta < 360$:
    (i) $2 \sin \theta° + 1 = 0$ (ii) $\sin \theta° \cos 2\theta° = 0$
    (iii) $(2 \cos \theta° - 1)^2 = 0$ (iv) $(1 + 3 \sin \theta°)(4 - \cos \theta°) = 0$.
2   Find the general solutions of the equations:
    (i) $\sin 2\theta° \cos \theta° = 0$ (ii) $\sin 2\theta° = \sin 3\theta°$
    (iii) $\sin 2\theta° = \cos \theta°$ (iv) $\sin \theta° + \cos \theta° = 0$.
3   By factorisation, solve the equations for $-180 < \theta \leqslant 180$:
    (i) $\cos^2 \theta° + \cos \theta° - 2 = 0$ (ii) $\cos \theta° \sin \theta° - \cos \theta° - \sin \theta° + 1 = 0$
    (iii) $\cos \theta° \sin \theta° - \cos \theta° + \sin \theta° = 1$ (iv) $2 \cos \theta° \sin \theta° - \sin \theta° + 2 \cos \theta° = 1$.
4   Use Pythagoras' theorem to solve for $0 \leqslant \theta \leqslant 180$:
    (i) $2 \sec^2 \theta° + 3 \tan \theta° = 1$ (ii) $\cos^2 \theta° = 3 \sin^2 \theta°$
    (iii) $\sin \theta° + \cos \theta° = 1$ (iv) $\tan \theta° + \cot \theta° = 2 \sec \theta°$.
5   Find all the values of x between 0 and 360 inclusive such that
    (a) $\cos x° = -\sqrt{3}/2$,   (b) $\cos x° = -\sin x°$.   *(L)*
6   Obtain the general solution of the equation $\sin \theta° = \cos \alpha°$ for θ in terms
    of α.   *(L)*
7   Given that $7\sin^2 \theta - 5 \sin \theta + \cos^2 \theta = 0$, find the possible values of
    $\sin \theta$.   *(L)*

3.4 Radian measure of angle

Although the measurement of angles in degrees is quite common, the division of a full circle into $360°$ is, in fact, quite arbitrary. It is connected with the division of a day into 24 × 60 minutes, so that the Earth rotates through one degree of longitude every four minutes.

There is a more natural way of measuring angles, which is more appropriate in the case of circular functions with real domains. Consider the unit circle, on which the point P corresponds to the angle x, equal to the angle AOP (see Fig. 3.8). Then the arc length AP on the circle is proportional to x. We make the factor of proportionality unity and define the measurement of angle in *radians*.

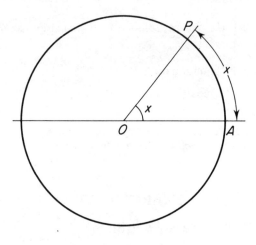

Fig. 3.8

Definition   The angle AOP is x *radians* if the arc length AP on the unit circle, centre O, is x units.

Since the circumference of the unit circle is of length 2π, we find the corresponding angular measure in degrees and radians:

Degrees	Radians
360	2π
180	π
90	$\frac{1}{2}\pi$
θ	$\dfrac{2\pi\theta}{360} = \dfrac{\pi\theta}{180} = \dfrac{\pi}{180}\theta.$

Note: The radian measure x of an angle is a real number, with no dimensions. The notation x^c is sometimes used for x radians, but we shall only use x.

When referred to radian argument, the circular functions are real functions. The properties of these functions follow from the properties of the functions with degree argument, obtained in §3.2. We summarise some of these properties, beginning with a table of their values for some key values of the argument.

Table 3.4A Values of circular functions

x	$\cos x$	$\sin x$	$\tan x$	$\sec x$	$\operatorname{cosec} x$	$\cot x$
0	1	0	0	1	—	—
$\dfrac{\pi}{6}$	$\dfrac{\sqrt{3}}{2}$	$\dfrac{1}{2}$	$\dfrac{1}{\sqrt{3}}$	$\dfrac{2}{\sqrt{3}}$	2	$\sqrt{3}$
$\dfrac{\pi}{4}$	$\dfrac{1}{\sqrt{2}}$	$\dfrac{1}{\sqrt{2}}$	1	$\sqrt{2}$	$\sqrt{2}$	1
$\dfrac{\pi}{3}$	$\dfrac{1}{2}$	$\dfrac{\sqrt{3}}{2}$	$\sqrt{3}$	2	$\dfrac{2}{\sqrt{3}}$	$\dfrac{1}{\sqrt{3}}$
$\dfrac{\pi}{2}$	0	1	—	—	1	0

EXERCISE 3.4A

1 Continue the above table for $x = \dfrac{2\pi}{3}, \dfrac{3\pi}{4}, \dfrac{5\pi}{6}, \pi$.

The functions $\cos x$ and $\sin x$ have domain $\mathbb{R}$ and are periodic with period 2π; $\tan x$ has domain $\mathbb{R} \backslash \{(n+\tfrac{1}{2})\pi : n \in \mathbb{Z}\}$ and has period π. The graphs of $\cos x$, $\sin x$ and $\tan x$ are shown in Fig. 3.9, and the results of question **2** of Exercise 3.2B may be rewritten

$$\cos(-x) = \cos x, \quad \sin(-x) = -\sin x, \quad \tan(-x) = -\tan x,$$
$$\cos(\pi+x) = -\cos x, \quad \sin(\pi+x) = -\sin x, \quad \tan(\pi+x) = \tan x,$$
$$\cos(\pi-x) = -\cos x, \quad \sin(\pi-x) = \sin x, \quad \tan(\pi-x) = -\tan x,$$
$$\cos(\tfrac{1}{2}\pi+x) = -\sin x, \quad \sin(\tfrac{1}{2}\pi+x) = \cos x, \quad \tan(\tfrac{1}{2}\pi+x) = -\cot x,$$
$$\cos(\tfrac{1}{2}\pi-x) = \sin x, \quad \sin(\tfrac{1}{2}\pi-x) = \cos x, \quad \tan(\tfrac{1}{2}\pi-x) = \cot x.$$

Repeating Table 3.2, for radian measure, shows, in Table 3.4B, how the real numbers, other than integer multiples of $\tfrac{1}{2}\pi$, can be divided into four sets, corresponding to the four quadrants:
in the first quadrant all the circular functions are positive;
in the second quadrant $\sin x$ is positive, $\cos x$ and $\tan x$ are negative;
in the third quadrant $\tan x$ is positive, $\sin x$ and $\cos x$ are negative;
in the fourth quadrant $\cos x$ is positive, $\sin x$ and $\tan x$ are negative.

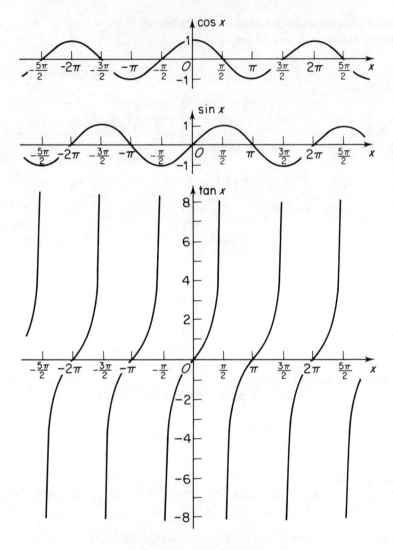

Fig. 3.9 Graphs of cos x, sin x and tan x.

Table 3.4B Signs of the trigonometric functions   For $n \in \mathbb{Z}$:

First quadrant	Second quadrant	Third quadrant	Fourth quadrant
$2n\pi < x < (2n+\frac{1}{2})\pi$	$(2n+\frac{1}{2})\pi < x < (2n+1)\pi$	$(2n+1)\pi < x < (2n+\frac{3}{2})\pi$	$(2n+\frac{3}{2})\pi < x < (2n+2)\pi$
$\cos x > 0$	$\cos x < 0$	$\cos x < 0$	$\cos x > 0$
$\sin x > 0$	$\sin x > 0$	$\sin x < 0$	$\sin x < 0$
$\tan x > 0$	$\tan x < 0$	$\tan x > 0$	$\tan x < 0$

EXAMPLE   *Solve the equation* $\cos x + \cos 5x = 0$
(i) *for* $-\pi \leqslant x \leqslant \pi$,   (ii) *for general values of* x.

Since we require $\cos 5x = -\cos x = \cos(\pi - x) = \cos(\pi + x)$, the solutions of the equation satisfy

either $5x = 2n\pi + \pi - x$ or $5x = 2n\pi + \pi + x$

that is, either $6x = (2n+1)\pi$ or $4x = (2n+1)\pi$,

so the solution set is $\left\{ \dfrac{2n+1}{6}\pi, \dfrac{2n+1}{4}\pi : n \in \mathbb{Z} \right\}$, in case (ii). In case (i) we choose

those values of n which give a solution in the range $-\pi \leqslant x \leqslant \pi$. That is for

$-3 \leqslant n \leqslant 2$ giving a solution set $\left\{ \dfrac{-5\pi}{6}, \dfrac{-\pi}{2}, \dfrac{-\pi}{6}, \dfrac{\pi}{6}, \dfrac{\pi}{2}, \dfrac{5\pi}{6}, \dfrac{-3\pi}{4}, \dfrac{-\pi}{4}, \dfrac{\pi}{4}, \dfrac{3\pi}{4} \right\}$.

Apart from working in radians, the next exercise can be done using the same methods as were used in §3.3.

EXERCISE 3.4B

1   Find all the solutions in the interval $0 \leqslant x \leqslant \pi$ of the equation
    $\sin 2x - \sin x = 0$.   (*JMB*)
2   Find all solutions in the interval $0 \leqslant x < 2\pi$ of the equation
    $\sin x = \cos 2x$.   (*JMB*)
3   Find, in radians, the general solution of the equation $\sin 2x = \cos x$.   (*L*)
4   Find, in radians, the general solution of the equation $\sin 2\theta + \sin \theta = 0$. (*L*)
5   Leaving all answers as multiples of π, find the values of x for which $0 < x < \pi$
    and $\cos x + \cos 3x = 0$.   (*L*)
6   Find all the values of x in the range; $0 < x < \pi$ for which $\sin 5x + \sin 3x = 0$.
                                                                                          (*L*)
7   In $\triangle ABC$, $BC = 12$ cm, $AB = 4$ cm and angle C is acute with $\sin C = \frac{1}{6}$. Find,
    in radians, the two possible values of the angle A, leaving your answer in terms
    of π.   (*L*)
8   Giving your answers in terms of π, solve for $0 \leqslant x \leqslant 2\pi$ the equations
    (a) $\tan 2x = -1$,
    (b) $\cos 2x = \cos x$.   (*L*)
9   Eliminate θ from the pair of simultaneous equations

$$x \cos \theta + y \sin \theta = 1$$
$$y \cos \theta + x \sin \theta = 2.$$ (*JMB*)

3.5 Circular arc and sector

Consider a circle of radius r, having an arc BQ which subtends an angle θ at
the centre O of the circle. Let OB and OQ meet the corresponding unit
circle with centre O at the points A and P (see Fig. 3.10).
    The circle of radius r is obtained from the unit circle by an all-round
enlargement with scale factor r, so that all linear dimensions are multiplied
by r. The arc length AP is θ and so the arc length BQ is $s = r\theta$. Notice that
this is the fraction $\theta/2\pi$ of the circumference $2\pi r$ of the circle.

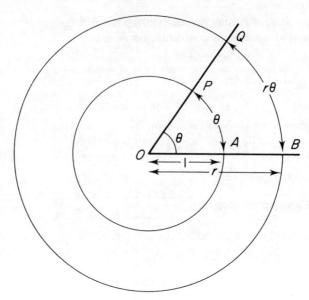

Fig. 3.10

To find the area S of the sector OBQ, we note that this is the same fraction $\theta/2\pi$ of the area of the circle, and so

$$S = (\theta/2\pi) \cdot \pi r^2 = \tfrac{1}{2} r^2 \theta.$$

EXAMPLE 1 *Find the area and the length of the curved boundary of a sector of a circle: (i) of radius 3 cm and angle 2/3; (ii) of radius 10 m and angle 20°.*

The area $S = \tfrac{1}{2} r^2 \theta$ and the arc length, s, is $r\theta$, where θ is measured in radians.

(i) $r = 3$ cm, $\theta = \tfrac{2}{3}$, so $S = \tfrac{1}{2} \cdot 9 \cdot \tfrac{2}{3} = \textbf{3 cm}^2$, and $s = 3 \cdot \tfrac{2}{3} = \textbf{2 cm}$.
(ii) $r = 10$ m, $\theta = 20 \cdot \pi/180 = \pi/9$, so $S = \tfrac{1}{2} \cdot 100 \cdot \pi/9 = \textbf{17·5 m}^2$, and $s = 10\pi/9$ $= \textbf{3·49 m}$.

EXAMPLE 2 *Find the area and the length of the boundary of a segment of a circle of radius r, bounded by a chord AB and the minor arc AB, where AB subtends an angle 2θ at the centre.*

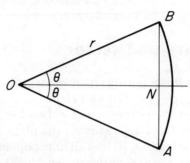

Fig. 3.11

Refer to Fig. 3.11, and let N be the midpoint of AB. The required area S is the area of the sector OAB less the area of the triangle, so

$$S = \tfrac{1}{2}r^2 . 2\theta - ON . AN = r^2\theta - r^2 \cos\theta \sin\theta = r^2(\theta - \cos\theta\sin\theta).$$

The length of the boundary $b = r2\theta + 2r\sin\theta = 2r(\theta + \sin\theta)$.

EXAMPLE 3 *Prove that, for $0 < \theta < \tfrac{1}{2}\pi$, $\sin\theta < \theta < \tan\theta$. Deduce that as $\theta \to 0$, $\sin\theta/\theta \to 1$, which is a notation for*
'as θ approaches zero, $\sin\theta/\theta$ approaches 1'.

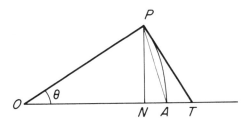

Fig. 3.12

In Fig. 3.12, let AP be an arc of a unit circle subtending an angle θ at the centre O. Let PN be the perpendicular from P on to OA and let PT be the tangent to the circle at P, meeting OA produced at T. Then the figure shows the situation for an acute angle θ and the area of the triangle OPA is less than the area of the sector OAP which is itself less than the area of the triangle OPT.

$$\tfrac{1}{2}OA . PN = \tfrac{1}{2}\sin\theta < \tfrac{1}{2}\theta < \tfrac{1}{2}OT . PN = \tfrac{1}{2}\sec\theta\sin\theta$$

and so, on dividing by $\tfrac{1}{2}$,

$$\sin\theta < \theta < \tan\theta.$$

Since θ and $\theta\sec\theta$ are both positive, we may divide the two inequalities by these numbers, when we obtain the inequalities

$$\cos\theta < \sin\theta/\theta < 1.$$

Now, as θ approaches zero, $\cos\theta$ approaches 1 and $\sin\theta/\theta$ is sandwiched between $\cos\theta$ and 1, so it also must approach 1, as was to be proved.

Note Referring to Fig. 3.11, the ratio of the lengths of the chord AB and the arc AB is $\dfrac{2r\sin\theta}{2r\theta} = \dfrac{\sin\theta}{\theta}$, and thus, by the result of the above example, as the point B approaches A along the circle of radius r, the ratio of the lengths of the chord AB and the arc AB approaches 1. These results will be used in Chapter 21.

EXERCISE 3.5

1   An arc of a circle of radius a subtends an angle θ at the centre. Find the length of the arc and the area of the corresponding sector when:

(i) $a = 5\,\text{m}$, $\theta = 2\frac{1}{2}$;   (ii) $a = 8\,\text{cm}$, $\theta = \frac{3}{4}\pi$;   (iii) $a = 2\cdot5\,\text{m}$, $\theta = 120°$;
(iv) $a = 1\cdot32\,\text{m}$, $\theta = 12°$.

2   Determine the angle, in degrees, subtended at the centre of a circle by an arc, given that the area of the corresponding sector is equal to the square of the length of the arc.

3   Two circles, of radii 3 m and 4 m respectively, lie in a plane with their centres a distance 5 m apart. Find the area common to these circles and the length of the boundary of this area.

4   Find the ratio of the areas of the two segments into which a circle is divided by a chord:
    (i) when the radius of the circle is equal to the length of the chord;
    (ii) when the radius of the circle is 2 m and the length of the chord is $2\sqrt{3}$ m;
    (iii) when the radius of the circle is 5 m and the chord is of length 8 m.

5   Find the ratio of the areas of two segments into which a circle is divided by a chord, if the chord divides the circumference into two arcs whose lengths are in the ratio $a:b$.

6   Find the area between three circles, each of radius a, which all touch each other externally.

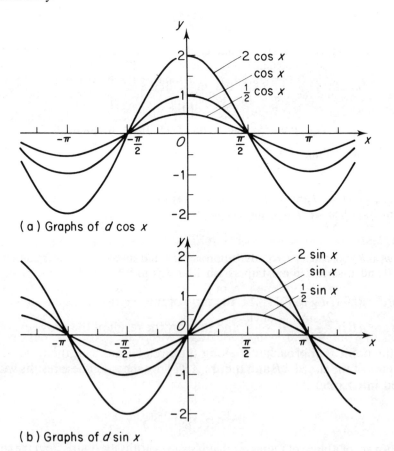

(a) Graphs of $d\cos x$

(b) Graphs of $d\sin x$

Fig. 3.13

3.6 Effect of changes of scale and origin upon the functions cos x and sin x

The graph of the function $\cos x$ is a curve with equation $y = \cos x$. A change in the scale for y is obtained by multiplying $\cos x$ by some constant, say d, giving the curve with equation $y = d \cos x$. The new function $d \cos x$ has the same period 2π as the function $\cos x$, since $d \cos (x + 2\pi) = d \cos x$. The new curve has its peaks at the same values of x as the original curve but the height of the peaks (the amplitude of the cosine oscillation) is multiplied by the factor d. Fig. 3.13(a) shows the effect of this scale change for the values $d = 2$ and $d = \frac{1}{2}$, and Fig. 3.13(b) shows the corresponding graphs for $d \sin x$.

EXERCISE 3.6A

1 Write down the values of (a) $2 \cos x$, (b) $\frac{1}{2} \sin x$, (c) $3 \cos x + 4 \sin x$, for:
   (i) $x = 0$, (ii) $x = \frac{\pi}{6}$, (iii) $x = \frac{\pi}{4}$, (iv) $x = \frac{\pi}{3}$, (v) $x = \frac{\pi}{2}$, (vi) $x = \frac{2\pi}{3}$,
   (vii) $x = \frac{3\pi}{4}$, (viii) $x = \frac{5\pi}{6}$, (ix) $x = \pi$.
2 Sketch the graphs of (a) $2 \cos x$, (b) $\frac{1}{2} \sin x$, (c) $3 \cos x + 4 \sin x$, with domain $-2\pi < x < 2\pi$, using your results from question 1. Comment on the shape and the amplitude of the graph (c).
3 Tabulate the values of $\cos 2x$ and $\sin 2x$, for the values of x given in question 1, (i) to (ix), and sketch the graphs of $\cos 2x$ and $\sin 2x$ with domain $-2\pi < x < 2\pi$. Use the graphs to solve the equation $\cos 2x = \sin 2x$.
4 In each of the following cases, state which of (a) or (b) is true:
   (i) the graph of $\cos 2x$ has (a) twice, (b) half as many peaks as the graph of $\cos x$;
   (ii) the period of $\cos 2x$ is (a) twice, (b) half the period of $\cos x$;
   (iii) the graph of $\sin dx$ has (a) d, (b) $1/d$ times as many peaks as the graph of $\sin x$;
   (iv) the period of $\sin dx$ is (a) $2\pi d$, (b) $2\pi/d$.

Questions 3 and 4 above give a clue to the effect of a change in the scale for x. The graph of the function $\cos 2x$ is the same as the graph of $\cos x$ with the x-scale halved. This means that for graphs on the same scale, the graph of $\cos 2x$ is obtained from the graph of $\cos x$ by a one-way stretch parallel to Ox with scale factor $\frac{1}{2}$. The period of $\cos 2x$ is half of the period of $\cos x$, namely π. Similarly, the graph of $\cos ax$ arises from the graph of $\cos x$ by a one-way stretch parallel to Ox with scale factor $1/a$, so the period of $\cos ax$ is $2\pi/a$. The same results apply to $\sin ax$.

These results are illustrated in Fig. 3.14, by showing the graphs of $\cos x$, $\cos 3x$ and $\cos \frac{1}{2}x$. Cos $3x$ has period $2\pi/3$ and $\cos \frac{1}{2}x$ has period 4π.

The addition of a constant c to x has the effect of moving the origin to the point $(c, 0)$ so that the graph of $f(x + c)$ is the same as the graph of $f(x)$ but translated a distance $(-c)$ in the direction Ox. One illustration of this is that the graph of $\cos x$ is the graph of $\sin x$ translated a distance $\frac{1}{2}\pi$ in the negative x-direction because $\cos x = \sin (x + \frac{1}{2}\pi)$. The graph of $\cos (x + 1)$

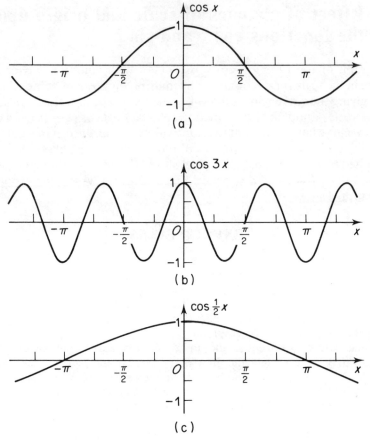

Fig. 3.14 Graphs of (a) cos x, (b) cos 3x, (c) $\cos\frac{1}{2}x$.

is the graph of cos x translated a unit distance parallel to the negative x-axis, as shown in Fig. 3.15(b).

Finally, combining scale change and origin shift, the graph of cos $(ax + b)$, that is, cos $a(x + b/a)$, is the graph of cos x stretched by a scale factor $1/a$ parallel to Ox and then translated $(-b/a)$ in the direction Ox. This is shown for the graph of cos $(3x + 2)$ in Fig. 3.15(c).

EXAMPLE   *Find a cosine function which has maximum and minimum values* $+2$ *and* -2 *respectively, period* $\pi/3$ *and the graph of which passes through the origin. What sine function has the same graph?*

The general form of a cosine function is $f(x) = d\cos a(x + c)$ and this function has maximum and minimum values $\pm d$. So we choose $d = 2$. The period of $2\cos a(x + c)$ is $2\pi/a$ since

$$\cos a\left(x + c + \frac{2\pi}{a}\right) = \cos[a(x+c) + 2\pi] = \cos a(x+c),$$

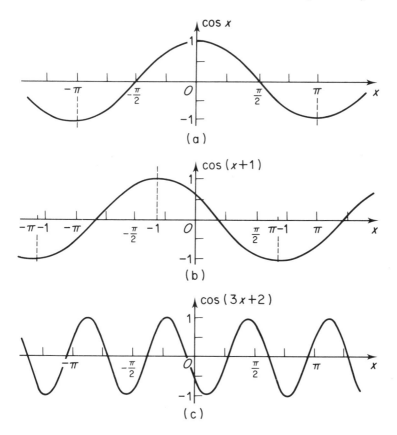

Fig. 3.15 Graphs of (a) cos x, (b) cos $(x+1)$, (c) cos $(3x+2)$

so we require $2\pi/a = \pi/3$ and $a = 6$. Finally, when $x = 0$,

$$2\cos 6(x + c) = 2\cos 6c = 0$$

when $6c$ is an odd multiple of $\frac{1}{2}\pi$. There are two essentially different cases, either $6c = \frac{1}{2}\pi$, or $6c = \frac{3}{2}\pi$, that is, $c = \pi/12$ or $c = \pi/4$, giving two functions which satisfy the given conditions, namely **$2\cos(6x+\frac{1}{2}\pi)$** and **$2\cos(6x+\frac{3}{2}\pi)$**. The corresponding sine functions are **$2\sin 6x$** and **$2\sin(6x+\pi)$**.

EXERCISE 3.6B

1 For the following functions, write down: (a) the maximum value, (b) the minimum value, (c) the period, (d) the coordinates of the three points, nearest to the origin, at which the graph of the function meets the coordinate axes Ox and Oy:

(i) $\cos 2x$ (ii) $\sin(x-1)$ (iii) $\cos(2+x)$

(iv) $2\sin\dfrac{x}{3}$ (v) $6\cos\frac{1}{2}(5x-4)$ (vi) $5\cos\dfrac{\pi}{4}(x+2)$.

2 Find a cosine function, with period $\pi/4$ and range $\{y: -3 \leqslant y \leqslant 3\}$, taking the value 3 when $x = \frac{1}{2}\pi$.

3 Show that there are two pairs of values of the constants a and b, giving two different functions $\sin(ax+b)$, both of which have period π and vanish when $x = 1$.

4 A particle moves on a straight line Ox and its distance x from O at time t is given by $x = 3 + 2\cos 3t$. Find:
(i) its greatest distance from O, (ii) its least distance from O, (iii) the time for one complete oscillation.

3.7 The addition formulae

On the unit circle, centre at the origin, let A and B be the points $(1,0)$ and $(0,1)$ on axes Ox and Oy. Let $P(x, y)$ be given by $(x, y) = (\cos\beta, \sin\beta)$, so that P corresponds to the angle β ($=$ angle AOP), (see Fig. 3.16(a)). The point P is reached from O by moving a distance x along OA and a distance y parallel to OB, that is

$$(x, y) = x(1,0) + y(0,1).$$

Consider now a rotation of the plane about O, through an angle α in the positive (anticlockwise) direction, in which A moves to A' $(\cos\alpha, \sin\alpha)$ and B moves to B' $(-\sin\alpha, \cos\alpha)$, while P moves to P' (Fig. 3.16(b)). Then P' is reached from O by moving a distance x along OA' and a distance y parallel to OB', so that the coordinates of P' are (x', y'), given by

$$\begin{aligned}(x', y') &= x(\cos\alpha, \sin\alpha) + y(-\sin\alpha, \cos\alpha) \\ &= (x\cos\alpha - y\sin\alpha, \ x\sin\alpha + y\cos\alpha) \\ &= (\cos\beta\cos\alpha - \sin\beta\sin\alpha, \ \cos\beta\sin\alpha + \sin\beta\cos\alpha).\end{aligned}$$

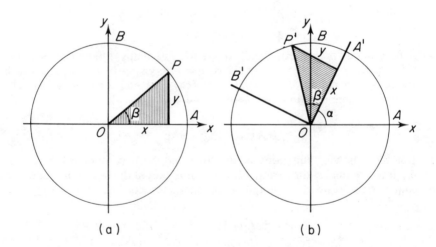

(a)   (b)

Fig. 3.16

But angle $AOP' = (\alpha + \beta)$ and so P' represents the angle $(\alpha + \beta)$ and has coordinates $(\cos\{\alpha + \beta\}, \sin\{\alpha + \beta\})$. Comparing these two forms for the coordinates of P', we find that

$$\cos(\alpha + \beta) = \cos\alpha\cos\beta - \sin\alpha\sin\beta,$$
$$\sin(\alpha + \beta) = \sin\alpha\cos\beta + \cos\alpha\sin\beta.$$

These formulae are the addition formulae for cosine and sine.

For negative angles, since $\cos(-\beta) = \cos\beta$ and $\sin(-\beta) = -\sin\beta$:

$$\cos(\alpha - \beta) = \cos\alpha\cos\beta + \sin\alpha\sin\beta,$$
$$\sin(\alpha - \beta) = \sin\alpha\cos\beta - \cos\alpha\sin\beta.$$

If we now put $\alpha = \beta = \theta$ into the addition formulae we obtain the double angle formulae

$$\cos 2\theta = \cos^2\theta - \sin^2\theta,$$
$$\sin 2\theta = 2\sin\theta\cos\theta.$$

Also, since $\cos^2\theta + \sin^2\theta = 1$, we may write $\sin^2\theta = 1 - \cos^2\theta$ and $\cos^2\theta = 1 - \sin^2\theta$ to obtain

$$\cos 2\theta = 2\cos^2\theta - 1$$
$$= 1 - 2\sin^2\theta.$$

These formulae are now summarised, using capital italic letters for the angles, instead of greek. They should be learned by heart so that they can be instantly recalled when needed. Access to tables of formulae is not a satisfactory alternative to knowing these formulae thoroughly.

The addition and double angle formulae

$$\cos(A + B) = \cos A\cos B - \sin A\sin B$$
$$\sin(A + B) = \sin A\cos B + \cos A\sin B$$
$$\cos(A - B) = \cos A\cos B + \sin A\sin B$$
$$\sin(A - B) = \sin A\cos B - \cos A\sin B$$
$$\cos 2A = \cos^2 A - \sin^2 A$$
$$= 2\cos^2 A - 1$$
$$= 1 - 2\sin^2 A$$
$$\sin 2A = 2\sin A\cos A$$

EXAMPLE 1   *Express $\cos 3A$ in terms of $\cos A$.*

$$\cos 3A = \cos(2A + A) = \cos 2A\cos A - \sin 2A\sin A$$
$$= \cos A\,(2\cos^2 A - 1) - 2\sin^2 A\cos A$$
$$= 2\cos^3 A - \cos A - 2(1 - \cos^2 A)\cos A$$
$$= \mathbf{4\cos^3 A - 3\cos A.}$$

EXAMPLE 2   *Simplify* $\dfrac{\sin 2A\,(2\cos 2A+1)}{2\sin 3A}$

$$\sin 3A = \sin (2A+A) = \sin 2A \cos A + \cos 2A \sin A$$
$$= 2 \sin A \cos^2 A + (2 \cos^2 A - 1)\sin A$$
$$= \sin A(4 \cos^2 A - 1).$$

So $$\frac{\sin 2A\,(2\cos 2A+1)}{2\sin 3A} = \frac{2 \sin A \cos A\,(2(2 \cos^2 A - 1)+1)}{2 \sin A\,(4 \cos^2 A - 1)}$$

$$= \frac{4 \cos^2 A - 1}{4 \cos^2 A - 1}\cos A = \cos A.$$

EXERCISE 3.7

1   Verify that a rotation α takes the point P $(\cos \beta, \sin \beta)$ into the point P' $(\cos \alpha \cos \beta - \sin \alpha \sin \beta,\ \cos \alpha \sin \beta + \sin \alpha \cos \beta)$ in the cases:
(i) $\alpha = \pi/3,\ \beta = \pi/3$;   (ii) $\alpha = \pi/3,\ \beta = \pi/6$;   (iii) $\alpha = \pi/3,\ \beta = \pi/2$;
(iv) $\alpha = 2\pi/3,\ \beta = 5\pi/6$;   (v) $\alpha = 5\pi/6,\ \beta = 5\pi/3$;
(vi) $\alpha = -\pi/3,\ \beta = 4\pi/3$.

2   Check that the sum and difference formulae for cosine and sine give the correct results in the cases when:
(i) $A = 2\pi,\ B = \theta$;   (ii) $A = \pi,\ B = \theta$;   (iii) $A = \tfrac{1}{2}\pi,\ B = \theta$;
(iv) $A = \theta,\ B = \pi$;   (v) $A = \theta,\ B = \tfrac{1}{2}\pi$.

3   Use the addition formulae for sine and cosine to prove that:
(i) $\tan (A+B) = \dfrac{\tan A + \tan B}{1 - \tan A \tan B}$;   (ii) $\tan (A-B) = \dfrac{\tan A - \tan B}{1 + \tan A \tan B}$;
(iii) $\tan 2A = \dfrac{2 \tan A}{1 - \tan^2 A}$.

4   Simplify the following:
(i) $\sin (A+B) + \sin (A-B)$;   (ii) $\cos (A+B) + \cos (A-B)$;
(iii) $\cos A \cos 2A - \sin A \sin 2A$;   (iv) $\cos A \cos 2A + \sin A \sin 2A$;
(v) $\cos A \cos (A+B) + \sin A \sin (A+B)$;   (vi) $\dfrac{\cos (A-B) - \cos (A+B)}{\sin (A+B) + \sin (A-B)}$;
(vii) $\dfrac{\cos (A+B) + \cos (A-B)}{\sin (A+B) - \sin (A-B)}$;
(viii) $\sin A + \sin B \cos (A+B) + \cos B \sin (B-A)$;
(ix) $\tfrac{1}{2} \tan 4A\,(1 - \tan^2 2A)$;   (x) $\dfrac{\cos 2A}{\cos A + \sin A}$;   (xi) $\dfrac{\sin 2A}{1 + \cos 2A}$;
(xii) $\dfrac{\sin 2A + \cos 2A + 1}{\sin 2A - \cos 2A + 1}$;   (xiii) $\dfrac{\sin 3A + \sin A}{2 \sin 2A}$;   (xiv) $\dfrac{\cos 3A + \cos A}{2 \cos 2A}$.

5   Find, without using tables or calculators, the values of $\cos 2A$, $\sin 2A$ and $\tan 2A$ in each of the following cases:
(i) $\sin A = 4/5$, and A is acute;   (ii) $\sin A = 4/5$, and A is obtuse;

(iii) $\cos A = 5/13$, and $0 < A < \pi$;   (iv) $\cos A = 5/13$, $-\pi < A < 0$;
(v) $\tan A = 9/40$, and A is acute.

6   Prove that
$$\frac{\sin\theta + \sin 2\theta}{1 + \cos\theta + \cos 2\theta} = \tan\theta,$$
where $\cos\theta \neq -\frac{1}{2}$ and $\cos\theta \neq 0$.   (L)

7   Prove that $\sin 3\theta = 3\sin\theta - 4\sin^3\theta$.
Given that $\sin 3\theta = \sin^2\theta$, find three possible values for $\sin\theta$. Hence find all the solutions of the equation $\sin 3\theta = \sin^2\theta$ for $90° \leqslant \theta \leqslant 270°$.
Using the same axes, sketch the graphs of the functions $\sin 3\theta$ and $\sin^2\theta$ for $90° \leqslant \theta \leqslant 270°$. Find the subset of values of θ for which $\sin 3\theta > \sin^2\theta$.   (L)

8   Prove that $\tan 3A = \dfrac{3\tan A - \tan^3 A}{1 - 3\tan^2 A}$.

9   Find the solutions in the range $0° \leqslant \theta \leqslant 180°$ of each of the following equations
(i) $\sin 2\theta = \cos\theta$,
(ii) $2\cos 2\theta = 1 + 4\cos\theta$.   (JMB)

10   When $\cos\theta \neq 0$, simplify $(\cos 2\theta + \tan\theta \sin 2\theta)^{-1}$.   (L)

11   Without using tables evaluate $\{\sin(7\pi/12) + \cos(7\pi/12)\}^2$.   (L)

12   Simplify $\dfrac{\sin 4\theta\,(1 - \cos 2\theta)}{\cos 2\theta\,(1 - \cos 4\theta)}$, where $\cos 2\theta\,(1 - \cos 4\theta) \neq 0$.   (L)

13   Express $\tan(45° + \theta)$ in terms of $\tan\theta$. Hence, or otherwise,
(i) express $\tan 75°$ in the form $a + b\sqrt{3}$ where a and b are integers;
(ii) express $\tan(45° + \theta) + \cot(45° + \theta)$ in terms of $\cos 2\theta$.   (JMB)

14   Given that X is the acute angle such that $\sin X = 4/5$ and Y is the obtuse angle such that $\sin Y = 12/13$, find the exact value of $\tan(X + Y)$.   (L)

3.8 The triangle formulae

Reminder   The three angles of the triangle ABC are denoted by A, B and C, and the sides BC, CA, AB are denoted by a, b, c respectively. Let BN be the altitude from B and consider the two cases in Fig. 3.17, (a) when the angle A is acute and (b) when A is obtuse. Of course, A is a right-angle if and only if $A = N$.

(a)

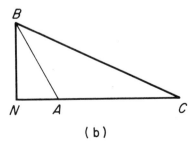
(b)

Fig. 3.17

Let the area of the triangle ABC be Δ, then $\Delta = \frac{1}{2}AC \cdot BN$ and in (a)

$$BN = AB \sin A = c \sin A,$$

while in (b)

$$BN = AB \sin BAN = c \sin (\pi - A).$$

But $\sin (\pi - A) = \sin A$ and so in each case

$$\Delta = \frac{1}{2}bc \sin A.$$

Similar results are obtained by permuting a, b, c and A, B, C, that is, by replacing a by b, b by c, c by a, A by B, B by C and C by A. We then obtain the sine formulae for a triangle ABC, the area of which is Δ:

$$\Delta = \frac{1}{2}ab \sin C = \frac{1}{2}bc \sin A = \frac{1}{2}ca \sin B,$$

and, on dividing these equations by $\frac{1}{2}abc$,

$$\frac{\sin A}{a} = \frac{\sin B}{b} = \frac{\sin C}{c}.$$

These ratios are also connected to the radius of the circumcircle of the triangle. Let this circumcircle have centre O and let BO meet the circle again at Q (see Fig. 3.18). Then angle BCQ is a right angle, being the angle in a semicircle, and angle BQC equals angle A in (a) and angle $(\pi - A)$ in (b), since these angles are subtended on the circle by BC. Applying sine formula to triangle BCQ, we find that $\sin A/a = 1/2R$ where R is the radius of the circumcircle, and so

$$\frac{a}{\sin A} = \frac{b}{\sin B} = \frac{c}{\sin C} = 2R.$$

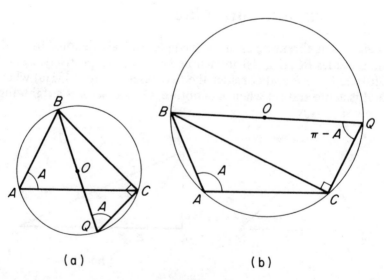

(a)   (b)

Fig. 3.18

Returning now to Fig. 3.17, $AN = AB \cos BAN$, so in (a) $AN = AB \cos A$ and in (b) $AN = AB \cos(\pi - A) = -AB \cos A$. We now use Pythagoras' theorem on the right-angled triangles, in the two cases.

(a) $\quad a^2 = BC^2 = BN^2 + NC^2 = AB^2 - AN^2 + (AC - AN)^2$

$\qquad = AB^2 - AN^2 + AC^2 - 2AC \cdot AN + AN^2$

$\qquad = AC^2 + AB^2 - 2AC \cdot AB \cos A = b^2 + c^2 - 2bc \cos A.$

(b) $\quad a^2 = BC^2 = BN^2 + NC^2 = AB^2 - AN^2 + (AC + AN)^2$

$\qquad = AB^2 - AN^2 + AC^2 + 2AC \cdot AN + AN^2$

$\qquad = AC^2 + AB^2 - 2AC \cdot AB \cos A = b^2 + c^2 - 2bc \cos A.$

Both cases give rise to the cosine formula for the triangle,

$$a^2 = b^2 + c^2 - 2bc \cos A.$$

Note that when the angle BAC is a right-angle, $A = \pi/2, \cos A = 0,$ and the cosine formula becomes Pythagoras' theorem, $a^2 = b^2 + c^2.$

Solution of triangles

The sine and cosine formulae are useful in calculating unknown angles and sides of a triangle. The list shows the appropriate formula, according to the given information, and the methods are then illustrated by examples.

Information given	Formula to use
2 angles and 1 side	sine formula
2 sides and non-included angle	sine formula
2 sides and included angle	cosine formula
3 sides	cosine formula

EXAMPLE 1 *In the triangle ABC, the angles $A = 42°$, $B = 73°$ and the side AB is of length 0·5 m. Solve the triangle and find the radius R of its circumcircle.*

Since $A + B + C = 180°$, $C = 180° - 42° - 73° = 65°$ and, on using the sine formula, since $AB = c = 0.5$ m,

$$\frac{a}{\sin 42°} = \frac{b}{\sin 73°} = \frac{0.5}{\sin 65°} = 2R \quad \text{(see Fig. 3.19(a)).}$$

Hence $\qquad a = \dfrac{0.5 \sin 42°}{\sin 65°} = 0.37 \text{ m}, \quad b = \dfrac{0.5 \sin 73°}{\sin 65°} = 0.53 \text{ m},$

and $R = \dfrac{1}{2} \dfrac{0.5}{\sin 65°} = 0.28 \text{ m}.$

When a triangle is to be determined given two sides and a non-included angle, there is some difficulty, since it is possible that two, one or no triangles fit the conditions. Suppose that, for triangle ABC, we are given the angle A and the sides $a = BC$ and $c = AB$ (Fig. 3.19(b)). Then C must

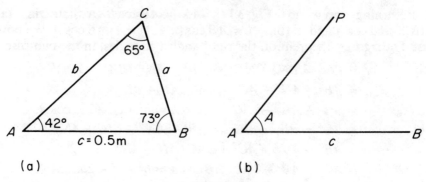

Fig. 3.19

lie on the line AP, such that angle BAP is the required angle A. Also C must lie on the circle, centre B and radius $a(= BC)$. Now this circle may meet AP in one or two points, or it may touch AP at one point, or it may not meet AP at all. The four possibilities are shown in Fig. 3.20, (a), (b), (c) and (d).

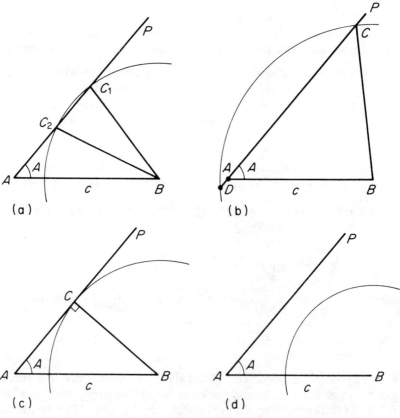

Fig. 3.20

(a) The circle meets AP in C_1 and C_2 and there are two possible triangles ABC_1 and ABC_2, satisfying the conditions.
(b) The circle meets AP at C and PA produced at D, so there is only one possible triangle ABC.
(c) The circle touches AP at C, giving a right-angled triangle ABC.
(d) The circle does not meet AP at all and no triangle exists.

The sine formula allows us to calculate the angle C, using $\sin C = (c/a) \sin A$, and the various possibilities are shown in Example **2**.

EXAMPLE 2 *Solve the triangle* ABC, *given that* $A = 40°$, $c = 10$ *and:*
(a) $a = 9$, (b) $a = 11$, (c) $a = 6{\cdot}428$, (d) $a = 6$.

(a) $\sin C = (10/9) \sin 40° = 0{\cdot}7142$, so $C = \mathbf{45{\cdot}6°}$ **or** $\mathbf{134{\cdot}4°}$. Then $B = \mathbf{94{\cdot}4°}$ **or** $\mathbf{5{\cdot}6°}$ and $b = a (\sin B/\sin A)$ so $b = \mathbf{14{\cdot}0}$ **or** $\mathbf{1{\cdot}4}$. This is a case where there are two possible triangles (see Fig. 3.20(a)).
(b) $\sin C = (10/11) \sin 40° = 0{\cdot}5843$, so $C = 35{\cdot}8°$ or $144{\cdot}2°$. In the latter case, $A + C = 184{\cdot}2°$, which is impossible since this is greater than $180°$. There is one triangle, as in Fig. 3.20(b), with $C = \mathbf{35{\cdot}8°}$, $B = \mathbf{104{\cdot}2°}$ and $b = \mathbf{16{\cdot}6}$.
(c) $\sin C = (10/6{\cdot}428) \sin 40° = 1$, so $C = \mathbf{90°}$ and we have the case (c) of Fig. 3.20. Then $B = \mathbf{50°}$ and $b = \mathbf{7{\cdot}660}$.
(d) $\sin C = (10/6) \sin 40° = 1{\cdot}071$, which is greater than 1 so **no solution** is possible, as in Fig. 3.20(d).

EXAMPLE 3 *Solve the triangle* ABC *where* $b = 9$, $c = 8$ *and* $A = 50°$.

Using the cosine formula,

$$a^2 = 9^2 + 8^2 - 2.9.8 \cos 50° = 81 + 64 - 92{\cdot}56 = 52{\cdot}44,$$

so $a = \mathbf{7{\cdot}24}$. The other angles may now be calculated using the sine formula.

$$\sin B = (b/a) \sin A = 0{\cdot}9521$$

and so $B = 72{\cdot}2°$ or $107{\cdot}8°$.

$$\sin C = (c/a) \sin A = 0{\cdot}8463$$

and so $C = 57{\cdot}8°$ or $122{\cdot}2°$. Since $A + B + C = 180°$, the only possible solution is $B = \mathbf{72{\cdot}2°}$, $C = \mathbf{57{\cdot}8°}$.

EXAMPLE 4 *Solve the triangle* ABC *when* $a = 8$, $b = 9$, $c = 10$, *and find its area.*

By the cosine formula,

$$\cos A = \frac{b^2 + c^2 - a^2}{2bc} = \frac{81 + 100 - 64}{180} = 0{\cdot}65$$

so $A = \mathbf{49{\cdot}5°}$. The triangle is clearly acute angled, so by the sine formula,

$$\sin B = (9/8) \sin 49{\cdot}5° = 0{\cdot}855$$

and $B = 58 \cdot 8°$. Then

$$C = 180° - 58 \cdot 8° - 49 \cdot 5° \text{ and } C = 72 \cdot 7°.$$

The area of the triangle is

$$\Delta = \tfrac{1}{2}bc \sin A = \tfrac{1}{2} . 9 . 10 . \sin 49 \cdot 5° = 34 \cdot 2.$$

EXERCISE 3.8

1 Solve the triangle ABC given that:
  (i) $A = 75°$, $B = 55°$, $c = 9$; (ii) $B = 68°$, $C = 82°$, $c = 15$;
  (iii) $A = 121°$, $C = 13°$, $a = 3$; (iv) $A = 32°$, $C = 87°$, $b = 22$.
2 Solve the triangle ABC given that:
  (i) $A = 15°$, $a = 2$, $b = 3$; (ii) $B = 82°$, $b = 5$, $c = 4$;
  (iii) $B = 38°$, $a = 12$, $b = 9$; (iv) $C = 150°$, $a = 6$, $c = 10$;
  (v) $A = 93°$, $a = 7$, $c = 2$; (vi) $A = 41°$, $b = 13$, $a = 18$.
3 Solve the triangle ABC given that:
  (i) $A = 34°$, $b = 5$, $c = 7$; (ii) $C = 58°$, $a = 12$, $b = 8$;
  (iii) $B = 111°$, $a = 9$, $c = 3$; (iv) $a = 4$, $b = 5$, $c = 6$;
  (v) $a = 13$, $b = 5$, $c = 12$; (vi) $a = 3$, $b = 7$, $c = 5$.
4 The area of an acute-angled triangle ABC is $12 \, \text{m}^2$. Given that $AB = 5 \, \text{m}$, $BC = 8 \, \text{m}$, find the length of CA. (L)
5 With the usual notation in a triangle ABC, $a = 7$, $b = 5$ and $c = 4$. Without using tables, find $\cos A$ as a fraction in its lowest terms, and prove that
$$\sin B = \frac{2\sqrt{6}}{7}.$$ (L)

6 Calculate in degrees and minutes the smallest angle of a triangle whose sides are of length 6, 7 and 8 cm. (L)
7 In $\triangle ABC$, $BC = 10 \, \text{cm}$ and $\angle BAC = 60°$.
  (a) Calculate the radius of the circle passing through A, B and C.
  (b) Given that AC is a diameter of this circle, calculate the area of $\triangle ABC$. (Answers may be left in surd form.) (L)
8 (i) In $\triangle ABC$, M is the mid-point of BC.
  (a) Show that $\cos \angle AMB + \cos \angle AMC = 0$.
  (b) By applying the cosine rule in $\triangle ABM$ and in $\triangle ACM$, or otherwise, prove that
$$4 \, AM^2 = 2 \, CA^2 + 2 \, AB^2 - BC^2.$$

  (ii) Giving your answers to one decimal place, solve, for $0 \leqslant \theta \leqslant 360$, the equations
  (a) $\sin \theta° = \tfrac{3}{5}$,
  (b) $\sin \theta° = -\tfrac{3}{4}$. (L)
9 Three forts A, B and C are situated in a flat desert region. A is 8 km due west of B, and C is 3 km due east of B. An oasis O is situated to the north of the line ABC and is 7 km from both A and C. Calculate
  (a) the distance between O and B,
  (b) the bearing of O from B.
  A mine M is situated to the south of ABC. The bearing of M from A is $135°$ and the bearing of M from C is $210°$.
  (c) Calculate the distance between M and B. (L)

MISCELLANEOUS EXERCISE 3

1 (i) Find the angles between $0°$ and $360°$ which satisfy the equations
    (a) $\cot 2x = 2 + \cot x$,
    (b) $\cos 3x - 3 \cos x = \cos 2x + 1$.
    (ii) Find the smallest angle of the triangle in which $a = 12 \cdot 45$, $b = 8 \cdot 76$ and
    $c = 13 \cdot 89$.   (*L*)

2 Prove that in *any* triangle ABC, with the usual notation,

$$a^2 = b^2 + c^2 - 2bc \cos A.$$

  A convex quadrilateral $ABCD$ has $AB = 5$ cm, $BC = 8$ cm, $CD = 3$ cm, $DA = 3$ cm and $BD = 7$ cm. Find the angles DAB, BCD and show that the quadrilateral is cyclic.
  Show also that $AC = 39/7$ cm.   (*L*)

3 The points A, B, C lie on a circle with centre O.
  Given that $AB = 11$ m, $BC = 13$ m, $CA = 20$ m, find the angles AOB, BOC, COA to the nearest tenth of a degree and the radius of the circle to the nearest tenth of a metre.   (*L*)

4 In a triangle ABC, $AB = x$, $BC = (x + 2)$ and $AC = (x - 2)$, where $x > 4$.
  Prove that

$$\cos A = \frac{x - 8}{2(x - 2)}.$$

  Find the set of integral values of x for which A is obtuse.   (*L*)

5 In the triangle ABC, given that $A - B = 90°$ and $a + b = 2c$,
  (a) prove that $\cos 2A - \cos 2B + 2 \sin C = 0$,

  (b) show that $\dfrac{a + b}{c} = \dfrac{\sin A + \sin B}{\sin C}$ and hence prove that $\sin \dfrac{C}{2} = \dfrac{1}{2\sqrt{2}}$.
         (*L*)

6 In the triangle ABC, AB is of unit length and $BC = CA = p$. The point P lies on AB at a distance x from A and is such that $\angle ACP = \theta$ and $\angle BCP = 2\theta$. By using the sine rule, or otherwise, show that

$$\cos \theta = \frac{1 - x}{2x}.$$

  State the range of possible values of θ as p varies and deduce that $\frac{1}{3} < x < \frac{1}{2}$. Express $\cos 3\theta$ in terms of p. Hence, or otherwise, find the value of x correct to two decimal places when $p = 1/\sqrt{2}$.   (*JMB*)

7 The triangle OMN is horizontal with angles NOM and ONM equal to θ and ϕ respectively. MA and NB are equal lines drawn vertically upwards and angles AOM and BON are α and β respectively. Prove that

$$\cot \phi = \tan \alpha \cot \beta \operatorname{cosec} \theta - \cot \theta.$$

8 Use standard formulae to prove that, for any angles A, B,

$$\cos (A + B) - \sin (A - B) = (\cos A - \sin A)(\cos B + \sin B).$$

  If $\cos (A + B)$ is equal to $\sin (A - B)$, what can you deduce about the values, in degrees, of A and/or B?   (*SMP*)

9 Solve, for $0 \leqslant \theta \leqslant 2\pi$, the equation $\sin \left(\theta + \dfrac{\pi}{4} \right) = 2 \cos \left(\theta - \dfrac{\pi}{4} \right)$.   (*L*)

10 Find all the angles θ between $0°$ and $360°$ such that $2\cos 2\theta = 1$.   *(SMP)*

11 Given that $\sin x = 0.6$ and that $\cos x = -0.8$, evaluate $\cos(x + 270°)$ and $\cos(x + 540°)$.   *(L)*

12 (i) Solve, for $0 \leqslant \theta \leqslant 2\pi$, the equation $6\sin^2\theta + \cos\theta - 5 = 0$.

(ii) Given that $5\cos\theta° - 12\sin\theta° \equiv R\cos(\theta° + \alpha°)$, where $R > 0$ and $0 < \alpha < 90$, calculate

(a) the value of R,

(b) the value of α to 1 decimal place.

Hence solve, for $0 \leqslant \theta \leqslant 360$, the equation $5\cos\theta° - 12\sin\theta° = 6\frac{1}{2}$.   *(L)*

13 (a) Starting with the formulae for $\sin(A - B)$ and $\cos(A - B)$ prove that

$$\tan(A - B) = \frac{\tan A - \tan B}{1 + \tan A \tan B}.$$

(b) State the values of $\tan\dfrac{\pi}{4}$ and $\tan\dfrac{\pi}{6}$ and hence prove that $\tan\dfrac{\pi}{12} = \dfrac{\sqrt{3} - 1}{\sqrt{3} + 1}$.

(c) Given that $\sin\left(\theta - \dfrac{\pi}{12}\right) = 2\cos\left(\theta + \dfrac{\pi}{12}\right)$, prove that $\tan\theta = \dfrac{3\sqrt{3} + 1}{3\sqrt{3} - 1}$.

(L)

14 The depth of water at the entrance to a harbour t hours after high tide is D metres, where $D = p + q\cos(rt°)$ for suitable constants p, q, r. At high tide the depth is 7 m; at low tide 6 hours later the depth is 3 m.

(a) Show that $r = 30$ and find the values of p and q.

(b) Sketch the graph of D against t for $0 \leqslant t \leqslant 12$.

(c) Find how soon after low tide a ship which requires a depth of at least 4 m of water will be able to enter harbour.   *(L)*

15 Students have been known to make the mistake of writing $\sin A + \sin B$ in place of $\sin(A + B)$.

Prove that these two expressions are equal only if

(a) $\sin\frac{1}{2}A = 0$ or (b) $\sin\frac{1}{2}B = 0$ or (c) $\sin\frac{1}{2}(A + B) = 0$.

What can you deduce about the values of A and B in these three cases?

(SMP)

4 Differentiation I

4.1 Linear relations and scale changes

Linear functions (see Chapter 1)

A linear function f is given by $f(x) = mx + c$, where m and c are constants. The graph of f is a straight line. The equation of a line in two-dimensional Cartesian coordinates is

$$ax + by + d = 0,$$

with a, b, d constant, and, if $a \neq 0 \neq b$, this equation gives a linear relation between x and y.

Gradient

The *gradient* of a linear function is defined to be the gradient, or slope, of its graph. Let f be a linear function with $f(x) = mx + c$; then the graph of f is the line with equation $y = mx + c$ and gradient m. On this graph consider the two points:

P with coordinates (x, y) where $y = mx + c$

and $\quad P_1$ with coordinates (x_1, y_1) where $y_1 = mx_1 + c$, (see Fig. 4.1).

From P to P_1 the change in the variable x is $(x_1 - x)$ and the change in y is given by $(y_1 - y) = m(x_1 - x)$, namely m times the change in x. Thus the function f implies a change of scale between x and y. We say that:

m is the *rate of change* of y with respect to x.

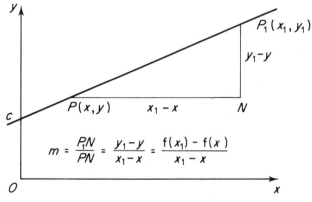

Fig. 4.1 Graph of f, where $f(x) = mx + c$, $m > 0$.

Note: This graph is drawn with the gradient m of f positive so that y increases as x increases. When m is negative, y decreases as x increases.

EXERCISE 4.1

1 Redraw the graph of Fig. 4.1 in the cases:
   (i) $c < 0 < m$; (ii) $m < 0 < c$; (iii) $c < 0$ and $m < 0$.
2 The points A, B, C have coordinates $(-1, 2), (3, 5), (2, -3)$, respectively. Draw the three lines AB, BC, CA on a graph and find their gradients.
3 Plot the points A (1, 1) and B (4, 2) on a graph and find the gradient of the line AB. Draw lines through A and B with gradients 1.5 and -2 respectively and find the coordinates of the point C where these two lines intersect.
4 Given that the x-coordinates of P and Q are 1 and 2 respectively, find the gradient of the chord PQ of the curve with equation:
   (i) $y = 3x - 2$; (ii) $y = 5x^2 + 3x - 4$; (iii) $y = 4 - 3x^2$; (iv) $y = x^2 - x^3$.
5 Sketch the graph of the function f where $f(x) = 2x^2 - 1$ for values of x between 1 and 3. Let P be the point (2, 7) on the graph and Q the point $(x, f(x))$ on the graph. Complete the table:

x	1·0	1·3	1·6	1·8	1·9	2·0	2·1	2·2	2·4	2·7	3·0
$f(x)$	1·0					7·0					17·0
Gradient PQ	6·0					—					10·0

From this table, deduce the value that you think the gradient of PQ approaches as the value of x tends to 2·0. Use a ruler to draw a tangent to the graph of f at P, as carefully as you can, judging the position by eye. Measure the gradient of this tangent and compare your result with the limit of the gradient of PQ which you previously deduced.

4.2 Speed

If a car is travelling at a steady speed of 60 km/h, then it will travel 60 kilometres in 1 hour, or 1 kilometre in 1 minute. The distance travelled in x hours will be y kilometres, where $y = 60x$, so y is a linear function of x. In practice, the speed of the car is not constant for a journey; the car has to start and stop at zero speed, otherwise travelling would be most uncomfortable!

When the car travels y kilometres in x hours, the ratio y/x is the average speed in km p h. However the speedometer in the car measures the speed at each instant of time, and this speed will vary throughout the journey. Whatever the speed changes that are made during the journey, suppose that the car travels a total distance y kilometres in a time x hours after the start of the journey. Then the relationship between x and y will be given by some function f, with $y = f(x)$. When the speed is constant, say m km p h, then f is a linear function with gradient m. In general, f will not be a linear function and its graph might be as shown in Fig. 4.2. On taking two points, P (x, y) and P_1 (x_1, y_1), on the graph, the car is seen to travel the distance

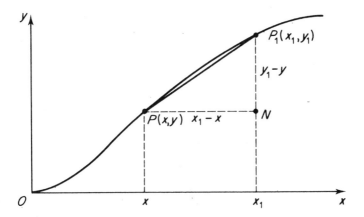

Fig. 4.2 Distance-time graph for a car journey.

$(y_1 - y)$ km in the time $(x_1 - x)$ hours, so that the average speed in this time interval is $(y_1 - y)/(x_1 - x)$ km p h. Now

$$\frac{y_1 - y}{x_1 - x} = \frac{f(x_1) - f(x)}{x_1 - x}$$

and this is the slope (or gradient) of the line PP_1.

The speed of the car at P, that is, x hours after the start of the journey, measured by the speedometer, may be interpreted from the graph in the following way. Keep x (and so P) fixed and consider a succession of points $P_n (x_n, y_n)$ on the graph, $n = 1, 2, 3, \ldots$, approaching P (Fig. 4.3).

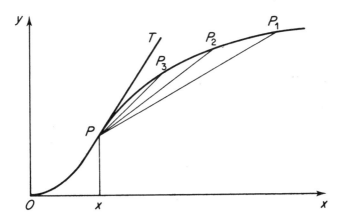

Fig. 4.3 Graph of $y = f(x)$ with chords PP_n and tangent PT.

In the time interval $(x_n - x)$ hours, the car moves $(y_n - y)$ kilometres, so its average speed in km p h is $(y_n - y)/(x_n - x)$, the gradient of the chord PP_n. As P_n approaches P along the graph, the time interval $x_n - x$ becomes very small and the speed in this time interval approaches the instantaneous speed at P. Also, as P_n approaches P, the chord PP_n approaches the tangent PT to the graph at P. Thus, the gradient of the tangent PT will give the speed at P, that is, x hours after the start.

EXERCISE 4.2

1   The distance travelled by a racing car in x seconds after starting is y metres where $y = \frac{1}{4}x^2 \, (64 - x^2)$.
   (a) Draw the distance-time graph for $x = 0$ to $x = 5$.
   (b) Draw a sequence of chords PP_1, PP_2, ..., where $P_n \, (x_n, y_n)$ is approaching the point $P \, (2, 60)$ with $x_n > 2$, and calculate the gradients of these chords.
   (c) Repeat (b) for chords PP_n, where $x_n < 2$.
   (d) Use the above calculations to estimate the speed of the car 2 seconds after starting.

4.3 The gradient of a function

The *gradient* of the function f at the point $P(x, f(x))$ is defined to be the slope (or gradient) of the tangent at P to the graph of f and is denoted by $f'(x)$.

   If $y = f(x)$ then $f'(x)$ is denoted by $\dfrac{dy}{dx}$ and is called the *derivative* of y with respect to x or, alternatively, the *differential coefficient* of y with respect to x.

   In the case of a linear function f (see §4.1), $f'(x) = \dfrac{dy}{dx}$ is the rate of change of y with respect to x. For a general function, $\dfrac{dy}{dx}$ is the instantaneous rate of change of y with respect to x, but the word 'instantaneous' is usually omitted. The speed of the car in §4.2 at a time x hours after the start of the journey is $f'(x)$ km p h.

Note: the symbol $\dfrac{dy}{dx}$ is read as 'dee y by dee x' and is *not a fraction*. In fact, the three letters $\dfrac{d}{dx}$ form a differential operator which changes y into its derivative. Thus, when $y = 2x^2 + x$ we write $\dfrac{dy}{dx} = \dfrac{d}{dx}(2x^2 + x)$.

4.4 Estimating the gradient of a function using the tangent to its graph

If the graph of the function f is carefully drawn, the value of $f'(x)$ can be estimated by drawing a tangent to the graph at $(x, f(x))$ and measuring its slope.

EXAMPLE *Draw a graph of the function* f, *with domain* $-2 \leqslant x \leqslant 4$ *and* $f(x) = x^3$. *Draw a tangent to the graph at each point for which* $x \in \{-1, 0, 1, 2, 3\}$ *and estimate the values of* $f'(x)$, $x \in \{-1, 0, 1, 2, 3\}$. *Compare these estimates with the corresponding values of* $g(x)$, *where* $g(x) = 3x^2$, *by drawing the graph of* g *and on it marking the points* $(x, f'(x))$, $x \in \{-1, 0, 1, 2, 3\}$.

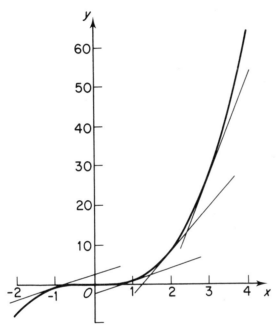

(a) Graph of x^3 with tangents used to measure gradient

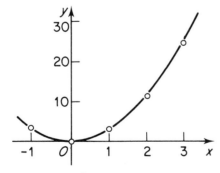

(b) Graph of $3x^2$, with measured values of the gradient of x^3

Fig. 4.4

The results are displayed in the form of a table overleaf and Fig. 4.4.

x	-2	-1	0	1	2	3	4
$f(x) = x^3$	-8	-1	0	1	8	27	64
Gradient of tangent $= f'(x)$ (from graph)	—	3.2	0	$3{\cdot}1$	$11{\cdot}3$	25	—
$g(x) = 3x^2$	—	3	0	3	12	27	—

Note that the estimate for $f'(x)$ is close to the value of $g(x)$.

EXERCISE 4.4

1   In each of the cases below, draw the graph of the function f and draw tangents at each of the points given by values of x in the set S. Measure the gradients of these tangents to estimate values of $f'(x)$. Mark the points $(x, f'(x))$ on a graph of $g(x)$ for the given function g.
    (i) $f(x) = x^2$, $-3 \leqslant x \leqslant 3$, $S = \{-2, -1, 0, 1, 2\}$, $g(x) = 2x$;
    (ii) $f(x) = x^2 - 4$, $-3 \leqslant x \leqslant 3$, $S = \{-2, -1, 0, 1, 2\}$, $g(x) = 2x$;
    (iii) $f(x) = x^2 - 4x$, $-1 \leqslant x \leqslant 5$, $S = \{0, 1, 2, 3, 4\}$, $g(x) = 2x - 4$;
    (iv) $f(x) = x^3 - 3x^2$, $-2 \leqslant x \leqslant 4$, $S = \{-1, 0, 1, 2, 3\}$, $g(x) = 3x^2 - 6x$.

4.5 Use of chords of the graph of a function to estimate its gradient

We saw in §4.3 that the tangent to a graph at a point P is the limiting position of chords PP_n as the point P_n approaches P along the graph, and the gradient at P is the limiting value of the gradient of PP_n. Hence, we can find $f'(x)$ by taking P as the point $(x, f(x))$ and choosing points $P_1, P_2, P_3, \ldots$ near to P on the graph and plotting a graph of the slopes of the chords $PP_1, PP_2, PP_3, \ldots$ as is shown in the next example.

EXAMPLE   *On the graph of the function* f, *where* $f(x) = x^3$, *mark the points* $P(x, f(x))$, $P_n(x_n, f(x_n))$, *where* $x = 2$, $x_1 = -1$, $x_2 = 0$, $x_3 = 1$, $x_4 = 3$, $x_5 = 4$. *For each of the five values of n, find* y_n *the gradient of the chord* PP_n *and on another graph plot the points* (x_n, y_n). *Join these points by a smooth curve and hence estimate* $f'(x)$; *the gradient of* f *at* P.

Point	P	P_1	P_2	P_3	P_4	P_5
x	2	-1	0	1	3	4
$f(x) = x^3$	8	-1	0	1	27	64
$f(x) - f(2)$	0	-9	-8	-7	19	56
$x - 2$	0	-3	-2	-1	1	2
Gradient PP_n $\dfrac{f(x) - f(2)}{x - 2}$	—	3	4	7	19	28

The graph of the gradient of PP_n passes through $(2, 12)$, so $f'(2) = 12$, as can be seen in Fig. 4.5.

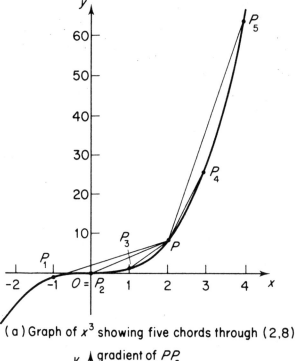

(a) Graph of x^3 showing five chords through $(2,8)$

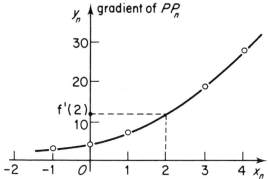

(b) Graph of the gradient of PP_n plotted against x_n

Fig. 4.5

EXERCISE 4.5

1 Repeat the above example taking P to be the given point and P_1, P_2, P_3, P_4, P_5, to be the other 5 points from the set of points $\{(-1, -1), (0, 0), (1, 1), (2, 8), (3, 27)\}$ for the following:
(i) P is $(-1, -1)$; (ii) P is $(0, 0)$; (iii) P is $(1, 1)$; (iv) P is $(3, 27)$.
2 Repeat the above example using the functions given in Exercise 4.4, (i), (ii), (iii) and (iv), and using the x-coordinate chosen as each member in turn of the

appropriate set S. This exercise involves five choices of P for each of four functions, that is, twenty cases. If a group of students are doing the exercise, the labour could be shared out with advantage and the results collected together.

3   The results of Exercise 4.4 and question **2** above should give estimates of $f'(x)$ which are close to the values of $g(x)$ in each case. The method of using the gradients of chords is more accurate than the method of measuring slopes of the tangents. The values of the functions used in these exercises are now tabulated:

$f(x)$:	x^2	x^3	$x^2 - 4$	$x^2 - 4x$	$x^3 - 3x^2$
$g(x)$:	$2x$	$3x^2$	$2x$	$2x - 4$	$3x^2 - 6x$

Consider the above table and given that for all the entries $g(x) = f'(x)$, try and discover a rule for finding $f'(x)$ when given $f(x)$.

4.6 Estimation of the derivatives of cos x and sin x

The method of §4.4 is used to estimate the derivative of $\cos x$ by measuring the gradients to the graph of the function at various points. Remember that x is always measured in radians when dealing with trigonometrical functions as real functions. Values of $\cos x$ and $\sin x$ and the gradients of some tangents to the graph of $\cos x$, as measured from Fig. 4.6 are tabulated.

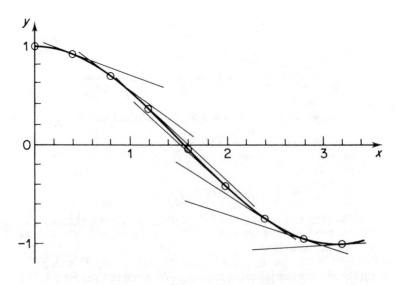

Fig. 4.6 Tangents to the graphs of cos x.

x	0	0·2	0·4	0·6	0·8	1·0	1·2	1·4	1·6
cos x	1·00	0·98	0·92	0·83	0·70	0·54	0·36	0·17	−0·03
sin x	0	0·20	0·39	0·56	0·72	0·84	0·93	0·9	1·00
Gradient of tangent to graph of cos x	0		−0·37		−0·73		−0·89		−1·00

x	1·8	2·0	2·2	2·4	2·6	2·8	3·0	3·2	3·4
cos x	−0·23	−0·42	−0·59	−0·74	−0·86	−0·94	−0·99	−1·00	−0·97
sin x	0·97	0·91	0·81	0·68	0·52	0·33	0·14	−0·06	−0·26
Gradient of tangent to graph of cos x		−0·92		−0·62		−0·31		−0·07	

EXERCISE 4.6

1 Using the above table, draw the graph of sin x and draw tangents to this graph at intervals of 0·4 radians. Measure the slopes of these tangents to estimate $\dfrac{d}{dx}\sin x$ and compare the values found with the corresponding values of cos x.

The above results should suggest that $\dfrac{d}{dx}\cos x = -\sin x$ and $\dfrac{d}{dx}\sin x = \cos x$, and this is the case. In elementary kinematics, the derivatives of cos nx and sin nx, where n is constant, are also required. Since $\dfrac{dy}{dx}$ is the rate of change of y with respect to x and is therefore a (local) change of scale between y and x (cf. §4.1), the replacement of x by nx gives a further change of scale and so we may expect that $\dfrac{d}{dx}f(nx) = nf'(x)$, which is, in fact, the case.

The addition of a constant to x changes the position of the graph of a function with respect to the origin but does not change the shape of the graph, so it leaves the derivative of a function unaltered, that is, if $f'(x) = g(x)$ then $f'(x+c) = g(x+c)$.

4.7 Rules for finding the derivatives of a function

The previous sections suggest that the following rules are plausible. They are stated without proof in order that they can be used in examples. Proof of these rules will be given in Chapter 18.

Rule 1 The derivative of a linear combination of functions is the corresponding linear combination of their derivatives. If a and b are constants and f and g are functions then

$$\text{if } h = af + bg \quad \text{then} \quad h' = af' + bg',$$

$$\text{if } y = au + bv \quad \text{then} \quad \frac{dy}{dx} = a\frac{du}{dx} + b\frac{dv}{dx}.$$

Rule 2 For any constant n,

$$\text{if } f(x) = x^n \text{ then } f'(x) = nx^{n-1},$$

$$\text{if } y = x^n \quad \text{then} \quad \frac{dy}{dx} = nx^{n-1},$$

$$\frac{d}{dx}\cos(nx+c) = -n\sin(nx+c),$$

$$\frac{d}{dx}\sin(nx+c) = n\cos(nx+c).$$

These rules may be used to find the derivatives of many functions.

EXAMPLE 1   *Find the derivative* f' *of the function* f *where* $f(x) = 3x^2 - 2x + 1$.

Using rule 2, $\dfrac{d}{dx}x^2 = 2x, \dfrac{d}{dx}x = 1, \dfrac{d}{dx}1 = \dfrac{d}{dx}x^0 = 0$, so by rule 1,
$f'(x) = 3(2x) - 2 = 6x - 2$.

EXAMPLE 2   *Differentiate the function* $(x - 1/x)^2$.

Expanding the square, $(x - 1/x)^2 = x^2 - 2 + x^{-2}$, and by rule 2 $\dfrac{d}{dx}x^{-2} = -2x^{-3}$.
Hence,

$$\frac{d}{dx}\left(x - \frac{1}{x}\right)^2 = 2x - 0 - 2x^{-3} = 2x - \frac{2}{x^3}.$$

EXAMPLE 3   *Find the equation of the tangent to the curve given by* $y = x + \sin x$ *at the point* $(\pi, 0)$.

Using the rules,

$$\frac{dy}{dx} = 1 + \cos x,$$

so the gradient of the tangent when $x = \pi$ is given by

$$m = 1 + \cos\pi = 0.$$

Thus the equation of the tangent is $y = \pi$.

EXAMPLE 4 *The displacement of a particle moving in a straight line is y metres after it has been moving t seconds, where $y = f(t) = t^3 - 2t^2 + t$. Find the time elapsed and the position of the particle at each instant when the particle is at rest. During what interval of time is the particle moving backwards towards its initial position?*

In our previous formula, x is now replaced by t, so the speed v of the particle at time t is given by

$$v = \frac{dy}{dt} = 3t^2 - 4t + 1,$$

on using the two rules. Hence

$$v = (3t - 1)(t - 1)$$

and $v = 0$, that is, the particle is stationary, at times $t = \frac{1}{3}$ and $t = 1$, that is, after the particle has been moving for **1/3 second** and **1 second**. The particle moves backwards when $v < 0$ and this occurs **between 1/3 second and 1 second** after the motion starts.

EXERCISE 4.7

1 Differentiate with respect to x:
(i) x^5, (ii) x^{-4}, (iii) $2x^7$, (iv) $3/x$, (v) $2/x^2$, (vi) $x^2 + 2x$, (vii) $x^2 + 3$,
(viii) $1 + 3x + 2x^2$, (ix) $3x^3 + 2x$, (x) $x^4 - 4x^3 + 2x^2$, (xi) $2 - 3x - 4x^2$,
(xii) $x^5 - 5x^4$, (xiii) $2 \sin x - 3 \cos x$, (xiv) $\cos x - \sin x$, (xv) $\sin 3x$.

2 Expand and then differentiate with respect to x:
(i) $(2x - 3)^2$, (ii) $(x + 1)(x - 2)$, (iii) $x^2(2x + 3)$, (iv) $(x^2 + 1)/x$,
(v) $(x^2 + 1)(x^2 - 1)$, (vi) $\left(x + \dfrac{1}{x}\right)^2$.

3 Find $f'(x)$ when:
(i) $f(x) = x^3 - 2x + 1$, (ii) $f(x) = 2 \cos 3x + x$, (iii) $f(x) = (x + 1)^2/x$,
(iv) $f(x) = 2x^3 - 5x$,   (v) $f(x) = 4x - 2 + x^{-2}$,   (vi) $f(x) = 2x - \cos 2x$,
(vii) $f(x) = 3x^2 - 2x^4$, (viii) $f(x) = (2x + 1)^3$, (ix) $f(x) = 2x + \dfrac{2}{x}$,
(x) $f(x) = \left(x - \dfrac{1}{x}\right)^3$.

4 (i) Given that $v = 2 + t - 3t^2$, find $\dfrac{dv}{dt}$;

(ii) Given that $V = \frac{4}{3}\pi r^3$,   find $\dfrac{dV}{dr}$;

(iii) Given that $s = ut + \frac{1}{2}at^2$, find $\dfrac{ds}{dt}$, u, a are constants;

(iv) Given that $PV = 25$,   find $\dfrac{dP}{dV}$.

5 Find the gradient of the tangent to the curve $y = 2x^3 - 3x^2$ at the point where (i) $x = 2$, (ii) $x = 1$, and, hence, write down the equation of the tangent at the given point.

6 Find the equation of the tangent to the curve $y = f(x)$ at the point where $x = b$, given that:
(i) $f(x) = x^2 - 2x - 1$, $b = 2$; (ii) $f(x) = (x - 1)^3$, $b = -1$;
(iii) $f(x) = \left(x + \dfrac{1}{x}\right)^2$, $b = 1$.

7 The displacement of a particle, moving in a straight line, is x metres after it has been moving for t seconds, where

$$x = f(t) = 2t^2 - 10t.$$

Find the speed of the particle when $t = 0, 1, 2, 3$ and 4. Find at what time the particle is stationary, at what time it returns to its starting point and at what speed it is then travelling.

8 The height of the tide x hours after midnight is h metres, where

$$h = 8 + 5 \cos \frac{\pi}{12}(x + 3).$$

Find, in terms of x, the rate of change of height of the tide at time x. Find also the maximum height of the tide.

9 A particle P moves in a horizontal straight line and passes through a fixed point O. After t seconds the distance s metres of P from O is given by

$$s = 12t - t^3, \text{ where } t \geq 0.$$

Calculate
(a) the value of t when P is instantaneously at rest,
(b) the speed of P at the instant when it again passes through O.   (L)

5 Vectors I

In this chapter, we consider the elementary algebra of vectors, based on vector addition and multiplication by a scalar, with the vectors represented by displacements. In Chapter 12, Vectors II, we shall consider units of length and direction, Cartesian frames of reference and column vectors.

5.1 Displacements

Suppose that we wish to describe a movement, or *displacement*, from a point P to a point Q. It is necessary to specify two things:

(i) a distance PQ explained by reference to a known unit of length,
(ii) a direction explained by reference to a known set of directions.

For example, if the known directions are compass bearings, then we could describe a displacement by (a) 3 km North West or (b) 200 miles on a bearing $060°$.

It is useful to have a notation which combines the two pieces of information, distance and direction, and we use the arrow notation:
$\overrightarrow{PQ}$ meaning a displacement through the distance PQ in the direction of PQ.
$\overrightarrow{PQ}$ is a vector quantity and the distance PQ is called the *magnitude* of the vector $\overrightarrow{PQ}$ (see Fig. 5.1 (a)).

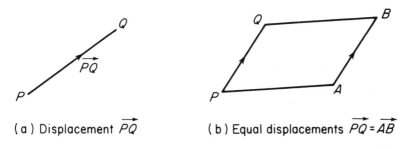

(a) Displacement $\overrightarrow{PQ}$ (b) Equal displacements $\overrightarrow{PQ} = \overrightarrow{AB}$

Fig. 5.1

Two displacements are *equal* when they have the same magnitude and the same direction. Thus in Fig. 5.1(b) $\overrightarrow{PQ} = \overrightarrow{AB}$ when $PQ = AB$ and PQ is parallel to AB, that is, when $PQBA$ is a parallelogram.

If a displacement $\overrightarrow{PQ}$ is followed by another $\overrightarrow{QR}$, then the total displacement is $\overrightarrow{PR}$ and this is defined as the sum of $\overrightarrow{PQ}$ and $\overrightarrow{QR}$, thus

$$\overrightarrow{PQ} + \overrightarrow{QR} = \overrightarrow{PR}.$$

$$\overrightarrow{PR} = \overrightarrow{PQ} + \overrightarrow{QR} = \overrightarrow{PS} + \overrightarrow{SR}$$

Fig. 5.2

Let $PQRS$ be a parallelogram, then $\overrightarrow{PQ} = \overrightarrow{SR}$ and $\overrightarrow{PS} = \overrightarrow{QR}$, hence in Fig. 5.2.

$$\overrightarrow{PR} = \overrightarrow{PQ} + \overrightarrow{QR} = \overrightarrow{PS} + \overrightarrow{SR}$$

The *sum* of two displacements is equal to the third side of a triangle whose two sides represent the given displacements (*the triangle rule*).

The *sum* is also represented by the diagonal of a parallelogram whose edges represent the given displacements (*the parallelogram rule*).

5.2 Vector and scalar quantities

A scalar quantity or *scalar* is a quantity which is completely specified by its magnitude, in terms of a given unit. For example, mass, distance, speed, area, volume and energy are all scalars.

A vector quantity or *vector* is a quantity which is completely specified by its magnitude in terms of a given unit and its direction relative to some agreed set of directions, and which can be added to another vector, of the same kind, by means of the triangle, or parallelogram, rule. For example, displacement, velocity, momentum and force are all vectors.

Notation   Italic letters are used for scalars, for example mass m, distance s, speed v, area S and volume V.

The arrow notation and bold type are used for vectors, for example, displacement $\overrightarrow{PQ}$, velocity $\mathbf{v}$ and force $\mathbf{F}$.

A vector, $\mathbf{a}$, may be represented by a directed line segment $\overrightarrow{PQ}$, with respect to some given unit, and we then write $\mathbf{a} = \overrightarrow{PQ}$.

Equality of vectors

Let $\mathbf{a} = \overrightarrow{PQ}$ and $\mathbf{b} = \overrightarrow{RS}$ be two vectors, then $\mathbf{a} = \mathbf{b}$ means that $\overrightarrow{PQ}$ and $\overrightarrow{RS}$ have the same magnitude and direction so that $PQSR$ is a parallelogram, as seen in Fig. 5.3(a).

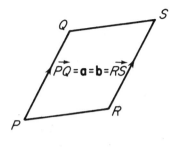

$\overrightarrow{PQ} = a = b = \overrightarrow{RS}$

(a) Equal vectors

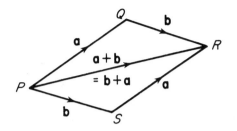

$a + b$
$= b + a$

(b) Vector addition

Fig. 5.3

Addition of vectors

In Fig. 5.3(b), let $\mathbf{a} = \overrightarrow{PQ}$ and $\mathbf{b} = \overrightarrow{QR}$, then we add $\mathbf{a}$ and $\mathbf{b}$ by the triangle rule

$$\mathbf{a} + \mathbf{b} = \overrightarrow{PQ} + \overrightarrow{QR} = \overrightarrow{PR}.$$

Let *PQRS* be a parallelogram, then $\mathbf{a} = \overrightarrow{PQ} = \overrightarrow{SR}$ and $\mathbf{b} = \overrightarrow{QR} = \overrightarrow{PS}$ so that

$$\mathbf{a} + \mathbf{b} = \overrightarrow{PQ} + \overrightarrow{QR} = \overrightarrow{PR} = \overrightarrow{PS} + \overrightarrow{SR} = \mathbf{b} + \mathbf{a}$$

and so we see that vector addition is commutative, $\mathbf{a} + \mathbf{b} = \mathbf{b} + \mathbf{a}$.

Multiplication of a vector by a scalar

Suppose that $\overrightarrow{PQ} = \mathbf{a} = \overrightarrow{QR}$ (Fig. 5.4(a)); then Q is the midpoint of *PR*. Thus

$$\overrightarrow{PR} = \overrightarrow{PQ} + \overrightarrow{QR} = \mathbf{a} + \mathbf{a} = 2\mathbf{a},$$

and so $2\mathbf{a}$ is the vector with magnitude twice the magnitude of $\mathbf{a}$ and with the same direction as $\mathbf{a}$. We extend this idea and define, for a vector $\mathbf{a}$ and a scalar $k, k > 0$:

$k\mathbf{a}$ is the vector with the same direction as $\mathbf{a}$
and of magnitude k times the magnitude of $\mathbf{a}$.

(a) Product by scalar

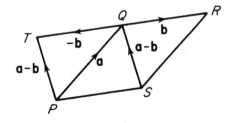

(b) Vector difference

Fig. 5.4

The negative of the vector **a** is −**a** and has the same magnitude as **a** but with a direction which is parallel and opposite to the direction of **a**.

In Fig. 5.4(a), if $\mathbf{a} = \overrightarrow{PQ}$ then $-\mathbf{a} = \overrightarrow{QP}$ and

$$\mathbf{a} + -\mathbf{a} = \overrightarrow{PQ} + \overrightarrow{QP} = \overrightarrow{PP} = \mathbf{0},$$

where **0** is the zero vector, which has zero magnitude and no particular direction. The zero vector **0** corresponds to no displacement at all.

If $k < 0$, say $k = -h, h > 0$, then $k\mathbf{a} = (-h)\mathbf{a} = h(-\mathbf{a})$ by definition, and then it will be seen that

$$h(-\mathbf{a}) = -(h\mathbf{a}).$$

Subtraction of vectors

We define $\mathbf{a} - \mathbf{b} = \mathbf{a} + -\mathbf{b}$ and, therefore, in Fig. 5.4(b), if $\overrightarrow{PQ} = \mathbf{a}$ and $\overrightarrow{QR} = \mathbf{b}$, let $\overrightarrow{QT} = -\mathbf{b} = \overrightarrow{RQ}$ so that Q is the midpoint of TR. Then

$$\mathbf{a} - \mathbf{b} = \overrightarrow{PQ} - \overrightarrow{QR} = \overrightarrow{PQ} + \overrightarrow{QT} = \overrightarrow{PT} = \overrightarrow{SQ}.$$

Thus the sum and difference of two vectors are represented by the two diagonals of the parallelogram whose sides represent the two vectors.

Distributive and associative laws

Since multiplication by a positive scalar only changes the magnitude of a vector and multiplication by a negative scalar changes the magnitude and reverses the direction, the associative law

$$h(k\mathbf{a}) = (hk)\mathbf{a}$$

holds for any vector **a** and scalars h, k.

Similarly, one distributive law follows at once from the definition

$$h\mathbf{a} + k\mathbf{a} = (h + k)\mathbf{a}.$$

The other distributive law that, for any scalar h and vectors **a**, **b**,

$$h\mathbf{a} + h\mathbf{b} = h(\mathbf{a} + \mathbf{b})$$

is proved by using corresponding displacements. Let **a** and **b** be represented by displacements $\overrightarrow{OA}$ and $\overrightarrow{OB}$ so that $\mathbf{a} + \mathbf{b}$ is represented by the diagonal $\overrightarrow{OC}$ of the parallelogram $OACB$ (Fig. 5.5).

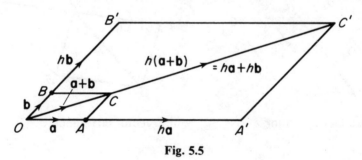

Fig. 5.5

Multiplication by h corresponds to an enlargement by a scale factor h, $h\mathbf{a}$ and $h\mathbf{b}$ being represented by $\overrightarrow{OA'}$ and $\overrightarrow{OB'}$ and then $h\mathbf{a} + h\mathbf{b}$ is represented by

$$\overrightarrow{OA'} + \overrightarrow{OB'} = \overrightarrow{OC'} = h(\mathbf{a} + \mathbf{b})$$

since $OA'C'B'$ is a parallelogram obtained from $OACB$ by an all-round enlargement with scale factor h.

The proof of the associative law of addition is given as question 1 in Exercise 5.2. It states that for any three vectors $\mathbf{a}$, $\mathbf{b}$ and $\mathbf{c}$,

$$\mathbf{a} + (\mathbf{b} + \mathbf{c}) = (\mathbf{a} + \mathbf{b}) + \mathbf{c}$$

so we may omit the brackets and write the sum $\mathbf{a} + \mathbf{b} + \mathbf{c}$.

EXERCISE 5.2

1   Given three vectors $\mathbf{a}$, $\mathbf{b}$ and $\mathbf{c}$, represent them on a diagram by $\overrightarrow{PQ} = \mathbf{a}$, $\overrightarrow{QR} = \mathbf{b}$, $\overrightarrow{RS} = \mathbf{c}$, and hence show that

$$\mathbf{a} + (\mathbf{b} + \mathbf{c}) = (\mathbf{a} + \mathbf{b}) + \mathbf{c}.$$

2   Two sets of equally spaced parallel lines are shown in Fig. 5.6 with a number of their intersections labelled by letters. Represent each of the following vectors as a displacement from O given that $\mathbf{a} = \overrightarrow{OA}$ and $\mathbf{b} = \overrightarrow{OB}$; for example, $\mathbf{a} + \mathbf{b} = \overrightarrow{OC}$:
(i) $2\mathbf{a}$,   (ii) $3\mathbf{b}$,   (iii) $2\mathbf{a} + \mathbf{b}$,   (iv) $3\mathbf{a} + 2\mathbf{b}$,   (v) $-\mathbf{b}$,   (vi) $-\mathbf{a} + 3\mathbf{b}$,
(vii) $2\mathbf{a} + -\mathbf{b}$,   (viii) $4\mathbf{a} + \mathbf{b}$,   (ix) $\mathbf{b} - \mathbf{a}$.
3   Using the same diagram, Fig. 5.6, as in question 2 above, express in terms of

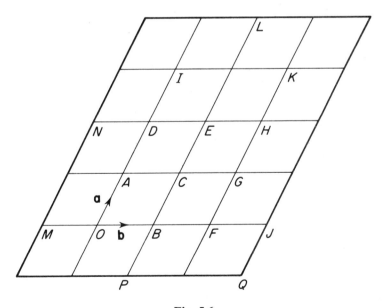

Fig. 5.6

a and **b** the vector represented by the following displacements:

(i) $\overrightarrow{AI}$,   (ii) $\overrightarrow{CL}$,   (iii) $\overrightarrow{AG}$,   (iv) $\overrightarrow{CK}$,   (v) $\overrightarrow{PJ}$,   (vi) $\overrightarrow{PA}$,   (vii) $\overrightarrow{AQ}$,
(viii) $\overrightarrow{GO}$,   (ix) $\overrightarrow{JM}$,   (x) $\overrightarrow{KP}$.

4   Again using the same diagram, Fig. 5.6, as in question **2**, write down three displacements equal to the following vectors, for example, $\mathbf{a} + 2\mathbf{b} = \overrightarrow{OG} = \overrightarrow{MC} = \overrightarrow{DK}$:

(i) $\mathbf{a} + \mathbf{b}$,   (ii) $\mathbf{b} + -\mathbf{a}$,   (iii) $-2\mathbf{a} + -\mathbf{b}$,   (iv) $-\mathbf{a} - 2\mathbf{b}$.

5   Let $\overrightarrow{OS} = \mathbf{s}$, $\overrightarrow{OT} = \mathbf{t}$ and let T be the mid-point of SU. Find, in terms of **s** and **t**:

(i) $\overrightarrow{ST}$,   (ii) $\overrightarrow{TS}$,   (iii) $\overrightarrow{OU}$,   (iv) $\overrightarrow{US}$,   (v) $\overrightarrow{TU}$.

5.3 Origin and position vectors

Again, refer to Fig. 5.6. In Exercise 5.2, several questions involved the point O which was used as a reference point for displacements. Thus $\overrightarrow{OA} = \mathbf{a}$ gives the position of the point A as a displacement **a** from the reference point O. A point O, used in this way as a reference point, is called the *origin* and **a** is the *position vector* for the point A. In other words, once an origin O is fixed, the position of every other point R in space can be defined by a unique position vector $\mathbf{r} = \overrightarrow{OR}$.

Thus, in Fig. 5.6, the position vectors of F, G, H and K are given by

$$\overrightarrow{OF} = 2\mathbf{b}, \quad \overrightarrow{OG} = 2\mathbf{b} + \mathbf{a}, \quad \overrightarrow{OH} = 2\mathbf{b} + 2\mathbf{a}, \quad \overrightarrow{OK} = 2\mathbf{b} + 3\mathbf{a}.$$

Given a scalar parameter λ, $(\lambda \in \mathbb{R})$, consider the set of points

$$S = \{R : \overrightarrow{OR} = \mathbf{r} = 2\mathbf{b} + \lambda\mathbf{a}\}.$$

Clearly, the points F, G, H and K are all elements of the set S, the corresponding values of λ being 0, 1, 2 and 3. Also, the point with position vector $\mathbf{r} = 2\mathbf{b} + \frac{1}{2}\mathbf{a}$ is the midpoint of FG, and $\mathbf{r} = 2\mathbf{b} + 2\frac{3}{4}\mathbf{a}$ is the position vector of the point R between H and K such that $\overrightarrow{HR} = \frac{3}{4}\overrightarrow{HK}$.

In general, if the point R has position vector $\mathbf{r} = 2\mathbf{b} + \lambda\mathbf{a}$, then

$$\overrightarrow{FR} = \overrightarrow{OR} - \overrightarrow{OF} = \mathbf{r} - 2\mathbf{b} = \lambda\mathbf{a} = \lambda\overrightarrow{FG},$$

and R lies on the line FG. Conversely, any point on FG has a position vector of the form $2\mathbf{b} + \lambda\mathbf{a}$, for some value of λ. Thus, the equation $\mathbf{r} = 2\mathbf{b} + \lambda\mathbf{a}$ defines an infinite set of points, parameterised by λ, and these points form the *line* through F, G, H and K, produced in both directions, that is, the line FG. We say that

$$\mathbf{r} = 2\mathbf{b} + \lambda\mathbf{a}$$

is *the equation of the line FG*.

EXAMPLE 1   *Using Fig. 5.6, find the equation of the line through the points P, B, C, E and L.*

The position vectors of the five given points are $\overrightarrow{OP} = \mathbf{b} - \mathbf{a}$, $\overrightarrow{OB} = \mathbf{b}$, $\overrightarrow{OC} = \mathbf{b} + \mathbf{a}$, $\overrightarrow{OE} = \mathbf{b} + 2\mathbf{a}$, $\overrightarrow{OL} = \mathbf{b} + 4\mathbf{a}$. Hence the equation of the line PL is $\mathbf{r} = \mathbf{b} + \lambda\mathbf{a}$, $\lambda \in \mathbb{R}$.

EXAMPLE 2   *Again with reference to Fig. 5.6, find the locus of points with position vector* **r**, *satisfying the equation*

$$\mathbf{r} = \mathbf{a} + \lambda(\mathbf{a} + \mathbf{b}), \lambda \in \mathbb{R}.$$

Consider the values of **r** for some values of λ:
if $\lambda = 0$, $\mathbf{r} = \mathbf{a}$ so A lies on the locus;
if $\lambda = 1$, $\mathbf{r} = \mathbf{a} + (\mathbf{a} + \mathbf{b}) = 2\mathbf{a} + \mathbf{b}$ so E lies on the locus;
if $\lambda = 2$, $\mathbf{r} = \mathbf{a} + 2(\mathbf{a} + \mathbf{b}) = 3\mathbf{a} + 2\mathbf{b}$ so K lies on the locus,
if $\lambda = -1$, $\mathbf{r} = \mathbf{a} - (\mathbf{a} + \mathbf{b}) = -\mathbf{b}$ so M lies on the locus.
We know that the equation is the equation of a line which must be the line through M, A, E and K.

Note: The equation $\mathbf{r} = \mathbf{a} + \lambda(\mathbf{a} + \mathbf{b})$, of Example 2, has two main parts in it. Firstly, the part independent of λ, obtained by putting $\lambda = 0$, gives a value $\mathbf{r} = \mathbf{a} = \overrightarrow{OA}$, so that A lies on the line. The second part, which contains the factor λ, is $\lambda(\mathbf{a} + \mathbf{b})$, which shows that the line is in the direction of the vector $(\mathbf{a} + \mathbf{b}) = \overrightarrow{OC} = \overrightarrow{AE}$. Similarly, in Example 1, the term independent of λ gives $\mathbf{r} = \mathbf{b}$, showing that B lies on the line. The other term $\lambda\mathbf{a}$ shows that the line is parallel to $\mathbf{a} = \overrightarrow{OA} = \overrightarrow{BC}$.

EXAMPLE 3   *Using Fig. 5.6, write down one point on the line with equation* $\mathbf{r} = 2\mathbf{a} + \mathbf{b} + \lambda(\mathbf{b} - \mathbf{a})$ *and find a vector displacement which is parallel to the line.*

The line passes through the point E with position vector $\mathbf{r} = 2\mathbf{a} + \mathbf{b} = \overrightarrow{OE}$, corresponding to $\lambda = 0$. The term $\lambda(\mathbf{b} - \mathbf{a})$ in the equation shows that the line is parallel to $\mathbf{b} - \mathbf{a} = \overrightarrow{OP}$.

EXERCISE 5.3

1   Use the diagram of Fig. 5.7 to find the equation of the line which passes through the following set of points:
(i) $\{E, C, F, G\}$;   (ii) $\{G, H, I\}$;   (iii) $\{G, J, L, K\}$;   (iv) $\{M, H, L\}$;
(v) $\{J, F, H\}$;   (vi) $\{E, N\}$.
2   Again using Fig. 5.7, find the locus of the points R, with position vector **r** satisfying the equation:
(i) $\mathbf{r} = 2\mathbf{c} + \mathbf{d} + \lambda\mathbf{c}, \lambda \in \mathbb{R}$;   (ii) $\mathbf{r} = \mathbf{c} + 2\mathbf{d} + \lambda(\mathbf{c} + \mathbf{d}), \lambda \in \mathbb{R}$;
(iii) $\mathbf{r} = \lambda(3\mathbf{c} + 2\mathbf{d}), \lambda \in \mathbb{R}$;   (iv) $\mathbf{r} = \mathbf{c} + \mu(2\mathbf{d} - \mathbf{c}), \mu \in \mathbb{R}$;
(v) $\mathbf{r} = \mathbf{d} + k(\mathbf{c} - \mathbf{d}), k \in \mathbb{R}$.
3   Let A and B be two points, with position vectors **a** and **b** respectively, with respect to an origin O. Find the equation of the line:
(i) through A parallel to $\overrightarrow{OB}$, (ii) through O parallel to $\overrightarrow{BA}$, (iii) through the midpoint of OB parallel to $\overrightarrow{OA}$, (iv) through A and B.
4   The points P and Q have position vectors **p** and **q**, relative to an origin O. Describe the locus of the points R with position vectors **r**, given by $\mathbf{r} = \lambda\mathbf{p} + \mu\mathbf{q}$, when:
(i) $\lambda = \mu$;   (ii) $\lambda = 1$, $\mu \in \mathbb{R}$;   (iii) $\lambda = -\mu$;   (iv) $\lambda + \mu = 1$;   (v) there is no restriction on the values of λ and μ, which take all real values.

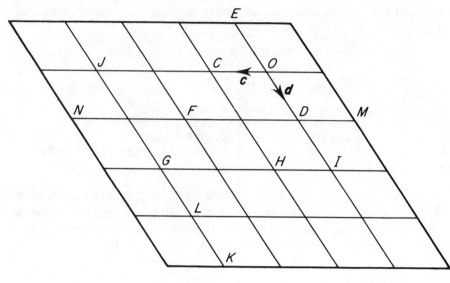

Fig. 5.7

5   (i) Three points P, Q and R have position vectors $\mathbf{p}$, $\mathbf{q}$ and $k(2\mathbf{p}+\mathbf{q})$ respectively, relative to a fixed origin. Find the numerical value of k if
(a) $\overrightarrow{QR}$ is parallel to $\mathbf{p}$,
(b) $\overrightarrow{PR}$ is parallel to $\mathbf{q}$,
(c) P, Q and R are collinear.
(ii) A hexagon $OABCDE$ has its pairs of opposite sides parallel and equal. The position vectors of A, B and C relative to O are $\mathbf{a}$, $\mathbf{a}+\mathbf{b}$, $\mathbf{a}+\mathbf{b}+\mathbf{c}$ respectively. Find the position vectors of D and E relative to O.   (L)

6   The points P and Q have position vectors $\mathbf{p}$ and $\mathbf{q}$ respectively relative to an origin O, which does not lie on PQ. Three points R, S, T have respective position vectors $\mathbf{r} = \frac{1}{4}\mathbf{p}+\frac{3}{4}\mathbf{q}$, $\mathbf{s} = 2\mathbf{p}-\mathbf{q}$, $\mathbf{t} = \mathbf{p}+3\mathbf{q}$. Show in one diagram the positions of O, P, Q, R, S and T.   (JMB)

7   The points A, B, C have position vectors $\mathbf{a}$, $\mathbf{b}$, $\mathbf{c}$ respectively with respect to an origin O. Write down, in terms of $\mathbf{a}$ and $\mathbf{b}$, the vector $\overrightarrow{BA}$ and find the position vector of the fourth vertex D of the parallelogram $ABCD$.   (L)

5.4 The ratio theorem

Let the two points A and B have position vectors $\mathbf{a}$ and $\mathbf{b}$ with respect to an origin O and let M be the midpoint of AB with position vector $\mathbf{m}$ (Fig. 5.8(a)). Then $\overrightarrow{AB} = \overrightarrow{AO}+\overrightarrow{OB} = \mathbf{b}-\mathbf{a}$, and so $\overrightarrow{AM} = \frac{1}{2}(\mathbf{b}-\mathbf{a})$. Now

$$\mathbf{m} = \overrightarrow{OM} = \overrightarrow{OA}+\overrightarrow{AM} = \mathbf{a}+\frac{1}{2}(\mathbf{b}-\mathbf{a}) = \mathbf{a}+\frac{1}{2}\mathbf{b}-\frac{1}{2}\mathbf{a} = \frac{1}{2}(\mathbf{a}+\mathbf{b}).$$

The same result is demonstrated in Fig. 5.8(b). If A_1 and B_1 are the respective midpoints of OA and OB, then

$$\overrightarrow{OA_1} = \frac{1}{2}\mathbf{a}, \quad \overrightarrow{A_1M} = \overrightarrow{OB_1} = \frac{1}{2}\mathbf{b},$$

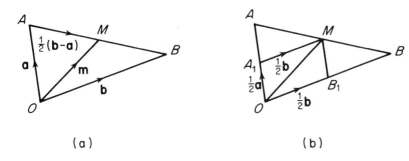

(a)   (b)

Fig. 5.8

so $$\overrightarrow{OM} = \overrightarrow{OA_1} + \overrightarrow{A_1M} = \tfrac{1}{2}(\mathbf{a} + \mathbf{b}).$$

This result can be generalised by using any real number instead of the fraction $\tfrac{1}{2}$. Let R be a point on AB with $\overrightarrow{AR} = \mu\overrightarrow{AB}$.

Then $$\overrightarrow{RB} = \overrightarrow{AB} - \overrightarrow{AR} = \overrightarrow{AB} - \mu\overrightarrow{AB} = (1 - \mu)\overrightarrow{AB}.$$

Put $1 - \mu = \lambda$, then

$$\overrightarrow{AR} = \mu\overrightarrow{AB}, \quad \overrightarrow{RB} = \lambda\overrightarrow{AB}, \quad \lambda + \mu = 1.$$

If $\lambda = 0$, then $R \equiv B$. If $\lambda \neq 0$, let $k = \dfrac{\mu}{\lambda}$, then, since

$$\overrightarrow{AR} = \mu\overrightarrow{AB} = \frac{\mu}{\lambda}\overrightarrow{RB} = k\overrightarrow{RB},$$

taking its sign into account, k represents the ratio $AR : RB$ and fixes the position of R on the line AB. When $k > 0$, $\overrightarrow{AR}$ and $\overrightarrow{RB}$ are in the same direction and, when $k < 0$, $\overrightarrow{AR}$ and $\overrightarrow{RB}$ are in opposite directions. As an example, in Fig. 5.9, three values of k are chosen:
(a) if $k = 3$, $\mu = 3\lambda$ so $\mu = \tfrac{3}{4}$, $\lambda = \tfrac{1}{4}$, $\overrightarrow{AR} = 3\overrightarrow{RB} = \tfrac{3}{4}\overrightarrow{AB}$, so R lies between A and B;
(b) if $k = -3$, $\mu = -3\lambda$ so $\mu = \tfrac{3}{2}$, $\lambda = -\tfrac{1}{2}$, $\overrightarrow{AR} = -3\overrightarrow{RB} = \tfrac{3}{2}\overrightarrow{AB}$, so R lies on AB produced;

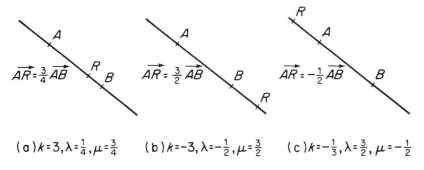

(a) $k = 3, \lambda = \tfrac{1}{4}, \mu = \tfrac{3}{4}$ (b) $k = -3, \lambda = -\tfrac{1}{2}, \mu = \tfrac{3}{2}$ (c) $k = -\tfrac{1}{3}, \lambda = \tfrac{3}{2}, \mu = -\tfrac{1}{2}$

Fig. 5.9

(c) if $k = -\frac{1}{3}, \mu = -\frac{1}{3}\lambda$ so $\mu = -\frac{1}{2}, \lambda = \frac{3}{2}, \overrightarrow{AR} = -\frac{1}{3}\overrightarrow{RB} = -\frac{1}{2}\overrightarrow{AB}$, so R lies on BA produced.

The general situation is shown in Fig. 5.10.
If $k > 0$, then R lies between A and B;
if $k = 0$, then $R = A$, and if $k = \infty$, then $R = B$;
if $-1 < k < 0$, then R lies on BA produced;
if $k < -1$, then R lies on AB produced.

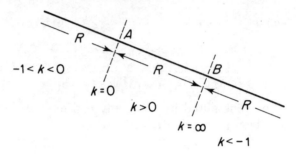

k is the ratio $AR : RB$, given by $\overrightarrow{AR} = k\overrightarrow{RB}$

Fig. 5.10

These results provide a vector theorem which fixes the position of a point R on the line AB in terms of the ratio k of AR to RB.

The Ratio Theorem

Let $\mathbf{a} = \overrightarrow{OA}$ and $\mathbf{b} = \overrightarrow{OB}$ be the position vectors of points A and B with respect to an origin O, and let $\mathbf{r} = \overrightarrow{OR}$ be the position vector of any point R in space. Then

R lies on AB with $\overrightarrow{AR} = \mu\overrightarrow{AB}, \overrightarrow{BR} = \lambda\overrightarrow{BA} \Leftrightarrow \mathbf{r} = \lambda\mathbf{a} + \mu\mathbf{b}$ and $\lambda + \mu = 1$.

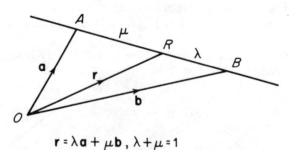

$\mathbf{r} = \lambda\mathbf{a} + \mu\mathbf{b}, \lambda + \mu = 1$

Fig. 5.11

Proof The implications have to be proved in each direction. Using Fig. 5.11:
(i) suppose that R lies on AB with $\overrightarrow{AR} = \mu\overrightarrow{AB}$ and $\overrightarrow{BR} = \lambda\overrightarrow{BA}$. Then $\overrightarrow{RB} = -\lambda\overrightarrow{BA} = \lambda\overrightarrow{AB}$, so

$$\overrightarrow{AB} = \overrightarrow{AR} + \overrightarrow{RB} = \mu\overrightarrow{AB} + \lambda\overrightarrow{AB} = (\lambda + \mu)\overrightarrow{AB},$$

and thus $\lambda + \mu = 1$. Also

$$\mathbf{r} = \overrightarrow{OR} = \overrightarrow{OA} + \overrightarrow{AR} = \mathbf{a} + \mu\overrightarrow{AB} = \mathbf{a} + \mu(\mathbf{b} - \mathbf{a})$$
$$= (1 - \mu)\mathbf{a} + \mu\mathbf{b} = \lambda\mathbf{a} + \mu\mathbf{b};$$

(ii) conversely, suppose that $\mathbf{r} = \lambda\mathbf{a} + \mu\mathbf{b}$ and $\lambda + \mu = 1$. Then $\lambda = 1 - \mu$. Then

$$\overrightarrow{AR} = \mathbf{r} - \mathbf{a} = \lambda\mathbf{a} + \mu\mathbf{b} - \mathbf{a} = (1 - \mu)\mathbf{a} + \mu\mathbf{b} - \mathbf{a} = \mu(\mathbf{b} - \mathbf{a}) = \mu\overrightarrow{AB},$$

so R lies on AB. Also

$$\overrightarrow{BR} = \mathbf{r} - \mathbf{b} = \lambda\mathbf{a} + \mu\mathbf{b} - \mathbf{b} = \lambda\mathbf{a} + (\mu - 1)\mathbf{b} = \lambda(\mathbf{a} - \mathbf{b}) = \lambda\overrightarrow{BA}.$$

Note that the equation relating $\mathbf{r}$, $\mathbf{a}$ and $\mathbf{b}$ depends only upon the position of R on the line AB. It is independent of the origin O.

EXAMPLE 1   *Find the position of the point R on the line AB, given that the position vectors of A and B are* $\mathbf{a}$ *and* $\mathbf{b}$ *and that* $AR:RB = 3:2$.

The given ratio means that $2\overrightarrow{AR} = 3\overrightarrow{RB}$ so that $\overrightarrow{AR} = \frac{3}{5}\overrightarrow{AB}$ and $\overrightarrow{BR} = \frac{2}{5}\overrightarrow{BA}$. By the ratio theorem, $\mathbf{r} = \frac{2}{5}\mathbf{a} + \frac{3}{5}\mathbf{b}$. See Fig. 5.12(a).

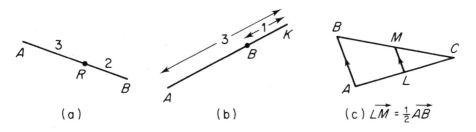

Fig. 5.12

EXAMPLE 2   *Describe the position of the point K with respect to the points A and B given that the position vectors* $\mathbf{k}$, $\mathbf{a}$ *and* $\mathbf{b}$ *of the three points satisfy the equation* $2\mathbf{k} = 3\mathbf{b} - \mathbf{a}$.

We note that $\mathbf{k} = \frac{3}{2}\mathbf{b} - \frac{1}{2}\mathbf{a}$, and $\frac{3}{2} + (-\frac{1}{2}) = 1$, so by the ratio theorem, with $\lambda = \frac{3}{2}$ and $\mu = -\frac{1}{2}$, K is the point on the line AB produced with $\overrightarrow{AK} = \frac{3}{2}\overrightarrow{AB}$ and $\overrightarrow{BK} = \frac{1}{2}\overrightarrow{AB}$. See Fig. 5.12(b).

EXAMPLE 3   *Given that L and M are the midpoints of the sides AC and BC of the triangle ABC show that LM is parallel to AB and LM is half the length of AB.*

By the ratio theorem, $\overrightarrow{AM} = \frac{1}{2}\overrightarrow{AB} + \frac{1}{2}\overrightarrow{AC} = \frac{1}{2}\overrightarrow{AB} + \overrightarrow{AL}.$

So, $\qquad\qquad \overrightarrow{LM} = \overrightarrow{AM} - \overrightarrow{AL} = \frac{1}{2}\overrightarrow{AB} + \overrightarrow{AL} - \overrightarrow{AL} = \frac{1}{2}\overrightarrow{AB}.$

Therefore, LM is parallel to AB and is half its length. See Fig. 5.12(c).

EXERCISE 5.4

1   In the parallelogram $ABCD$, E is the midpoint of CD and F is the point of trisection of DB. Let $\overrightarrow{AB} = \mathbf{b}$ and $\overrightarrow{AD} = \mathbf{d}$. Express $\overrightarrow{AC}$, $\overrightarrow{AE}$, $\overrightarrow{AF}$ in terms of $\mathbf{b}$ and $\mathbf{d}$ and deduce that F is the point of trisection of EA.

2   In the quadrilateral $ABCD$, E, F, G, H are the midpoints of AB, BC, CD, DA respectively. The position vectors of A, B, C, D are $\mathbf{a}$, $\mathbf{b}$, $\mathbf{c}$, $\mathbf{d}$ respectively. Express the position vectors of E, F, G, H in terms of $\mathbf{a}$, $\mathbf{b}$, $\mathbf{c}$, $\mathbf{d}$ and prove that:
   (i) $EFGH$ is a parallelogram;
   (ii) the diagonals of $EFGH$ meet at the point with position vector $\frac{1}{4}(\mathbf{a} + \mathbf{b} + \mathbf{c} + \mathbf{d})$.

3   Given three non-parallel vectors in space, $\mathbf{a} = \overrightarrow{OA}$, $\mathbf{b} = \overrightarrow{OB}$ and $\mathbf{c} = \overrightarrow{OC}$:
   (i) if C lies in the plane OAB, use a parallelogram with diagonal OC and edges parallel to $\mathbf{a}$ and $\mathbf{b}$ to show that, for some real numbers h, k, $\mathbf{c} = h\mathbf{a} + k\mathbf{b}$;
   (ii) conversely, prove that if $\mathbf{c} = h\mathbf{a} + k\mathbf{b}$ then C lies in the plane OAB.

4   The six points P, Q, R, S, T, U are equally spaced on a circle, centre O, so that they form the vertices of a regular hexagon. Given that $\overrightarrow{OP} = \mathbf{p}$, $\overrightarrow{OQ} = \mathbf{q}$, express in terms of $\mathbf{p}$ and $\mathbf{q}$ the vectors $\overrightarrow{OR}$, $\overrightarrow{OS}$, $\overrightarrow{OT}$, $\overrightarrow{OU}$, $\overrightarrow{RU}$, $\overrightarrow{RT}$.

5    $PQRS$ is a parallelogram and $\overrightarrow{PR} = \mathbf{a}$, $\overrightarrow{QS} = \mathbf{b}$. Express the edges $\overrightarrow{PQ}$, $\overrightarrow{QR}$, $\overrightarrow{RS}$, $\overrightarrow{SP}$ of the parallelogram in terms of $\mathbf{a}$ and $\mathbf{b}$.

6   In the triangle ABC, the points P, Q and R are respectively the midpoints of the sides BC, CA and AB. Find the position vectors of P, Q and R in terms of the position vectors $\mathbf{a}$, $\mathbf{b}$ and $\mathbf{c}$ of A, B and C and prove that the three medians AP, BQ and CR intersect at a point which is two-thirds down the length of each median from its corresponding vertex.

7   The centroid of n points A_1, A_2, $\ldots$, A_n is defined to be the point with position vector $\frac{1}{n}(\mathbf{a}_1 + \mathbf{a}_2 + \ldots + \mathbf{a}_n)$, where $\mathbf{a}_i$ is the position vector of A_i
   (i) Prove that the centroid of two points is the point midway between them.
   (ii) Prove that the centroid of three non-collinear points A, B and C is the point G where the three medians of triangle ABC intersect (see question 6).
   (iii) Generalise the above to the case of four points A, B, C and D which do not lie in one plane.

8   In the quadrilateral $OABC$, D is the mid-point of BC and G is the point on AD such that $AG:GD = 2:1$. Given that $\overrightarrow{OA} = \mathbf{a}$, $\overrightarrow{OB} = \mathbf{b}$ and $\overrightarrow{OC} = \mathbf{c}$, express $\overrightarrow{OD}$ and $\overrightarrow{OG}$ in terms of $\mathbf{a}$, $\mathbf{b}$ and $\mathbf{c}$.   (L)

9   The points A, B, C have position vectors $\mathbf{a}$, $\mathbf{b}$, $\mathbf{c}$ respectively referred to an origin O. State the position vector of P, the mid-point of AB.
   Find the position vector of the point which divides the line segment PC internally in the ratio $3:1$.   (L)

10   The position vectors of the vertices of a triangle ABC referred to a given origin are $\mathbf{a}$, $\mathbf{b}$, $\mathbf{c}$. P is a point on AB such that $AP/PB = \frac{1}{2}$, Q is a point on AC such that $AQ/QC = 2$, and R is a point on PQ such that $PR/RQ = 2$. Prove that the position vector of R is $\frac{4}{9}\mathbf{a} + \frac{1}{9}\mathbf{b} + \frac{4}{9}\mathbf{c}$.
   Prove that R lies on the median BM of the triangle ABC, and state the value of BR/RM.   (SMP)

11   Points X and Y are taken on the sides QR and RS, respectively, of a parallelogram $PQRS$, so that $\overrightarrow{QX} = 4\overrightarrow{XR}$ and $\overrightarrow{RY} = 4\overrightarrow{YS}$. The line XY cuts the line PR at Z. Prove that $\overrightarrow{PZ} = \frac{21}{25}\overrightarrow{PR}$.   (JMB)

12   (i) In the quadrilateral $ABCD$, X and Y are the mid-points of the diagonals

AC and *BD* respectively. Show that

(a) $\overrightarrow{BA} + \overrightarrow{BC} = 2\overrightarrow{BX}$,

(b) $\overrightarrow{BA} + \overrightarrow{BC} + \overrightarrow{DA} + \overrightarrow{DC} = 4\overrightarrow{YX}$.

(ii) The point P lies on the circle through the vertices of a rectangle $QRST$. The point X on the diagonal QS is such that $\overrightarrow{QX} = 2\overrightarrow{XS}$. Express $\overrightarrow{PX}$, $\overrightarrow{QX}$ and $(\overrightarrow{RX} + \overrightarrow{TX})$ in terms of $\overrightarrow{PQ}$ and $\overrightarrow{PS}$. (L)

5.5 Basis of the set of vectors in one plane

A plane Π through the origin O may be defined by any two non-parallel vectors **a** and **b** which lie in Π. This was the situation in Exercise 5.2, in those questions which used Fig. 5.6, and again in Exercise 5.3 in those questions which used Fig. 5.7.

In Fig. 5.13, let $\overrightarrow{OA} = \mathbf{a}$ and $\overrightarrow{OB} = \mathbf{b}$, then Π is the plane of the triangle OAB. Also, since **a** and **b** are not parallel,

$$r\mathbf{a} = s\mathbf{b} \Rightarrow r = 0 = s.$$

We now prove that

[a point P lies in Π] $\Leftrightarrow$ [$\mathbf{r} = \overrightarrow{OP} = \lambda\mathbf{a} + \mu\mathbf{b}$, for some scalars λ, μ].

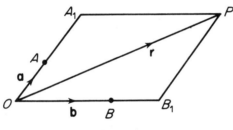

Fig. 5.13

Proof

(i) Suppose that P is a point in space with $\overrightarrow{OP} = \mathbf{r} = \lambda\mathbf{a} + \mu\mathbf{b}$, for some scalars λ and μ. Then define points A_1 and B_1, on OA and OB respectively, produced if necessary, such that $\overrightarrow{OA_1} = \lambda\overrightarrow{OA}$ and $\overrightarrow{OB_1} = \mu\overrightarrow{OB}$. Then

$$\overrightarrow{OP} = \lambda\mathbf{a} + \mu\mathbf{b} = \lambda\overrightarrow{OA} + \mu\overrightarrow{OB} = \overrightarrow{OA_1} + \overrightarrow{OB_1},$$

so A_1PB_1O is a parallelogram and hence P lies in the plane OA_1B_1, which is the plane OAB, that is, Π.

(ii) Conversely, let P be any point in the plane Π. Construct two lines through P, one parallel to **b** meeting OA at A_1, and one parallel to **a** meeting OB at B_1, where OA and OB are produced if necessary. Then OA_1PB_1 is a parallelogram and so $\overrightarrow{OP} = \overrightarrow{OA_1} + \overrightarrow{OB_1}$. Because $\overrightarrow{OA_1}$ and $\overrightarrow{OB_1}$ are respectively parallel to $\overrightarrow{OA}$ and $\overrightarrow{OB}$, $\overrightarrow{OA_1} = \lambda\overrightarrow{OA}$ and $\overrightarrow{OB_1} = \mu\overrightarrow{OB}$ for some scalars λ and μ. Hence

$$\mathbf{r} = \overrightarrow{OP} = \overrightarrow{OA_1} + \overrightarrow{OB_1} = \lambda\overrightarrow{OA} + \mu\overrightarrow{OB} = \lambda\mathbf{a} + \mu\mathbf{b}.$$

We can take this idea one step further and prove that, for every point P in Π, $\mathbf{r}$ is expressed *uniquely* as a sum of multiples of $\mathbf{a}$ and $\mathbf{b}$.

Suppose that $\overrightarrow{OP} = \mathbf{r} = \lambda\mathbf{a} + \mu\mathbf{b} = \lambda_1\mathbf{a} + \mu_1\mathbf{b}$. Then

$$\lambda\mathbf{a} - \lambda_1\mathbf{a} = \mu_1\mathbf{b} - \mu\mathbf{b}$$

so that $\qquad\qquad\qquad (\lambda - \lambda_1)\mathbf{a} = (\mu_1 - \mu)\mathbf{b}.$

But $\mathbf{a}$ and $\mathbf{b}$ are not parallel, so only their zero multiples are equal, hence

$$(\lambda - \lambda_1) = 0 = (\mu_1 - \mu)$$

and so $\qquad\qquad\qquad \lambda = \lambda_1,\ \mu = \mu_1,$

and the expression for $\mathbf{r}$ as a sum of multiples of $\mathbf{a}$ and $\mathbf{b}$ is unique.

We combine these two results in the following theorem.

Theorem 5.5 Let $\mathbf{a}$ and $\mathbf{b}$ be non-parallel vectors in the plane Π through O and let $\overrightarrow{OP} = \mathbf{r}$. Then

P lies in $\Pi \Leftrightarrow$ there exist unique λ, μ with $\mathbf{r} = \lambda\mathbf{a} + \mu\mathbf{b}$.

Note: In the proof of the theorem, we proved a result which is useful in its own right:

For non-parallel vectors $\mathbf{a}$ and $\mathbf{b}$,

$$[\lambda\mathbf{a} + \mu\mathbf{b} = \lambda_1\mathbf{a} + \mu_1\mathbf{b}] \Leftrightarrow [\lambda = \lambda_1 \text{ and } \mu = \mu_1].$$

The situation of theorem **5.5**, when every point P in a plane Π has a position vector $\mathbf{r}$ which is the sum of unique multiples of $\mathbf{a}$ and $\mathbf{b}$, is described by saying that the pair of vectors

$\{\mathbf{a},\ \mathbf{b}\}$ is a *basis* for the set of all position vectors of points in Π.

Since we began with any two non-parallel vectors $\mathbf{a}$ and $\mathbf{b}$ in the plane Π, it will follow that any two non-parallel vectors in a plane form a basis for the set of position vectors of all points in the plane.

In three dimensions, we can choose three vectors, not in one plane, to form a similar basis for all the position vectors in three dimensional space. This we shall consider in Chapter 12.

EXAMPLE 1   *Relative to an origin O, the points A, B and C have position vectors $\mathbf{a}$, $\mathbf{b}$ and $\mathbf{c}$, respectively. Given that C lies in the plane OAB with $\mathbf{c} = \lambda\mathbf{a} + \mu\mathbf{b}$, and that BC is not parallel to OA, find, in terms of $\mathbf{a}$, λ, μ, the position vector $\mathbf{d}$ of D, the point of intersection of OA and BC (Fig. 5.14).*

$\overrightarrow{BC} = \overrightarrow{OC} - \overrightarrow{OB} = \mathbf{c} - \mathbf{b} = \lambda\mathbf{a} + \mu\mathbf{b} - \mathbf{b} = \lambda\mathbf{a} + (\mu - 1)\mathbf{b} \neq k\mathbf{a}$, since $\overrightarrow{BC}$ is not parallel to $\overrightarrow{OA}$, and so $\mu \neq 1$. Now, for some constant v,

$$\overrightarrow{BD} = v\overrightarrow{BC} = v\lambda\mathbf{a} + v(\mu - 1)\mathbf{b}$$

and so $\quad \overrightarrow{OD} = \mathbf{d} = \overrightarrow{OB} + \overrightarrow{BD} = \mathbf{b} + v\lambda\mathbf{a} + v(\mu - 1)\mathbf{b} = v\lambda\mathbf{a} + (1 + v\mu - v)\mathbf{b} = k\mathbf{a}.$

Hence $1 + v\mu - v = 0$ and $k = v\lambda$. Solving $1 - v + \mu v = 0$ for v, gives $v = \dfrac{1}{1 - \mu}$

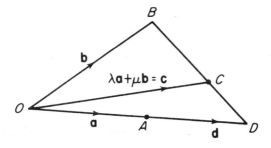

Fig. 5.14

and so

$$\mathbf{d} = \nu\lambda\mathbf{a} = \frac{\lambda}{1-\mu}\mathbf{a}.$$

EXAMPLE 2 *With reference to an origin O in a plane and a basis* $\{\mathbf{a}, \mathbf{b}\}$, *the equations of two lines are* $\mathbf{r} = \mathbf{a} + \mathbf{b} + \lambda(\mathbf{a} - \mathbf{b})$ *and* $\mathbf{r} = 2\mathbf{a} - 3\mathbf{b} + \lambda(\mathbf{a} + 2\mathbf{b})$. *Find the position vector of the point of intersection of the two lines.*

In the two equations of the lines, the same symbol λ is used for the parameter. Since the point P of position vector $\mathbf{r}$, where the lines intersect, will have different parameters in the equations of the two lines, we use two symbols λ and μ. Then we have to solve the equation

$$\mathbf{r} = \mathbf{a} + \mathbf{b} + \lambda(\mathbf{a} - \mathbf{b}) = 2\mathbf{a} - 3\mathbf{b} + \mu(\mathbf{a} + 2\mathbf{b}).$$

We separate the terms containing $\mathbf{a}$ and $\mathbf{b}$, to give

$$\mathbf{a} + \lambda\mathbf{a} - 2\mathbf{a} - \mu\mathbf{a} = -\mathbf{b} + \lambda\mathbf{b} - 3\mathbf{b} + 2\mu\mathbf{b},$$

that is, $(1 + \lambda - 2 - \mu)\mathbf{a} = (-1 + \lambda - 3 + 2\mu)\mathbf{b}$ and, since $\mathbf{a}$ and $\mathbf{b}$ are not parallel, ($\{\mathbf{a}, \mathbf{b}\}$ being a basis for the plane), we must have

$$1 + \lambda - 2 - \mu = 0 \quad \text{and} \quad -1 + \lambda - 3 + 2\mu = 0.$$

Eliminating λ from these two equations, $\lambda = 1 + \mu$ and $\lambda = 4 - 2\mu$, so $1 + \mu = 4 - 2\mu$, $3\mu = 3$, $\mu = 1$ and $\lambda = 1 + 1 = 2$. Putting these values of the parameters into the equations of the two lines, we find the position vector $\mathbf{r}$ of their common point to be $\mathbf{r} = 3\mathbf{a} - \mathbf{b}$.

EXERCISE 5.5

1   In the parallelogram $ABCD$, E is the midpoint of CD, and AE meets BD at F. Let $\overrightarrow{AB} = \mathbf{b}$ and $\overrightarrow{AD} = \mathbf{d}$. Express $\overrightarrow{AC}$, $\overrightarrow{AE}$, $\overrightarrow{AF}$ in terms of $\mathbf{b}$ and $\mathbf{d}$ and deduce that F is the point of trisection of DB. (Note: This question is a converse of question 1 of Exercise 5.4).

2   The position vectors, relative to O, of the vertices A and B of the rectangle $OACB$ are $\mathbf{a}$ and $\mathbf{b}$, respectively. The point P divides OC internally in the ratio $3:1$ $(= OP:PC)$. The lines BP and OA meet at Q and the lines AP and OB meet at R. In terms of $\mathbf{a}$ and $\mathbf{b}$, find the position vectors of P, Q and R.

3   In the parallelogram $ABCD$, $\overrightarrow{AB} = \mathbf{b}$ and $\overrightarrow{AC} = \mathbf{c}$. L is the midpoint of AD and $\overrightarrow{AM} = 2\overrightarrow{AB}$. The lines LM and BC meet at N. Find, in terms of $\mathbf{b}$ and $\mathbf{c}$, the vectors $\overrightarrow{AL}$, $\overrightarrow{AM}$, $\overrightarrow{AN}$.

4   Given a triangle ABC, with R equal to the mid point of AB, and Q the point such that C is the midpoint of AQ. Let RQ meet BC at P. Express the vector $\overrightarrow{AP}$ in terms of $\overrightarrow{AB}$ and $\overrightarrow{AC}$.

5.6 Vector equation of a line in three dimensions

Most examples considered so far have been two dimensional. However, the theory applies to a three-dimensional situation. We shall consider briefly the equations of lines in three dimensions. They will be dealt with in more detail in §12.5. The vector equation of a line, which was used in §5.3, applies equally well to a line in space.

Theorem 5.6   Given a point A, with position vector $\mathbf{a} = \overrightarrow{OA}$, and any vector $\mathbf{u}$, the equation of the line L through A in the direction of $\mathbf{u}$ is $\mathbf{r} = \mathbf{a} + t\mathbf{u}$, where t is a scalar parameter.

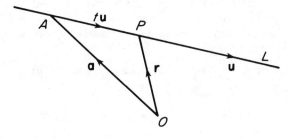

Fig. 5.15

Proof
Consider Fig. 5.15. Let P be any point in space, with position vector $\mathbf{r} = \overrightarrow{OP}$. Then

$$P \text{ lies on } L \Leftrightarrow \overrightarrow{AP} \text{ is parallel to } \mathbf{u}$$
$$\Leftrightarrow \overrightarrow{AP} = \mathbf{r} - \mathbf{a} = t\mathbf{u}, \text{ for some scalar } t,$$
$$\Leftrightarrow \mathbf{r} = \mathbf{a} + t\mathbf{u}.$$

So the equation of L is $\mathbf{r} = \mathbf{a} + t\mathbf{u}$.

Intersecting lines

Consider two coplanar lines which are not parallel. One line passes through A in the direction $\mathbf{u}$, and the other passes through B in the direction $\mathbf{v}$. If $\overrightarrow{OA} = \mathbf{a}$ and $\overrightarrow{OB} = \mathbf{b}$, the two lines have equations $\mathbf{r} = \mathbf{a} + t\mathbf{u}$ and $\mathbf{r} = \mathbf{b} + s\mathbf{v}$. See Fig. 5.16. Note that we use different scalar parameters t and s for the two lines. Let the two lines intersect at Q, where $\overrightarrow{OQ} = \mathbf{q}$, then

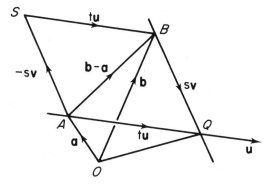

Fig. 5.16

q satisfies both equations, $\mathbf{q} = \mathbf{a} + t\mathbf{u} = \mathbf{b} + s\mathbf{v}$, for some numbers t and s. Therefore, $\overrightarrow{AB} = \mathbf{b} - \mathbf{a} = t\mathbf{u} - s\mathbf{v}$ and, as we saw in theorem 5.5, t and s can be found by construction of a parallelogram with diagonal AB and edges parallel to **u** and **v**.

Note that if the lines are parallel, $\mathbf{u} = k\mathbf{v}$, then it is no longer possible to find t and s such that $\overrightarrow{AB} = t\mathbf{u} - s\mathbf{v}$. This corresponds to the fact that parallel lines do not meet.

Skew lines

In three dimensions, two lines which are not parallel may not intersect, and then they are said to be *skew* (Fig. 5.17).

This is indicated in the algebra. There will be no values of t and s such that $\mathbf{a} + t\mathbf{u} = \mathbf{b} + s\mathbf{v}$, because $(\mathbf{b} - \mathbf{a})$, **u** and **v** do not lie in one plane.

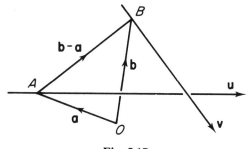

Fig. 5.17

MISCELLANEOUS EXERCISE 5

1   *AOB* is a triangle with $\overrightarrow{OA} = \mathbf{a}$, $\overrightarrow{OB} = \mathbf{b}$, and P, Q are the mid-points of OB, OA, respectively. Find the position vector of
(a) a general point on AP, (b) a general point on BQ, each in terms of **a**, **b** and a scalar parameter. Find also the position vector of the point in which AP and BQ intersect.   (*L*)

2   The points A, B have position vectors $\mathbf{a}, \mathbf{b}$ respectively, referred to an origin O.
    The point C lies on AB between A and B and is such that $\dfrac{AC}{CB} = \dfrac{2}{1}$, and D is
    the mid-point of OC. The line AD produced meets OB at E. Find, in terms of
    $\mathbf{a}$ and $\mathbf{b}$,
    (i) the position vector of C (referred to O),
    (ii) the vector $\overrightarrow{AD}$.
    Find the values of $\dfrac{OE}{EB}$ and $\dfrac{AE}{ED}$.   (C)

3   The position vectors of the vertices A, B, C of a triangle relative to an origin O
    are $\mathbf{a}, \mathbf{b}, \mathbf{c}$. The side BC is produced to D so that $BC = CD$. We define X as the
    point dividing the side AB in the ratio $2:1$, and Y as the point dividing AC in
    the ratio $4:1$. Express the position vectors $\mathbf{d}, \mathbf{x}, \mathbf{y}$ of D, X, Y relative to O in
    terms of $\mathbf{a}, \mathbf{b}, \mathbf{c}$, and use these to prove that the three points D, X, Y are in a
    straight line.   (SMP)

4   $ABCDEF$ is a regular hexagon. If $\overrightarrow{AB} = \mathbf{a}$ and $\overrightarrow{BC} = \mathbf{b}$, express the following
    vectors on terms of $\mathbf{a}$ and $\mathbf{b}$:
    (a) $\overrightarrow{CD}$,   (b) $\overrightarrow{CE}$,   (c) $\overrightarrow{EB}$.   (L)

5   The points A, B, C have position vectors $\mathbf{a}, \mathbf{b}, \mathbf{c}$ respectively referred to an
    origin O. State the position vector of P, the mid-point of AB.
    Find the position vector of the point which divides the line segment PC
    internally in the ratio $3:1$.   (L)

6   The points A, B and C have position vectors $\mathbf{a}, \mathbf{b}$ and $\mathbf{c}$ with respect to an
    origin O. The point R in the plane ABC has position vector $\mathbf{r}$ where
    $\mathbf{r} = \frac{1}{2}(\frac{2}{3}\mathbf{a} + \frac{1}{3}\mathbf{b}) + \frac{1}{2}\mathbf{c}$. Use the ratio theorem to obtain a geometrical description
    of the position of R with reference to the points A, B and C. Illustrate your
    answer with a diagram.
    By writing $\mathbf{r}$ in the form $\lambda\mathbf{a} + \mu(m\mathbf{b} + n\mathbf{c})$ where $\lambda + \mu = 1$, obtain an
    alternative description of the position of R. Given that the point S has
    position vector $\frac{2}{3}\mathbf{a} + \frac{1}{12}\mathbf{b} + \frac{1}{4}\mathbf{c}$, show that S bisects the line segment AR.
                                                                              (JMB)

7

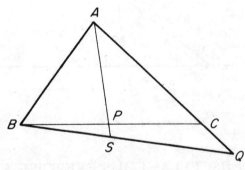

    In the diagram P is the mid-point of the side BC of the triangle ABC and Q lies
    on AC produced, so that $AC:CQ = 3:1$. Find vector equations for the lines
    AP and BQ in terms of $\mathbf{a}, \mathbf{b}$ and $\mathbf{c}$, which are, respectively, the position vectors
    of the points A, B and C relative to an origin O. Hence obtain, in terms of $\mathbf{a}, \mathbf{b}$
    and $\mathbf{c}$, the position vector of the point S at which the lines AP and BQ intersect.
                                                                              (JMB)

8　The tetrahedron $OABC$ has edges $\overrightarrow{OA} = \mathbf{a}$, $\overrightarrow{OB} = \mathbf{b}$, $\overrightarrow{OC} = \mathbf{c}$. The points $L, M,$ N are midpoints of OA, OB, OC, respectively, and P, Q, R are the midpoints of BC, CA, AB, respectively. Prove that PL and QM lie in one plane and find the position of their point of intersection, in terms of $\mathbf{a}$, $\mathbf{b}$ and $\mathbf{c}$. Deduce that the lines joining the midpoints of opposite edges of a tetrahedron all meet at their common midpoint.

9　The position vectors of P, Q with reference to an origin O are $\mathbf{p}, \mathbf{q}$, and M is the point on PQ such that

$$\beta \overrightarrow{PM} = \alpha \overrightarrow{MQ}.$$

Prove that the position vector of M is $\mathbf{m}$, where

$$\mathbf{m} = \frac{\beta \mathbf{p} + \alpha \mathbf{q}}{\alpha + \beta}.$$

The vectors $\mathbf{p}, \mathbf{q}$ are given by $u\mathbf{a}, v\mathbf{b}$ respectively, where u, v are positive scalars and $\mathbf{a}, \mathbf{b}$ are unit vectors. Prove that the position vector of any point on the internal bisector of $P\hat{O}Q$ has the form $r(\mathbf{a} + \mathbf{b})$, and deduce that, if M is the point where this bisector meets PQ, then

$$\frac{\alpha}{\beta} = \frac{u}{v}. \tag{C}$$

6 Integration I

6.1 A function and its derivative (revision)

EXERCISE 6.1

1 Complete the following table of functions and derivatives:

$f(x)$	$f'(x)$
x^4	$4x^3$
$x^3 + 2x$	
	$3x^2$
	$2x + 1$

2 Find the derivative function $f'(x)$ for the function $f(x)$:

    (i) x^2 (ii) $\frac{1}{3}x^3$ (iii) $x + 2$
    (iv) $x^3 + 3$ (v) $x^3 - 1$ (vi) 2
    (vii) $x^4 + c$ (viii) $x^4 - c$ (ix) $x^{3/2}$
    (x) $x^2 + 2x$ (xi) $2x^{1/2} - 2x^{-1/2}$ (xii) $x^{1/4} + x^{-3/4}$.

3 Find the function $f(x)$ with the following derivative:

    (i) x^2 (ii) x^3 (iii) $x^{1/2}$
    (iv) $x - x^{1/2}$ (v) $x^2 + 7x + 7$ (vi) $x^2 + 7x$
    (vii) 7 (viii) $\frac{1}{4}x^3 + c$ (ix) $x^{3/4} + x^{-1/4}$.

You will see that, when you are given $f(x)$, there is a unique expression for $f'(x)$. However, when $f'(x)$ is given, then $f(x)$ is not known uniquely because any constant may be added to $f(x)$ without affecting $f'(x)$. For example, if $f'(x) = 3x^2$, then $f(x)$ can be any function of the form $f(x) = x^3 + c$, where c is some real constant.

6.2 Integration

The reverse process of differentiation, that is to find $f(x)$ given $f'(x)$, is called *integration*. Given a function $g(x)$, then a function $f(x)$, such that $g(x) = f'(x)$, is called an *integral*, or *antiderivative*, of $g(x)$. When the integral includes the addition of an arbitrary constant c, then it is written

$\int g(x)dx$ = the (*indefinite*) integral of $g(x)$ with respect to x.

(The word 'indefinite' is often omitted.)

Thus $\qquad\qquad\qquad\qquad \int 3x^2 dx = x^3 + c.$

In reading this expression, the symbols have the following meaning:

$\int$ means 'the integral of',

dx means 'with respect to x'.

When the constant c is given a particular value, then we obtain a function whose derivative is $g(x)$, thus

$\qquad\qquad x^3 + c$ is the indefinite integral of $3x^2$

and $\qquad\quad$ if $f(x) = x^3 + 2$ then $f'(x) = 3x^2$

so $\qquad\qquad x^3 + 2$ is an integral of $3x^2$.

6.3 Rules for integration

The rules for differentiation, given in §4.7, lead to corresponding rules for integration, that is, the process of finding the integral of a function.

Rule 1 The integral of a linear combination of functions is the corresponding linear combination of their integrals, (with the linear combination of the constants of integration combined into one arbitrary constant). If a and b are constants and f and g are functions,

$$\int [af(x) + bg(x)]dx = a\int f(x)dx + b\int g(x)dx.$$

Rule 2 For any constants n and a,

$$\int x^n dx = \frac{1}{n+1}x^{n+1} + c, \text{ provided } n \neq -1,$$

$$\int \cos (nx + a)dx = \frac{1}{n}\sin (nx + a) + c,$$

$$\int \sin (nx + a)dx = \frac{-1}{n}\cos (nx + a) + c.$$

EXAMPLE 1   *Find the integral with respect to x of:*
(i) $2 + 3x$;   (ii) $x^4 - x^2$;   (iii) $3\cos (2x + 5)$.

Using the rules:
(i) $\int (2 + 3x)dx = 2\int 1dx + 3\int xdx = 2x + \frac{3}{2}x^2 + c$;
(ii) $\int (x^4 - x^2)dx = \int x^4 dx - \int x^2 dx = \frac{1}{5}x^5 - \frac{1}{3}x^3 + c$;
(iii) $\int 3\cos (2x + 5)dx = 3\int \cos (2x + 5)dx = \frac{3}{2}\sin(2x + 5) + c.$

Sometimes it is necessary to change the form of the *integrand*, that is, the function being integrated. The independent variable may also be something other than x.

EXAMPLE 2   *Integrate* (i) $(1+2x)^3$, (ii) $\cos^2 \theta$.

(i) $\int(1+2x)^3\,dx = \int(1+6x+12x^2+8x^3)dx = x+3x^2+4x^3+2x^4+c.$
(ii) $\int\cos^2\theta\,d\theta = \int\frac{1}{2}(1+\cos 2\theta)d\theta = \frac{1}{2}\theta+\frac{1}{4}\sin 2\theta+c.$

EXERCISE 6.3

1   Check the results of the above examples, by differentiation.
2   Write down
    (i) $\int 6x^2\,dx$ (ii) $\int(4x-3)dx$ (iii) $\int x^4\,dx$
    (iv) $\int\cos 2x\,dx$ (v) $\int(x^3-2x)dx$ (vi) $\int x^6\,dx$.
3   Find the integral of:
    (i) $\frac{3}{2}x$ (ii) $\dfrac{-2}{x^2}$ (iii) $5/x^2+1$
    (iv) $(x^2-1)/x^2$ (v) $(1+x)^2$ (vi) $(2+x)(x-3)$.
4   Integrate, with respect to x, the following:
    (i) $3x^2+2x+1$ (ii) $(3x-4)(2x-1)$ (iii) $(\cos x+\sin x)^2$
    (iv) $(x^2+1/x^2)^2$ (v) ax^2+bx+c (vi) $2x^{-\frac{1}{2}}+3x^{\frac{1}{2}}$.
5   Find
    (i) $\int(x^2+2x)dx$ (ii) $\int(t^2+2t)dt$ (iii) $\int\sin 2\theta\,d\theta$
    (iv) $\int(2u+u^{\frac{1}{2}})du$ (v) $\int(s+4)^3\,ds$ (vi) $\int(u+u^{-1})^2\,du$.

6.4 Evaluation of the arbitrary constant of integration

The process of integrating $f'(x)$ to obtain $f(x)$ involves an arbitrary constant c. Then c may be chosen so as to satisfy a condition that f takes a particular value for a given value of x. The graphs of the functions obtained by giving some set of values to the arbitrary constant of integration c are all translations of one another parallel to the y-axis (see Fig. 6.1). By choosing a suitable value of c we are choosing one particular graph, and we make this graph pass through some point (a, b).

EXAMPLE   *The gradient of the function f is given by $f'(x) = 2x+1$. Integrate $f'(x)$ and, by choosing the arbitrary constant c from the set $\{-1, 1, 3\}$, draw the graphs of three functions which all have the same gradient as f at any given value of x. Draw also the graph of f, given that $f(1) = 2$.*

Since $f'(x) = 2x+1$, $\mathbf{f}(x) = x^2+x+c$, for some constant c. The graphs of the functions corresponding to $c = -1$, $c = 1$, and $c = 3$ are shown in Fig. 6.1. For the required function f, $f(1) = 1+1+c = 2$, so $c = 0$, $f(x) = x^2+x$ and the graph of this function is also shown in Fig. 6.1.

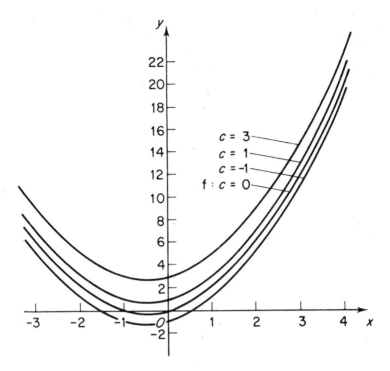

Fig. 6.1 Graphs of the functions $f(x) = x^2 + x + c$.

EXERCISE 6.4

1   Write down $\int 4x\,dx$ and for $c \in \{0, 1, 2\}$ draw the graph of the indefinite integral, where c is the constant of integration. For what value of c does the graph pass through $(3, 4)$?

2   The equation of a curve is $y = f(x)$. Find $f(x)$ given that:

   (i) $\dfrac{dy}{dx} = 4x$ and the curve passes through $(0, 4)$;

   (ii) $\dfrac{dy}{dx} = 3x^2 - 6x + 3$ and the curve passes through $(1, 0)$;

   (iii) $\dfrac{dy}{dx} = 3(x + 2)^2$ and the curve passes through $(0, 8)$;

   (iv) $\dfrac{dy}{dx} = 2\cos 2x - 2\sin 2x$ and the curve passes through $(0, 1)$.

3   At time t, the velocity of a particle moving in a straight line is $v = 3t^2 - 2t$. Given that the displacement s of the particle takes the value 2 when $t = 1$, find the value of s when $t = 2$.

4   At time t, the velocity of a particle moving in a straight line is $v = t^3 + 1$.
   (i) Through what distance does the particle move between $t = 3$ and $t = 4$?
   (ii) What is the average velocity between $t = 1$ and $t = 3$?

5 The velocity of a particle thrown vertically upwards is given by $v = u - gt$, at
   time t, where u, g are constants. Find:
     (i) an expression for the displacement s of the particle at time t,
    (ii) the maximum height h reached by the particle,
   (iii) the time elapsed before the particle returns to its point of projection.

7 Polynomials

7.1 Definitions

A *polynomial* is an algebraic expression consisting of a linear combinaton of positive integer powers of some indeterminate x. The *degree* of the polynomial is the highest exponent of x occurring in the expression. For example, the polynomials $2x - 3$, $x^3 + 4x$, $ax^2 + bx + c$, have degrees 1, 3, 2, respectively. The general polynomial of degree n is

$$p(x) = a_n x^n + a_{n-1} x^{n-1} + \ldots + a_1 x + a_0, a_n \neq 0.$$

Then $a_n, a_{n-1}, \ldots, a_1, a_0$ are the *coefficients* of $p(x)$,
a_n is the *leading coefficient* of $p(x)$,
a_0 is the *constant term* of $p(x)$,
$a_i x^i$ is the *term of degree i* of $p(x)$.
If p is a function whose value $p(x)$ is a polynomial then p is a *polynomial function*. The polynomial functions of low degree are:

constant function   : $n = 0$, $p(x) = a_0$;

linear function   : $n = 1$, $p(x) = a_1 x + a_0$;

quadratic function : $n = 2$, $p(x) = a_2 x^2 + a_1 x + a_0$.

Two polynomials are *equal* if they have the same degree and the same term of each degree. Equal polynomial functions are, of course, equal as functions.

EXERCISE 7.1

1   For the following polynomials state (a) the degree, (b) the constant term, (c) the leading coefficient, (d) $p(0)$, (e) $p(2)$:

     (i) $p(x) = 2x + 3$ (ii) $p(x) = x^2 - 4x$ (iii) $p(x) = x^3 + x - 1$
     (iv) $p(x) = 4$ (v) $p(x) = x - 2$ (vi) $p(x) = x^2 - 4$
     (vii) $p(x) = 5 - 2x$ (viii) $p(x) = 4x - 3x^2 - 7$ (ix) $p(x) = x^3 + 2x^4 - x^5$.

2   In question **1**, your answers to (b) and (d) should be the same in each case. Explain why this is so.

7.2 Algebra of polynomials

Polynomials may be added, subtracted or multiplied by a constant, and a linear combination of polynomials is also a polynomial. A linear combination of polynomials is obtained by multiplying each polynomial by a real number and adding the results. For example

$$(x^2 + 2x + 3) + (2x^2 - 4x - 2) = 3x^2 - 2x + 1.$$

The calculation of linear combinations may be laid out so that terms of the same degree are placed under each other.

EXAMPLE 1   *Given* $p(x) = x^3 - 2x^2 + 3x - 4$ *and* $q(x) = 2x^3 + x^2 + 2$, *find* $r(x) = 3p(x) - 2q(x)$.

$$
\begin{aligned}
3p(x) = &\ \ 3x^3 - 6x^2 + 9x - 12 \\
-2q(x) = &\ -4x^3 - 2x^2 \qquad\ \ - 4 \\
\hline
r(x) = &\ -x^3 - 8x^2 + 9x - 16
\end{aligned}
$$

The product of two polynomials is also a polynomial and is calculated by multiplying one polynomial by each term of the other polynomial in turn, and then adding. Again the work is assisted by using the long multiplication layout.

EXAMPLE 2   *Find* $r(x) = p(x).q(x)$ *where* $p(x) = x^2 + 3x - 4$ *and* $q(x) = 2x - 1$.

$$
\begin{aligned}
p(x) = &\ \qquad x^2 + 3x - 4 \\
q(x) = &\ \qquad\qquad 2x - 1 \\
\hline
(-1)p(x) = &\ \qquad - x^2 - 3x + 4 \\
2x\,p(x) = &\ \ 2x^3 + 6x^2 - 8x \\
\hline
p(x)\,q(x) = &\ \ 2x^3 + 5x^2 - 11x + 4
\end{aligned}
$$

In Example 3 note that a gap is left in a line where a term of a given degree is absent, that is, has zero coefficient.

EXAMPLE 3   *Find* $p(x).q(x)$, *where* $p(x) = 2x^3 - x^2 + 4$, $q(x) = x^2 - 2x + 2$.

$$
\begin{aligned}
p(x) = &\ \qquad\qquad 2x^3 - x^2 \qquad\ + 4 \\
q(x) = &\ \qquad\qquad\qquad x^2 - 2x + 2 \\
\hline
2p(x) = &\ \qquad\qquad 4x^3 - 2x^2 \qquad + 8 \\
-2x\,p(x) = &\ \qquad -4x^4 + 2x^3 \qquad\ - 8x \\
x^2 p(x) = &\ 2x^5 - x^4 \qquad\ + 4x^2 \\
\hline
p(x).q(x) = &\ 2x^5 - 5x^4 + 6x^3 + 2x^2 - 8x + 8
\end{aligned}
$$

Another method, which we might call the 'loops method', allows the multiplication to be done mentally, with a minimum of writing. Each step consists of picking out all the terms in the product of a certain degree by multiplying appropriate terms in each bracket. These terms are indicated by connecting loops and each time a term is used it is marked with a tick. When finished, each term should have as many ticks as there are terms in the other bracket. The steps for the product of Example 3 are as follows:

$(2x^3 - x^2 + 4)(x^2 - 2x + 2)$ $2x^3 x^2 = 2x^5$

$(2x^3 - x^2 + 4)(x^2 - 2x + 2)$ $2x^3(-2x) - x^2 x^2 = -5x^4$

$(2x^3 - x^2 + 4)(x^2 - 2x + 2)$ $2x^3 2 + x^2 2x = 6x^3$

$(2x^3 - x^2 + 4)(x^2 - 2x + 2)$ $-2x^2 + 4x^2 = 2x^2$

$(2x^3 - x^2 + 4)(x^2 - 2x + 2)$ $4(-2x) = -8x$

$(2x^3 - x^2 + 4)(x^2 - 2x + 2)$ $4.2 = 8.$

Now sum the terms on the right-hand side for the answer.

Note 1 The product of two polynomials of degrees m and n has degree $m + n$, since its leading coefficient is the product of their leading coefficients.

Note 2 The degree of a linear combination of two polynomials will be less than or equal to the larger of the two degrees. For example:

$$2(x^2 - 4) - (2x^2 - 6x) = 6x - 8,$$
$$2(x^2 - 4) - 3(x - 8) = 2x^2 - 3x + 16.$$

EXERCISE 7.2

1 Express as a polynomial the linear combination:
   (i) $(2x + 4) - (x + 3)$, (ii) $2(x + 5) + 3(x^2 - 2)$,
   (iii) $4(x^2 - 2x + 1) - 2(2x^2 + 3)$, (iv) $4(x - 2) - 3(x^2 - 2x + 5)$,
   (v) $5(1 - 3x + x^3) - 2(3x^2 - 2x + 4)$, (vi) $9(3x^2 + 4x + 1) - 7(3 - x - 2x^2)$.

2 Using long multiplication, express the product as a polynomial:
   (i) $(x - 2)(x^2 + x + 3)$, (ii) $(x^2 - 2x - 5)(x^3 + x)$, (iii) $(2x^2 + x + 1)^2$,
   (iv) $(x + 2)^2(x - 3)$, (v) $(x + 4)^3$, (vi) $(x^2 + 2)(x^3 - 3x)$.

3 Multiply the following polynomials, using the loop method:
   (i) $(x^2 + 2)(3x - 1)$, (ii) $(2x + 1)(3x^2 - 4x + 1)$, (iii) $(4x^3 - 2x^2)(3x^2 - 1)$,
   (iv) $(5x + 2)(5x^2 - x - 3)$, (v) $(4x^2 - 2x + 1)(1 + 3x - 2x^2)$,
   (vi) $(1 - 3x - 6x^2)(x + 2x^2 - 5x^3)$, (vii) $(3x - 1)(x^4 - 2x^3 + 3x^2 - 4x + 5)$,
   (viii) $(x^3 - 3x^2 + 2x - 1)(4 - 2x + 3x^2)$.

4 Given that $p(x) = 2x^2 - 3x + 4$, $q(x) = x^2 + 1$, find the polynomial:
   (i) $p(x) + q(x)$, (ii) $2p(x) + 3q(x)$, (iii) $3p(x) - 4q(x)$, (iv) $p(x)q(x)$,
   (v) $p(x)p(x)$, (vi) $\{q(x)\}^2$, (vii) $\{p(x) + q(x)\}\{p(x) - q(x)\}$.

5 Find the product of $1 + 2x + 3x^2 + 4x^3$ and $1 - 2x + x^2$.

6 (i) Find the coefficient of x^3 in the product $(3x^2 - 2x - 1)(2x^2 + 3x - 4)$.
   (ii) Find the coefficient of x^4 in the product $(3 + 2x - 4x^2)(2 - x^2 + 3x^3 - x^4)$.

7 Expand in ascending powers of x, as far as x^3:
   (i) $(1 - x + 2x^2 - x^3 + x^4)^2$, (ii) $(1 + x)^2(2 - x)(1 + 3x - x^2)$,
   (iii) $(2 + x)(1 - x^2)(3x - 4)^2$, (iv) $(3x^2 - 2x + 4)(4x - 2)(x^2 - x)$.

7.3 Rational functions

When polynomials are divided the result may not always be a polynomial. For example, $(x+2)/(x+1)$ is not a polynomial. Such fractions are called *rational functions* and may be manipulated in the usual way.

EXAMPLE   *Simplify* (i) $\dfrac{x+2}{x+1} - \dfrac{x+1}{x+2}$,   (ii) $\dfrac{x^2-1}{x+1}$.

(i) Use a common denominator:

$$\frac{x+2}{x+1} - \frac{x+1}{x+2} = \frac{(x+2)^2 - (x+1)^2}{(x+1)(x+2)} = \frac{x^2 + 4x + 4 - x^2 - 2x - 1}{(x+1)(x+2)}$$

$$= \frac{2x+3}{(x+1)(x+2)}.$$

(ii) $\dfrac{x^2-1}{x+1} = \dfrac{(x-1)(x+1)}{x+1} = x-1$. In this case, the quotient of the two polynomials is also a polynomial. However, as a function, we must remember that the domain must exclude the point $x = -1$.

EXERCISE 7.3

1   Express as a rational function:

(i) $\dfrac{1}{x} - \dfrac{1}{x^2}$

(ii) $\dfrac{x}{1+x} + \dfrac{1}{1-x}$

(iii) $2x + \dfrac{1}{x+1}$

(iv) $\dfrac{2x}{3-x} + \dfrac{4}{x-3}$

(v) $x^2 + x - 1 + \dfrac{2}{x+3}$

(vi) $x - 1 + \dfrac{2x}{x^2+1}$

(vii) $\left(1 - \dfrac{7}{x+3}\right)\left(2 + \dfrac{16}{x-5}\right)$

(viii) $\dfrac{x^3+8}{x^3-8} - \dfrac{x^2}{x^2+2x+4}$

7.4 Division of a polynomial by a linear polynomial

A polynomial $p(x)$ of degree n can be divided by a linear polynomial $(x+a)$ to give a quotient $q(x)$ of degree $(n-1)$ and a constant remainder r. This is achieved by long division, in a sequence of steps. One step is described and the whole process is shown in an example.

Division step

When we are left with a polynomial $t(x)$ of degree m, with $m \geqslant 1$, we divide the leading term of $t(x)$ by x, giving $a_m x^{m-1}$ which then forms part of the quotient q(x). Then subtract $a_m x^{m-1}(x+a)$ from t(x) to give a new polynomial of degree less than *m*. This polynomial becomes t(x) for the next step, unless it is constant, when it becomes the remainder *r*. Initially t(x) = p(x). The work may be laid out as a long division.

EXAMPLE 1   *Divide $x^3 + 3x^2 - 3$ by $x + 1$.*

$$x^2 + 2x - 2 \longleftarrow \text{quotient}$$
$$x+1\overline{)x^3 + 3x^2 + 0x - 3}$$

Step 1
$$\underline{x^3 + x^2}$$
$$2x^2 + 0x$$

Step 2
$$\underline{2x^2 + 2x}$$
$$- 2x - 3$$

Step 3
$$\underline{- 2x - 2}$$
$$- 1 \longleftarrow \text{remainder}$$

Thus $x^3 + 3x^2 - 3 = (x+1)(x^2 + 2x - 2) - 1$. **The quotient is $x^2 + 2x - 2$ and the remainder is -1.**

The 'loop method' can also be used, the terms of the dividend being ticked off as they are accounted for, as in Example 2 below.

EXAMPLE 2   *Divide $x^3 - 4x + 5$ by $x - 2$.*

$$\underset{\checkmark}{x^3} + 0x^2 - 4x + 5 \quad :(x-2)x^2 = x^3 - 2x^2$$

$$\underset{\checkmark}{x^3} + \underset{\checkmark}{0x^2} - 4x + 5 \quad :(x-2)(x^2 + 2x) = x^3 - 4x$$

$$\underset{\checkmark}{x^3} + \underset{\checkmark}{0x^2} - \underset{\checkmark}{4x} + 5 = (x-2)(x^2 + 2x) + 5,$$

so **the quotient is $x^2 + 2x$ and the remainder is 5.**

EXERCISE 7.4

1   Find the quotient q(x) and the remainder *r* on dividing:
 (i) $x^2 + 4x - 5$ by $x + 2$ (ii) $x^3 + 1$ by $x + 1$
 (iii) $x^2 + 3x + 2$ by $x + 1$ (iv) $3x^2 - 11x + 8$ by $x - 3$
 (v) $x^3 - 2x^2 + 3x - 6$ by $x + 2$ (vi) $2x^3 + 4x$ by $x + 1$
 (vii) $x^3 + x^2 - 9x + 9$ by $x + 3$ (viii) $x^4 - 3x^2$ by $x - 2$
 (ix) $x^3 - x^2 - 5x + 6$ by $x - 2$ (x) $2x^3 - x + 8$ by $2x - 1$
 (xi) $3x^4 + 2x^3 - x^2 + 4x - 5$ by $x + 3$ (xii) $x^4 - 3x^2 + 2x$ by $2x - 3$.
2   Check your results in question 1 by multiplying the quotient q(x) by the linear divisor and adding the remainder.

7.5 Factors of a polynomial

If a polynomial $p(x)$ can be written $p(x) = p_1(x) \cdot p_2(x)$ where $p_1(x)$ and $p_2(x)$ are polynomials of degree at least one, then p_1 and p_2 are factors of the polynomial p.

If we divide $p(x)$ by a linear polynomial $(x - \alpha)$ and obtain a quotient $q(x)$ and remainder r, then

$$p(x) = (x - \alpha)q(x) + r$$

so clearly $(x - \alpha)$ is a factor of $p(x)$ if $r = 0$.

Regarding the polynomials as functions we see that

$$p(\alpha) = (\alpha - \alpha)q(\alpha) + r = r.$$

These results give us two useful theorems.

Remainder theorem

The remainder on dividing the polynomial $p(x)$ by $(x - \alpha)$ is $p(\alpha)$.

Factor theorem

$[(x - \alpha)$ is a factor of the polynomial $p(x)] \Leftrightarrow p(\alpha) = 0$.

When $p(\alpha) = 0$, α is called a *zero* of p, or a *root* of $p(x) = 0$.
Note the signs: $(x - \alpha)$ is a factor when $p(\alpha) = 0$,
                       $(x + \alpha)$ is a factor when $p(-\alpha) = 0$.
As a slight modification, suppose

$$p(x) = (ax + b)q(x) + r.$$

then $p(-b/a) = (-b + b) \, q(-b/a) + r = r,$

so the remainder on dividing $p(x)$ by $(ax + b)$ is $p(-b/a)$ and the remainder on dividing $p(x)$ by $(ax - b)$ is $p(b/a)$.

EXAMPLE 1   *Find the remainder on dividing* $x^3 + 2x^2 - 3x - 4$ *by:* (i) $x - 1$,
(ii) $x + 2$.

(i) The remainder is $p(1) = 1 + 2 - 3 - 4 = -4$.
(ii) The remainder is $p(-2) = -8 + 8 + 6 - 4 = 2$.

EXAMPLE 2   *Solve the equation* $x^3 - 2x^2 - 5x + 6 = 0$.

Since we cannot solve a cubic equation in general, we look for a factor $(x - \alpha)$ of $p(x) = x^3 - 2x^2 - 5x + 6$. Since the factors of 6 are $\pm 1, \pm 2, \pm 3, \pm 6$ we try some of these values for α.

$$p(-1) = -1 - 2 + 5 + 6 = 8,$$
$$p(1) = 1 - 2 - 5 + 6 = 0,$$

so $(x - 1)$ is a factor of $p(x)$.

On dividing p(x) by (x − 1) we find

$$p(x) = x^3 - 2x^2 - 5x + 6 = (x-1)(x^2 - x - 6)$$
$$= (x-1)(x+2)(x-3)$$

on factorising the quadratic factor.

Hence $p(1) = 0$, $p(-2) = 0$, $p(3) = 0$ and the solution set of $p(x) = 0$ is $\{1, -2, 3\}$.

EXERCISE 7.5

1 Use the remainder theorem to find the remainder on dividing:
   (i) $x^3 - 2x^2 + x - 1$ by $x - 1$
   (ii) $x + x^2 + 1$ by $x + 2$,
   (iii) $3x^2 + 2x - 1$ by $x - 2$
   (iv) $x^3 + x^2 + x + 1$ by $x + 1$
   (v) $4x^3 + x - 2$ by $2x - 1$
   (vi) $x^4 + x^2 + 1$ by $x + 2$.
   Check your answers by long division.

2 State whether the linear polynomial is a factor of the other polynomial:
   (i) $x - 1$, $2x^3 + x^2 - 2x - 1$
   (ii) $x - 1$, $x^4 - 2x + 1$
   (iii) $x + 2$, $x^3 - 3x^2 + 5x - 10$
   (iv) $x + 4$, $x^3 + 2x^2 + 5x - 12$
   (v) $x + 1$, $2x^3 + 3x^2 - 1$
   (vi) $2x - 1$, $4x^3 + 3x - 2$
   (vii) $2x - 3$, $x^4 - 2x - 3$
   (viii) $3x + 1$, $6x^3 - 13x^2 + 13x + 6$.

3 Factorise the polynomial completely (note that some quadratic factors can not themselves be factorised into two linear factors):
   (i) $2x^3 + x^2 - 2x - 1$
   (ii) $2x^3 + 3x^2 - 1$
   (iii) $x^3 + 3x^2 + 3x + 1$
   (iv) $x^4 - 1$
   (v) $x^3 - 1$
   (vi) $x^3 - x^2 - x + 1$
   (vii) $x^3 + x^2 - x + 2$
   (viii) $x^3 - x^2 + x - 1$
   (ix) $4x^3 + 3x - 2$
   (x) $6x^3 - 13x^2 + 13x + 6$
   (xi) $3x^3 - 7x^2 + 4$
   (xii) $x^3 - 4x^2 + x + 6$
   (xiii) $x^3 - 21x + 20$
   (xiv) $4x^3 - 8x^2 + x + 3$
   (xv) $6x^3 + 17x^2 - 4x - 3$.

4 Find the value of a, given that:
   (i) $x^3 - 2x^2 + 3x - a$ is divisible by $x - 2$,
   (ii) $x^3 + x^2 + ax + 8$ is divisible by $x - 1$,
   (iii) $x^3 + ax^2 - 2x + 1$ is divisible by $x + 2$,
   (iv) $x^3 - 3x^2 + ax + 5$ has remainder 8 when divided by $x - 2$,
   (v) $3x^3 + 2x^2 - ax + 3$ has remainder 1 when divided by $2x - 1$.

5 Find the values of a and b and factorise the polynomial p(x) completely, given that:
   (i) $p(x) = x^3 + ax^2 - x + b$ and p(x) is divisible by $x - 1$ and by $x + 3$,
   (ii) $p(x) = x^3 + ax^2 + 2x + b$ and p(x) is divisible by $(x + 1)(x - 2)$,
   (iii) $p(x) = 4x^3 + ax + b$ and p(x) is divisible by $(x + 2)(2x - 1)$.

6 Show that, for any constant a and any natural number n, $x - a$ is a factor of $x^n - a^n$. Find conditions (if any) on n that are required in order that:
   (i) $x + a$ is a factor of $x^n + a^n$,
   (ii) $x + a$ is a factor of $x^n - a^n$,
   (iii) $x - a$ is a factor of $x^n + a^n$.

7 Use the results of question 6 to state a linear factor of p(x) or to show that p(x) has no linear factors:
   (i) $p(x) = x^3 - 8$
   (ii) $p(x) = x^4 + 16$
   (iii) $p(x) = x^3 + 27$
   (iv) $p(x) = 8x^3 - 125$.

8 The polynomial $x^3 + ax + b$, where a, b are constants, leaves remainders of 11 and 41 when divided by $(x - 3)$ and $(x - 4)$ respectively. Find the remainder when this polynomial is divided by $(x - 5)$. (L)

9   Given that $(x+3)$ is a factor of $f(x)$ where
$$f(x) \equiv 2x^3 - ax + 12,$$
find the constant a. Express $f(x)$ as a product of linear factors.   (L)

10   Let $f(x) = 2x^4 + ax^2 + bx - 60$. The remainder when $f(x)$ is divided by $(x-1)$ is -94. One factor of $f(x)$ is $(x-3)$. Determine the constants a and b.   (L)

11   $f(x) \equiv x^3 - x^2 + ax + b$, where a and b are constants. When $f(x)$ is divided by $(x-1)$ the remainder is 1, and when $f(x)$ is divided by x the remainder is 0. Find the remainder when $f(x)$ is divided by $(x-2)$.   (L)

12   Use the factor theorem to find a linear factor of $P(x)$, where $P(x) = x^3 + 6x^2 - 7x - 60$. Hence express $P(x)$ as a product of three linear factors.

13   Show that if $(x+t)$ is a common factor of $x^3 + px^2 + q$ and $ax^3 + bx + c$, then it is also a factor of $apx^2 - bx + aq - c$. Show that $x^3 + \sqrt{7}x^2 - 14\sqrt{7}$ and $2x^3 - 13x - \sqrt{7}$ have a common factor and hence find all the roots of the equation $2x^3 - 13x - \sqrt{7} = 0$.   (L)

7.6 The sign of a polynomial function

When a polynomial function can be factorised into a product of linear factors, the sign of its value at any point will be given by the signs of its factors. This may be used to give a rough sketch of the graph of the function.

EXAMPLE   *Find the roots of the polynomial function* $p(x) = x^3 - 2x^2 - 5x + 6$ *and sketch its graph.*

Using the factor theorem we evaluate $p(x)$ for values of x dividing 6.
$p(1) = 1 - 2 - 5 + 6 = 0$ $p(-1) = -1 - 2 + 5 + 6 = 8$
$p(2) = 8 - 8 - 10 + 6 = -4$ $p(-2) = -8 - 8 + 10 + 6 = 0$
$p(3) = 27 - 18 - 15 + 6 = 0$ $p(-3) = -27 - 18 + 15 + 6 = -24$,
and so $p(x) = c(x-1)(x+2)(x-3)$, where c is a constant. By comparing coefficients of x^3 we see that $cx^3 = x^3$ and $c = 1$.

So $p(x) = (x-1)(x+2)(x-3)$ and the graph of p crosses the x-axis where $x = -2, 1, 3$.

We obtain the signs of x from the signs of its factors:

	$(x+2)$	$(x-1)$	$(x-3)$	$p(x)$
for $x < -2$	$-$ve	$-$ve	$-$ve	$-$ve
for $-2 < x < 1$	$+$ve	$-$ve	$-$ve	$+$ve
for $1 < x < 3$	$+$ve	$+$ve	$-$ve	$-$ve
for $3 < x$	$+$ve	$+$ve	$+$ve	$+$ve.

Thus, the graph of p is of the form shown in Fig. 7.1.

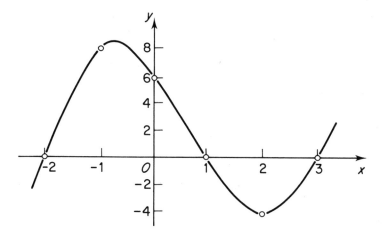

Fig. 7.1

EXERCISE 7.6

1 Using the signs of the factors of $p(x)$, sketch its graph:
   (i) $p(x) = (x + 1)(x - 2)$ (ii) $p(x) = (x + 2)(x - 3)(x + 4)$
   (iii) $p(x) = (2 - x)(3 - x)$ (iv) $p(x) = (2x + 1)(2 - x)$
   (v) $p(x) = (4x + 1)(x - 2)(x + 1)$ (vi) $p(x) = (x + 3)(2x - 1)(x + 1)(x - 4)$.

2 Find the points where the graph of $p(x)$ crosses the axes $O(x, y)$ and hence sketch the graph:
   (i) $p(x) = x^3 - 3x^2 + 2x$ (ii) $p(x) = x^4 - 2x^2 + 1$
   (iii) $p(x) = x - x^3$ (iv) $p(x) = 2x^3 - 3x^2 - 3x + 2$.

3 The cubic polynomial (that is, of degree 3) $p(x)$ has a graph which passes through the four points $(-2, 0)$, $(1, 0)$, $(4, 0)$ and $(0, 16)$. Find $p(x)$.

4 State a possible polynomial which has roots: (a) $\{-2, 4\}$; (b) $\{-4, -1, 3\}$; (c) $\{-3, 0, 2, 5\}$.

MISCELLANEOUS EXERCISE 7

1 Given that $f(x) = x^4 + 3x^3 - 5x^2 - 9x - 2$, find by trial two integer solutions of the equation $f(x) = 0$.
   Hence factorise $f(x)$ and solve the equation completely.   (*SMP*)

2 The cubic polynomial $x^3 + ax^2 + bx + c$ when divided by x, $(x - 1)$, $(x - 2)$ has remainders of 1, 2, 5 respectively. Find the values of a, b, and c.   (*L*)

3 Prove that the remainder on dividing a polynomial $f(x)$ by $(x - a)$ is $f(a)$.
   The remainder when a polynomial $f(x)$ is divided by $(x - 2)$ is 3 and the remainder when it is divided by $(x + 1)$ is 6. If the remainder when $f(x)$ is divided by $(x - 2)(x + 1)$ is $px + q$, find the numerical values of p and q.   (*JMB*)

4 The polynomial $P(x)$ leaves a remainder of 2 when divided by $(x-1)$ and a remainder of 3 when divided by $(x-2)$. The remainder when $P(x)$ is divided by $(x-1)(x-2)$ is $ax+b$. By writing

$$P(x) \equiv (x-1)(x-2)Q(x) + ax + b,$$

find the values of a and b.

Given also that $P(x)$ is a cubic polynomial with coefficient of x^3 equal to unity, and that -1 is a root of the equation $P(x)=0$, obtain $P(x)$. Show that the equation $P(x)=0$ has no other real roots.   (*JMB*)

5 Find the quotient and the remainder (of degree less than or equal to 1) when the polynomial $x(x+1)(2x-3)$ is divided by the polynomial x^2+1.   (*SMP*)

6 Given that the equations

$$x^3 - 2x + 4 = 0$$

and

$$x^2 + x + k = 0$$

have a common root, show that

$$k^3 + 4k^2 + 14k + 20 = 0.$$ (*JMB*)

7 Show that, when $f(x)$, a polynomial in x, is divided by $(x-a)(x-b)$, where $a \neq b$, the remainder is

$$\left(\frac{f(a)-f(b)}{a-b}\right)x + \left(\frac{af(b)-bf(a)}{a-b}\right).$$

Verify that $(2x-1)$ is a factor of

$$4x^3 - 3x + 1$$

and find the other linear factors.

Determine the remainder when $4x^3 - 3x + 1$ is divided by $x^2 + x - 6$.   (*L*)

8 Composition of Functions and Applications to Graphs

8.1 Composition of mappings

Suppose that A, B and C are sets and that two mappings of functions are defined:

$$f : A \rightarrow B, \quad \text{with domain } A \text{ and codomain } B;$$
$$g : B \rightarrow C, \quad \text{with domain } B \text{ and codomain } C.$$

The corresponding mappings of any element x in A and any element y in B are

$$f : x \mapsto f(x), \quad g : y \mapsto g(y),$$

and these are composed to form the *composite function* gf of f and g, by

$$gf : A \rightarrow C, \text{ for all } x \in A, \quad gf : x \mapsto gf(x) = g(f(x))$$

so that $\qquad gf(x) = g(y)$, where $y = f(x)$.

It may be helpful to consider the function composition in terms of a Venn diagram showing the mappings (Fig. 8.1).

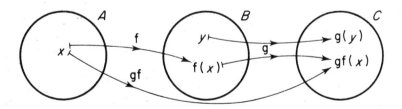

Fig. 8.1 Function composition: $gf(x) = g(f(x))$.

Note The composite function gf is sometimes referred to as a *function of a function*, because $gf(x) = g(f(x))$ may be read as g of f of x, and sometimes the notation used for gf is $g \circ f$, the small circle between g and f being read as 'of'. However, it is not good practice to refer to gf as a function of a function because this phrase suggests a function whose domain is a set of functions, which is not at all the case here. We shall always use the term 'composite function'. It is quite a different way of combining functions from the product of functions (Chapter 1).

It is important to remember that the function gf means that you perform the mapping f first and follow it by g, the reverse of the order in which the functions are written.

EXERCISE 8.1

1   Given the functions $f: A \rightarrow B$ and $g: B \rightarrow C$, state the meaning of gf(x), where:
(i) A is the set of children in a town, B is the set of all classes, C is the set of all schools in the town and x is John Smith, if f and g have the meanings 'the class containing' and 'the school of' respectively;
(ii) A, B and C are sets of people, x is you, f means 'the father of' and g means 'the mother of';
(iii) A is a set of football teams, B is a set of strips, C is a set of colours, f means 'the strip of', g means 'the colour of', and x is Manchester United.
2   In question 1 (ii), write down the meaning of $\{ \text{ff}(x), \text{fg}(x), \text{gf}(x), \text{gg}(x) \}$.
3   Using question 1 (i) and (iii) as examples, show that gf can have a meaning when fg has no meaning.
   Give a condition to be satisfied by the sets A, B and C in order that fg has a meaning.
4   The domains of f and g are the set of real numbers $\mathbb{R}$. Given that $f(x) = 2x - 1$ and $g(x) = x^2$, write down:
(i) fg(0), (ii) gf(0), (iii) ff(4), (iv) fg(4), (v) fgf(4), (vi) fg(x), (vii) gf(x), (viii) fg(t).

8.2 Composition of real functions

When f and g are real functions, their domains and their codomains are all subsets of $\mathbb{R}$. For example, let f and g have domain $\mathbb{R}$, and for $x \in \mathbb{R}$ let $f(x) = x^2 - 2x$ and $g(x) = x + 3$. Then

$$\text{gf}(x) = g(x^2 - 2x) = x^2 - 2x + 3,$$
whilst $$\text{fg}(x) = f(x + 3) = (x + 3)^2 - 2(x + 3) = x^2 + 4x + 3.$$

This shows that, in general, fg $\neq$ gf, that is, composition of functions is not commutative. The order of the functions in a composite is important.

However, the composition of functions is associative, because the composition of mappings generally is associative. Let f, g, h be real functions, then

$$(fg)h = f(gh) = fgh,$$

the second equality being one of notation, since there is no ambiguity. In other words, the brackets are unimportant in the composition of functions and so we omit them. To prove the result of associativity, for all x in the domain of fgh,

$$(fg)h(x) = fg(h(x)) = f(g(h(x))) = f(gh(x)) = f(gh)(x).$$

We recall from Chapter 1 that the domain of a real function may be a subset and not the whole of $\mathbb{R}$. In fact, when f is defined by means of a formula for $f(x)$, we assume that the domain of f is as large as possible and that it includes all the points where $f(x)$ is defined. When considering the domain of a composite function, we again assume that it is as large as possible, as a convention. Thus, if the domain of f is A and its range is B, $f(A) = B$; let the domain of g be C, then the domain of gf will be the subset of A which is mapped on to $B \cap C$. In words, the domain of gf is that subset of the domain of f which is mapped into the domain of g.

Notation   Since we do not need to use brackets when writing down the composite of three or more functions, there is only one meaning to fff or to ffff, and so we write $ff = f^2$, $fff = f^3$, $ffff = f^4$, and the composite of n copies of the function f is written f^n.

EXAMPLE 1   *Find the domain and the form of the function fgh given that*
$$f(x) = \frac{1}{x-1}, \, g(x) = 2x - 1, \, h(x) = x^2.$$

Following the convention that the domain of a real function is as large a subset of the real numbers as possible, the domains of g and h are each $\mathbb{R}$ and the domain of f is $\mathbb{R}\backslash\{1\}$. Then

$$fg(x) = f(2x - 1) = \frac{1}{(2x - 1) - 1} = \frac{1}{2(x - 1)} \quad \text{for } x \in \mathbb{R}\backslash\{1\}$$

$$(fg)h(x) = fg(x^2) = \frac{1}{2(x^2 - 1)} \quad \text{for } x \in \mathbb{R}\backslash\{1, -1\}.$$

Note also $f(gh)(x) = f(2x^2 - 1) = \dfrac{1}{2(x^2 - 1)} = (fg)h(x)$, as expected.

Hence, $fgh(x) = \dfrac{1}{2(x^2 - 1)}$ and fgh has domain $\mathbb{R}\backslash\{1, -1\}$.

When finding the value of a composite function, it is sometimes helpful to introduce some intermediate variables. For instance, if we put

$$h(x) = y \text{ and } g(y) = z \text{ then } fgh(x) = fg(y) = f(z).$$

In Example 1, $h(x) = y = x^2$, $g(y) = z = 2y - 1$,

$$fgh(x) = f(z) = \frac{1}{2y - 1} = \frac{1}{2(x^2 - 1)}.$$

EXAMPLE 2   *The real functions f, g and h are given by the equations*
$$f(x) = 1/x, \quad g(x) = \sqrt{x}, \quad h(x) = x^2 - 2x - 3.$$

Find the domain and the range of the real function:
(i) fg, (ii) gf, (iii) gh, (iv) gfh.

(i) $fg(x) = f(\sqrt{x}) = 1/\sqrt{x}$, g has domain $\mathbb{R}^+ \cup \{0\}$, f has domain $\mathbb{R}\backslash\{0\}$ and so fg has domain $\mathbb{R}^+$. Clearly, the range of fg is also $\mathbb{R}^+$.

(ii) $gf(x) = g(1/x) = \sqrt{(1/x)} = 1/\sqrt{x} = fg(x)$, so gf = fg, with domain and range each equal to $\mathbb{R}^+$, as in (i).

(iii) $gh(x) = g(x^2 - 2x - 3) = \sqrt{\{(x-3)(x+1)\}}$, which will only be defined when $(x-3)(x+1) \geqslant 0$, that is, when either $x \geqslant 3$ or $x \leqslant -1$. The domain of h is $\mathbb{R}$ so the domain of gh is $\{x \in \mathbb{R}: x \geqslant 3\} \cup \{x \in \mathbb{R}: x \leqslant -1\}$. Since, for all x in this domain, $gh(x) \geqslant 0$, $gh(3) = 0$ and $gh(x)$ can be made as large as we like by taking x large enough, the range of gh is $\mathbb{R}^+ \cup \{0\}$.

(iv) $gfh(x) = \sqrt{\dfrac{1}{(x-3)(x+1)}}$, so gfh has domain

$\{x \in \mathbb{R}: x > 3\} \cup \{x \in \mathbb{R}: x < -1\}$, since the points 3, -1 do not lie in the domain of fh. Also, since $(x-3)(x+1)$ can be made as small as we like as long as x is near enough to 3, and can be made as large as we like for large enough x, the range of gfh is $\mathbb{R}^+$.

EXERCISE 8.2

1   Find the domain and range of (a) fg, (b) gf, when the real functions f and g are given by:
   (i) $f(x) = 1/x$, $g(x) = \sqrt{x}$; (ii) $f(x) = x^2$, $g(x) = \sqrt{x}$;
   (iii) $f(x) = x - 3$, $g(x) = 1/(x^2 - 1)$;   (iv) $f(x) = \sqrt{(x^2 - 4)}$, $g(x) = 2/(x+1)$.

8.3 Translation of a graph

Consider the graph of the function f, which is the curve with the equation $y = f(x)$. If we wish to translate the graph by a distance b parallel to the y-axis, then this means that we add b to each value of y since the point (x, y) is to become $(x, y+b)$. Thus the equation of the translated graph will be $y = f(x) + b$. Let g be the real function given by $g(x) = x + b$, then $f(x) + b = gf(x)$ so the new graph is the graph of the composite function gf. Note that the equation of gf could be written $y - b = f(x)$ so we can regard the translation as given by either adding b to $f(x)$ or subtracting b from y in the equation. This translation with $b = 3$ and $f(x) = x^2$ is shown in Fig. 8.2(a).

Now consider the translation of the graph of f a distance a parallel to the x-axis, so that the point (x, y) becomes $(x + a, y)$. Since (x, y) satisfies the equation $y = f(x)$, the point $(x + a, y) = (x_1, y)$ must satisfy the equation $y = f(x_1 - a)$. This means that, to find the height of the translated graph at x, we move back a distance a to the point $(x - a)$ and find the height of the original graph at $(x - a)$, which is $f(x - a)$. Therefore, the equation of the translated graph is $y = f(x - a) = fh(x)$, where $h(x) = x - a$. This translation of the parabola $y = x^2$, with $a = 2$ is shown in Fig. 8.2(b).

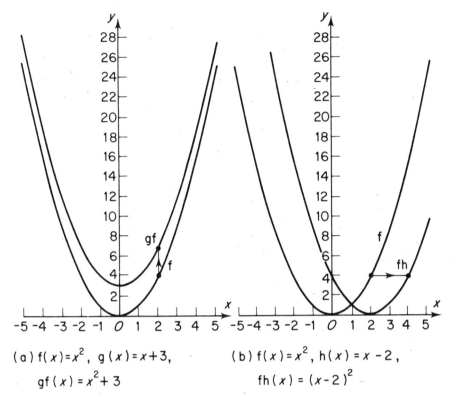

(a) $f(x) = x^2$, $g(x) = x + 3$,

    $gf(x) = x^2 + 3$

(b) $f(x) = x^2$, $h(x) = x - 2$,

    $fh(x) = (x - 2)^2$

Fig. 8.2 Translations of graphs

The above two translations may be combined, and we may translate the graph of f by a distance a parallel to Ox and a distance b parallel to Oy. This means that the origin moves to (a, b) and every point (x, y) moves to $(x + a, y + b) = (x_1, y_1)$. The new coordinates (x_1, y_1), where $x_1 = x + a$ and $y_1 = y + b$, will satisfy an equation obtained from the equation $y = f(x)$ by replacing x, y by $x_1 - a$, $y_1 - b$ respectively and so $y_1 - b = f(x_1 - a)$. Therefore, the equation of the translated graph is

$$y - b = f(x - a) \quad \text{or} \quad y = f(x - a) + b = gfh(x).$$

In the case when $f(x) = x^2$, $gfh(x) = (x - 2)^2 + 3$ and the parabola with this equation is shown in Fig. 8.3.

Summary Let $h(x) = x - a$ and $g(x) = x + b$, then a translation of the graph of the function f:

distance a along Ox is the graph of fh;
distance b along Oy is the graph of gf;
a along Ox and b along Oy is the graph of gfh.

Note that the different signs of the constants in h and g occur because in

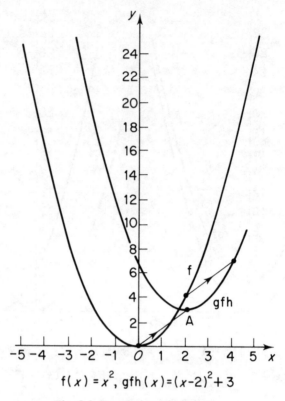

$$f(x) = x^2, \quad \text{gfh}(x) = (x-2)^2 + 3$$

Fig. 8.3 Translation of a graph

order to translate the point (x, y) on the graph of f to the point $(x + a, y + b)$ it is necessary to replace x and y in the equation of the graph by $x - a$ and $y - b$ respectively. In Fig. 8.3, the vertex O of the graph of f becomes the vertex A of the graph of gfh, since $f(0) = 0$, and

$$\text{gfh}(a) = \text{gf}(a - a) = \text{gf}(0) = g(0) = b.$$

It is, thus, necessary to subtract a from x and add b to $f(x)$.

8.4 One-way stretches of a graph

In order to stretch the graph of $f(x)$ in the Oy direction, with a scale factor 2, the point on the graph with coordinates $(x, f(x))$ has to become the point $(x, 2f(x))$. Hence, if g is the function given by $g(x) = 2x$, then $\text{gf}(x) = 2f(x)$ and the graph of gf will be the graph of f stretched with scale factor 2 in the Oy direction. In the case when $f(x) = x^2$, $\text{gf}(x) = 2x^2$, and this stretch is shown in Fig. 8.4(a).

On the other hand, in order to stretch the graph of f with scale factor 2 in the Ox direction, the point of the graph with coordinates $(x, f(x))$

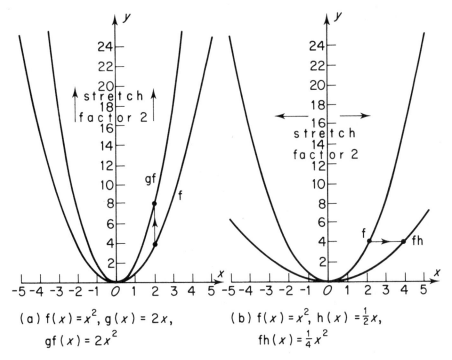

(a) $f(x) = x^2$, $g(x) = 2x$,

   $gf(x) = 2x^2$

(b) $f(x) = x^2$, $h(x) = \frac{1}{2}x$,

   $fh(x) = \frac{1}{4}x^2$

Fig. 8.4 One-way stretches of a graph.

becomes $(2x, f(x))$ and the point $(\frac{1}{2}x, f(\frac{1}{2}x))$ becomes $(x, f(\frac{1}{2}x))$. This is achieved by the composite function fh, where $h(x) = \frac{1}{2}x$ so $fh(x) = f(\frac{1}{2}x)$, and this stretch is shown in Fig. 8.4 (b) for the parabola $y = x^2$.

   The combination of the above two one-way stretches means that the graph of the function gfh, with $g(x) = 2x$, $h(x) = \frac{1}{2}x$, is obtained from the graph of f by stretch with scale factors 2 parallel to Ox and Oy, that is an all-round stretch, or magnification, of scale factor 2. Of course, stretches with different scale factors can be combined, as shown in the summary.

Summary   Let $h(x) = \dfrac{1}{a}x$ and $g(x) = bx$, then

the graph of fh is the graph of f stretched along Ox with scale factor a,
the graph of gf is the graph of f stretched along Oy with scale factor b,
the graph of gfh is the graph of f stretched both along Ox with scale factor a and along Oy with scale factor b.

   Again, note that x is divided by a in h and multiplied by b in g, because this corresponds to dividing y by b in the equation $y = f(x)$.

   Also, note that, instead of obtaining a new graph by one of these one-way stretches, the same graph could be used with a corresponding change of scale on the appropriate axis.

8.5 Reflections of a graph

The reflection of the point (x, y) in the axis Ox is the point $(x, -y)$, so the reflection in Ox of the point $(x, f(x))$ on the graph of f is the point $(x, -f(x))$. Let $g(x) = -x$. Then $-f(x) = gf(x)$, so the graph of gf is the reflection of the graph of f in the axis Ox. Similarly, $fg(x) = f(-x)$ and the point $(x, f(-x))$ is the reflection in Oy of the point $(x, f(x))$, and the graph of fg is the graph of f reflected in Oy. Combining these two transformations, the graph of gfg is the graph of f first reflected in Ox and then reflected in Oy (or the combination of these two reflections in the opposite order), and this can also be expressed as a rotation of the graph about O through $180°$ or as a reflection in the origin O, or as an enlargement with scale factor -1.

Summary   Let $g(x) = -x$, then

the graph of gf is the reflection of the graph of f in Ox,
the graph of fg is the reflection of the graph of f in Oy,
the graph of gfg is the graph of f rotated $180°$ about 0.

These reflections are shown for the graph of 2^x in Fig. 8.5.

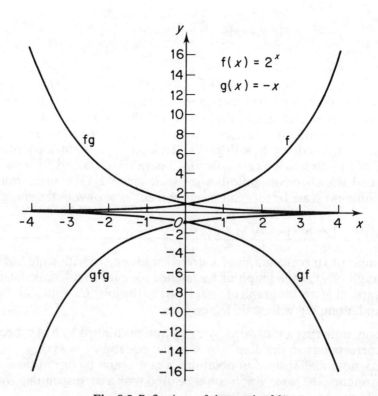

Fig. 8.5 Reflections of the graph of 2^x

8.6 Composition of a function with a linear function

The result of the composition of a function f with a linear function g can be found from the previous results as a combination of translations, stretches and reflections.

We illustrate this by an example where f and g are given by $f(x) = 2^{(\frac{1}{2}x+1)}$ and $g(x) = -2x + 3$ (Fig. 8.6). Then $g = g_1 g_2 g_3$, where

$$g_1(x) = x + 3, \quad g_2(x) = -x, \quad g_3(x) = 2x.$$

Thus, the graph of $gf = g_1 g_2 g_3 f$ is obtained from the graph of f by a succession of three transformations:

(i) $g_3 f$: a stretch with scale factor 2 in the direction Oy,
(ii) $g_2 g_3 f$: a reflection in the axis Ox,
(iii) gf: a translation of 3 units parallel to Oy.

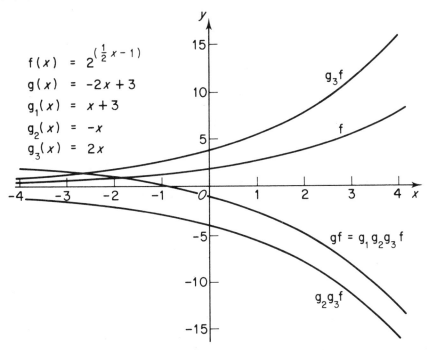

Fig. 8.6 Composition of $2^{(\frac{1}{2}x+1)}$ with $(-2x+3)$.

Similarly, the graph of the function fg can be obtained from the graph of f through three stages:

(i) fg_1: a translation by (-3) units in the Ox direction,
(ii) $fg_1 g_2$: a reflection in the axis Oy,
(iii) fg: a stretch with scale factor $\frac{1}{2}$ in the direction of Ox.

This is demonstrated in Fig. 8.7.

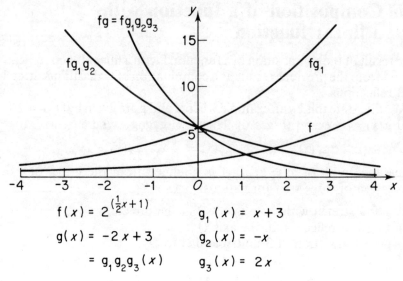

$$f(x) = 2^{\left(\frac{1}{2}x+1\right)}$$

$$g(x) = -2x+3$$

$$= g_1 g_2 g_3(x)$$

$$g_1(x) = x+3$$

$$g_2(x) = -x$$

$$g_3(x) = 2x$$

Fig. 8.7 Composition of $2^{\left(\frac{1}{2}x+1\right)}$ with $(-2x+3)$.

EXERCISE 8.6

1   Find (a) $fg(x)$, (b) $gf(x)$ in terms of the function f and describe how the graphs of fg and gf are obtained from the graph of f by means of translations, stretches and reflections, when g is given by:

   (i) $g(x) = x - 1$ (ii) $g(x) = 1 - x$ (iii) $g(x) = 3x$
   (iv) $g(x) = \frac{1}{2}x$ (v) $g(x) = -2x$ (vi) $g(x) = \frac{1}{2}(1-x)$.

2   Find the linear functions g and h such that the graph of gfh is obtained from the graph of f by:

   (i) an enlargement by a scale factor 3,
   (ii) a translation of 1 unit parallel to Ox followed by a reflection in Oy,
   (iii) a reflection in Oy and a stretch parallel to Oy with scale factor $\frac{1}{2}$,
   (iv) a reflection in the line $y = 2$.

8.7 Symmetries of a graph

Even functions

The graph of an even power of x, say x^{2n}, $n \in \mathbb{N}$, is symmetrical about the axis Oy, since $(-x)^{2n} = x^{2n}$. Any function $f: x \mapsto f(x)$ whose graph is symmetrical about Oy is called an *even* function.

f is an even function $\Leftrightarrow f(-x) = f(x)$, for all x in the domain of f.

Examples of even functions are x^2, $3x^4$, $x^4 + 2x^2 - 1$, $3\cos 2x$. Let $g(x) = -x$, then $f(-x) = fg(x)$ and so f is even if $fg = f$.

Odd functions

The graph of an odd power of x, say x^{2n+1}, $n \in \mathbb{N}$, is symmetrical about the origin O, that is, it is unaltered by a rotation through $180°$ about O, which displacement can also be described as an enlargement with scale factor -1. Any function f with the same symmetry satisfies the equation $f(-x) = -f(x)$, and is called an *odd* function.

f is an odd function $\Leftrightarrow f(-x) = -f(x)$, for all x in the domain of f.

Examples of odd functions are x, $2x^3$, $x^5 - 4x^3$, $2 \sin 3x$, $\tan 2x$. Using the same function g as before, with $g(x) = -x$, then f is an odd function if $fg = gf$. Fig. 8.8 shows graphs of an even function and an odd function.

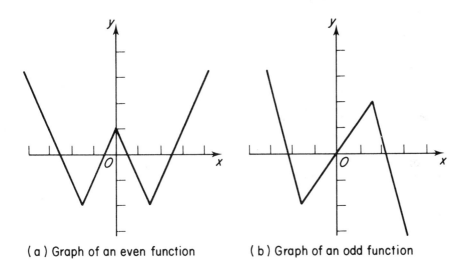

(a) Graph of an even function   (b) Graph of an odd function

Fig. 8.8

Periodic functions

Suppose that, for some fixed number k, $f(x+k) = f(x)$ for all x in the domain of f.
Then if $g(x) = x + k$, $fg = f$ and the graph of f is unaltered by a translation of amount k parallel to the x-axis. Then $fg^n = fgg^{n-1} = fg^{n-1} = \ldots = fg = f$, and the graph of f is unaltered by a translation of amount nk, parallel to Ox, with $n \in \mathbb{Z}$. Let k be the smallest positive number such that

$$f(x+k) = f(x), \text{ for all } x \text{ in the domain of f,}$$

then we say f is *periodic*, with period k.
For example, $\cos x$ and $\sin x$ are periodic, with period 2π,
$\qquad\qquad \tan x$ and $\cos 2x$ are periodic, with period π,
$\qquad\qquad \sin 3x$ is periodic with period $\frac{2}{3}\pi$.

EXERCISE 8.7

1 State which of the properties, odd, even, periodic or none of these, are held by the function:
   (i) $x^2 - 2$, (ii) $(x - 2)^2$, (iii) $\sqrt[3]{x}$, (iv) $\cos x$, (v) $\tan(x - \pi)$,
   (vi) $\sin x \cos x$, (vii) $x \sin x$, (viii) $x^3 \cos x$, (ix) $\sin(x^2)$.

2 Define the following real functions:
   (a) modulus of x: $|x| = \sqrt{(x^2)} =$ the positive square root of x^2, so $|x| = x$ for $x \geqslant 0$ and $|x| = -x$ for $x < 0$;
   (b) integer part of x: $[x] =$ the largest integer which is not greater than x. For example, $|2| = 2$, $|-3| = 3$, $[2\frac{1}{2}] = 2, [-2\frac{1}{2}] = -3 = [-3]$. Write down: (i) $[4\frac{1}{4}]$, (ii) $|-4\frac{7}{8}|$, (iii) $[4\frac{5}{8}]$, (iv) $[-4\frac{5}{8}]$.

3 Using the definitions of the functions in question 2, sketch the function f and state whether the function f is (a) odd, (b) even, (c) periodic and, if so, state the period:

   (i) $f(x) = |x|$, (ii) $f(x) = [x]$, (iii) $f(x) = \dfrac{|x|}{x}$, (iv) $f(x) = x - [x]$,

   (v) $f(x) = [|x|]$, (vi) $f(x) = |[x]|$, (vii) $f(x) = |x| - [|x|]$.

4 The function f has the following properties:
   (a) $f(x) = 4x$ for $0 \leqslant x < 2/3$,
   (b) $f(x) = 8(1 - x)$ for $2/3 \leqslant x \leqslant 1$,
   (c) $f(x)$ is an odd function,
   (d) $f(x)$ is periodic with period 2.
   Sketch the graph of $f(x)$ for $-3 \leqslant x \leqslant 3$.   (L)

5 For each of the following expressions state whether or not it is periodic, and, if it is periodic, give the period.
   (a) $\dfrac{\sin x}{x}$, $x \neq 0$,

   (b) $|\sin x|$.   (L)

6 Determine the period of the function

$$f : x \to \sin^2\left(\frac{x}{3}\right), \qquad x \in \mathbb{R}.$$ (JMB)

7 The function f is periodic with period π and

$$f(x) = \sin x \quad \text{for } 0 \leqslant x \leqslant \pi/2,$$
$$f(x) = 4(\pi^2 - x^2)/(3\pi^2) \quad \text{for } \pi/2 < x < \pi.$$

   Sketch the graph of $f(x)$ in the range $-\pi \leqslant x \leqslant 2\pi$.   (L)

8 A function $g(x)$ of period 2π is defined by

$$g(x) = x^2 \quad \text{for } 0 \leqslant x \leqslant \pi/2,$$
$$g(x) = \pi^2/4 \quad \text{for } \pi/2 < x \leqslant \pi.$$

   Given also that $g(x) = g(-x)$ for all x, sketch the graph of $g(x)$ for $-2\pi \leqslant x \leqslant +2\pi$.   (L)

9 The function f is periodic with period 2 and

$$f(x) = 4/x \qquad \text{for } 1 < x \leqslant 2,$$
$$f(x) = 2(x - 1) \qquad \text{for } 2 < x \leqslant 3.$$

   Sketch the graph of f when $-3 \leqslant x \leqslant 3$.   (L)

10 The functions f and g are defined by

$$f: x \mapsto \sin 2x, \qquad x \in \mathbb{R},$$
$$g: x \mapsto \cot x, \qquad x \in \mathbb{R}, \quad x \neq k\pi \, (k \in \mathbb{Z})$$

State the periods of f and g.
Find the period of the function f.g.
On separate axes, sketch the graphs of f, g and f.g for the interval $\{x : -\pi < x < \pi, x \neq 0\}$.
Find the range of the function f.g. (*JMB*)

11 The function f is defined by
   (i) f has domain $\mathbb{R}$,
   (ii) f is even,
   (iii) f is periodic with period 2,
   (iv) for $0 \leqslant x \leqslant 1$, $f(x) = x^3$.
   Sketch the graph of $f(x)$ for $-4 \leqslant x \leqslant 4$.

12 The function f is periodic with period 3 and

$$f(x) = \sqrt{(9 - 4x^2)} \quad \text{for } 0 < x \leqslant 1 \cdot 5,$$
$$f(x) = 2x - 3 \qquad \text{for } 1 \cdot 5 < x \leqslant 3.$$

Sketch the graph of $f(x)$ in the range $-3 \leqslant x \leqslant 6$. (*L*)

8.8 Inverse functions

Identity function

The function e, given by $e(x) = x$ for all $x \in \mathbb{R}$, has a graph with equation $y = x$, which is the line through O with unit gradient; e is an odd function and, for every real function f,

$$fe(x) = f(e(x)) = f(x) = e(f(x)) = ef(x)$$

for all x in the domain of f. Therefore, $fe = f = ef$ and so e is the identity of the operation of composition of real functions. The function e is called the *identity function*. In cases when we wish to restrict the domain to some subset X of $\mathbb{R}$, we shall still use the symbol e for the identity function with domain X.

Inverse function

Let the real function f have domain X and range Y,

$$f: X \to Y = f(X), \quad X \subseteq \mathbb{R}, \quad Y \subseteq \mathbb{R}.$$

We say that f has an inverse function f^{-1} if

$$f^{-1}: Y \to X, \text{ such that for all } x \in X, \ f^{-1}f(x) = x,$$

which means that if $y = f(x)$ then $f^{-1}(y) = x$, so that $f^{-1}f$ is the identity function with domain X. If such an f^{-1} exists, then for every $y \in Y$, there exists $x = f^{-1}(y) \in X$ such that

$$y = f(x) = f(f^{-1}(y)) = ff^{-1}(y) = e(y),$$

and so ff^{-1} is the identity function with domain Y.

Inverse image

The inverse of a function f may not exist. For example, if f has domain $\mathbb{R}$ and $f(x) = x^2$, then if $y = f(x)$, $y = f(-x)$, and we would not be able to give a unique meaning to $f^{-1}(y)$, since both x and $-x$ would be possible candidates. However, a meaning can still be given to f^{-1} by defining a function whose domain is the set of all subsets of Y. We define the *inverse image* of a subset A of Y as $f^{-1}(A)$ where

$$f^{-1}(A) = \{x \in X : f(x) \in A\},$$

then f^{-1} is a function with domain the set of all subsets of Y and range the set of all subsets of X.

There will not be any ambiguity in using the same symbol f^{-1} for the inverse image of a set, as well as for the inverse function of f when this happens to exist. If $y \in Y$, then the inverse image of y is $f^{-1}(\{y\})$ whereas, if f has an inverse function, then the inverse of y is $f^{-1}(y)$.

EXAMPLE 1   *The real function f is given by* $f(x) = 2x - 1$. *Show that f has an inverse function* f^{-1}, *given by* $f^{-1}(x) = \frac{1}{2}(x+1)$. *Write down:* (i) $f(3)$; (ii) $f(\{0, 1, 2\})$; (iii) $f(\mathbb{Z})$; (iv) $f^{-1}(-1)$; (v) $f^{-1}(\{0, 1, 2\})$; (vi) $f^{-1}(\mathbb{Z})$.

Let $2x - 1 = y$, then $2x = y + 1$ and $x = \frac{1}{2}(y+1)$. Therefore, f has domain and range equal to $\mathbb{R}$. The inverse function f^{-1} is obtained by interchanging x and y in the last equation. Then, for the inverse function $y = \frac{1}{2}(x+1)$ and so f has an inverse function f^{-1}, with $f^{-1}(x) = \frac{1}{2}(x+1)$.
(i) $f(3) = \mathbf{5}$;   (ii) $f(\{0, 1, 2\}) = \{-\mathbf{1}, \mathbf{1}, \mathbf{3}\}$;   (iii) $f(\mathbb{Z})$ is **the set of odd integers**;
(iv) $f^{-1}(-1) = \mathbf{0}$;   (v) $f^{-1}(\{0, 1, 2\}) = \{\frac{1}{2}, \mathbf{1}, \frac{3}{2}\}$;   (vi) $f^{-1}(\mathbb{Z}) = \{\frac{1}{2}n : n \in \mathbb{Z}\}$.

EXAMPLE 2   *Find the domain and range of the function f where* $f(x) = 1/(x^2 - 1)$. *Show that an inverse function* f^{-1} *does not exist. Write down:* (i) $f(3)$;   (ii) $f(-1)$;   (iii) $f(0)$;   (iv) $f(-\frac{1}{2})$;   (v) $f^{-1}(\{-1\})$;   (vi) $f^{-1}(\{0\})$; (vii) $f^{-1}(\{\frac{1}{3}, \frac{1}{8}, \frac{1}{15}\})$.

Since $x^2 - 1$ vanishes for $x \in \{1, -1\}$, the domain of f is $\mathbb{R} \backslash \{1, -1\}$. For $x > 1$ and for $x < -1$, $f(x)$ is positive, $f(x)$ tends to zero as x tends to infinity and tends to infinity as x tends to 1 or -1. For $-1 < x < 0$ and for $0 < x < 1$, $f(x)$ is negative and is less than or equal to -1 and it tends to negative infinity as x tends to 1 or to -1. Thus the range of f is $\{x : x > 0\} \cup \{x : x \leqslant -1\}$. Since $f(2) = f(-2) = \frac{1}{3}$, an inverse function cannot exist, since $f^{-1}(\frac{1}{3})$ cannot be defined.
(i) $f(3) = \frac{1}{8}$;   (ii) $f(-1)$ **does not exist**:   (iii) $f(0) = -\mathbf{1}$;   (iv) $f(-\frac{1}{2}) = -\frac{3}{4}$;
(v) $f^{-1}(\{-1\}) = \{\mathbf{0}\}$;   (vi) $f^{-1}(\{0\})$ **does not exist** (or is ϕ);
(vii) $f^{-1}(\{\frac{1}{3}, \frac{1}{8}, \frac{1}{15}\}) = \{\mathbf{2, -2, 3, -3, 4, -4}\}$.

EXERCISE 8.8

1   The following functions all have the domain $\mathbb{N}$ and are defined by the given value $f(n)$ for $n \in \mathbb{N}$:

(i) $1 - n$, (ii) n^2, (iii) $1/(n+1)$, (iv) n^3.

In each case find the range of f and show that f has an inverse function f^{-1}.

2 Given that the functions, defined in (i)–(iv) of question 1, are real functions, find, in each case, the domain and the range of the function and determine whether it has an inverse.

3 The linear function f is given by $f(x) = ax + b$, with domain $\mathbb{R}$. State the range of f, whether f has an inverse function f^{-1}, and the form of $f^{-1}(x)$ when the inverse exists. Distinguish between $a = 0$ and $a \neq 0$.

4 Prove that the following real functions have no inverse functions. In each case give a restricted domain such that the function then has an inverse and state the form of the inverse function:

(i) $2x^2 - 1$, (ii) $(x^2 - 1)^{-2}$, (iii) $\sin x$, (iv) $\cos 4x$, (v) $|x|$, (vi) $[x] - x$.

8.9 Conditions for an inverse function to exist

Suppose that a real function f has domain X and range Y and an inverse function f^{-1} with domain Y and range X. If $a, b \in X$ and $f(a) = f(b)$, then

$$a = f^{-1}f(a) = f^{-1}(f(a)) = f^{-1}(f(b)) = f^{-1}f(b) = b.$$

This implies that for every y in Y there is one and only one x in X such that $y = f(x)$. In other words, the inverse image of every one-element subset of Y is a one-element subset of X. We call such a function f *one-one*.

Definition   The function $f: X \to Y = f(X)$ is one-one if, for every $y \in Y$, there is a unique $x \in X$ such that $y = f(x)$.

We have proved that if f^{-1} exists then f is one-one. The converse is also true, namely that if f is one-one then f^{-1} exists.

Proof   Suppose that the function $f: X \to Y = f(X)$ is a one-one function. Then, given any element y of Y, there is a unique element x of X such that $f(x) = y$. So let the equation $x = g(y)$ define a function g with domain Y. Then the range of g is X and $gf(x) = g(y) = x$ for every x in X. Hence g is the inverse function f^{-1} of f.

We have now proved the following theorem.

Theorem   Let $f: X \to Y$ be a real function with range $Y = f(X)$. Then f is one-one $\Leftrightarrow$ f has an inverse function f^{-1}.

Another way of stating this theorem is:

the condition that the real function f is one-one is both necessary and sufficient for f to possess an inverse function f^{-1}.

Suppose that $f: X \to Y$ is a real one-one function with inverse function $f^{-1}: Y \to X$. Then the graph of f has equation $y = f(x)$. But $y = f(x)$ if $x = f^{-1}(y)$, so the graph of f^{-1}, which has equation $y = f^{-1}(x)$ is obtained from the graph of f by a reflection in the line $y = x$ since this reflection transforms (x, y) to (y, x). The equation of f^{-1} is obtained from the equation of f by interchanging x and y. This is done in §9.6 for the particular function 2^x, and the graphs of 2^x and its inverse function are shown in Fig. 9.2.

EXAMPLE   *Determine whether or not the function f has an inverse function f^{-1}, and illustrate your argument with Cartesian graphs, in the cases*
(i) $f(x) = x^2$ *and f has domain* $\mathbb{R}$,
(ii) $f(x) = x^2$ *and f has domain* $X = \{x \in \mathbb{R}: x < 0\}$.

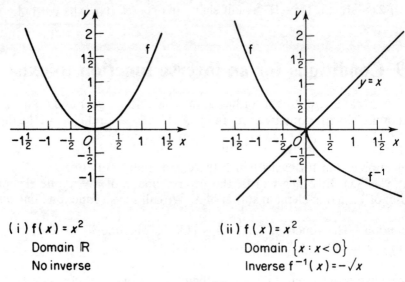

(i) $f(x) = x^2$
Domain $\mathbb{R}$
No inverse

(ii) $f(x) = x^2$
Domain $\{x : x < 0\}$
Inverse $f^{-1}(x) = -\sqrt{x}$

Fig. 8.9

The graphs of the two functions defined in (i) and (ii) are shown in Fig. 8.9 (i) and (ii). In (i), the range of f is $\mathbb{R}^+ \cup \{0\}$ and $f(1) = 1 = f(-1)$. So f is not one-one and has no inverse function. In fact, apart from 0, each value in the range of f arises from two points in its domain.

In case (ii), with the restricted domain f becomes a one-one function and its inverse function f^{-1}, with domain $\mathbb{R}^+$, is given by $f^{-1}(x) = -\sqrt{x}$.

EXERCISE 8.9

1   The function f is defined by $f(x)$ and a given domain, in each of the following cases. Find an expression for $f^{-1}(x)$, where f^{-1} is the inverse function of f. State the domain of f^{-1} and show that $f^{-1}f(x) = x$, for all x in the domain of f.
  (i) $f(x) = 2x$, domain $\mathbb{R}$ (ii) $f(x) = x - 3$, domain $\mathbb{Z}$
  (iii) $f(x) = 3x + 2$, domain $\mathbb{R}$ (iv) $f(x) = (x + 2)^2$, domain $\mathbb{R}^+$
  (v) $f(x) = x^3$, domain $\mathbb{R}$ (vi) $f(x) = \sqrt{x}$, domain $\mathbb{R}^+$
  (vii) $f(x) = x|x|$, domain $\mathbb{R}$ (viii) $f(x) = [x] - x$, domain $\{x : 2 \leqslant x < 3\}$
  (ix) $f(x) = \sqrt{(1 - x^2)}$, domain $\{x : 0 \leqslant x \leqslant 1\}$.

2 The function f, with domain $\mathbb{R}$, is given by $f(x) = x^2 - 4x + 5$. Find the range of f and sketch the graph of f. Find the real number d such that the following two conditions are both satisfied:
(i) the function g which is f with domain restricted to $\{x : d \leqslant x\}$ is a one-one function,
(ii) the function h which is f with domain restricted to $\{x : x \leqslant d\}$ is a one-one function.
State the domains of g^{-1} and h^{-1} and find $g^{-1}(x)$ and $h^{-1}(x)$.

3 Given that the real functions f, g and h, with domain $\mathbb{R}$, satisfy the condition that $fg = hf = e$ (the identity function), prove that $g = h$.

4 A condition P is a necessary condition for a function f to be one-one means that

$$\text{'f is one-one'} \Rightarrow \text{'}P\text{ is true'}.$$

P is a sufficient condition for a function f to be one-one means that

$$\text{'}P\text{ is true'} \Rightarrow \text{'f is one-one'}$$

For the following four conditions, state which is necessary, which is sufficient, which is both, and which is neither, for the function f to be one-one:
P(1) for all a, b in the domain of f, $\quad f(a) = f(a) \Rightarrow a = b$;
P(2) for all a, b in the domain of f, $\quad f(a) \neq f(b) \Rightarrow a \neq b$;
P(3) for all a, b in the domain of f, $\quad a = b \Rightarrow f(a) = f(b)$;
P(4) for all a, b in the domain of f, $\quad a \neq b \Rightarrow f(a) \neq f(b)$.

5 Given two functions, f with domain A and range B, and g with domain B and range A, such that gf is the identity function with domain A, prove that $g = f^{-1}$ and that fg is the identity function with domain B.

6 The function f, with domain D and range R, is $1-1$. Prove that its inverse function f^{-1}, with domain R and range D, is also $1-1$.

7 The function f, with domain D, and the function g, with domain C, satisfy the condition that gf is the identity function with domain D. Prove that f is one-one. Prove that g is not necessarily the inverse function of f by considering the case when $f(x) = \sqrt{x}$, $g = x^2$, $D = \mathbb{R}^+$, $C = \mathbb{R}$.

MISCELLANEOUS EXERCISE 8

1 Given that $f(x) = \dfrac{x+2}{x-1}$, where the domain of f is all real values of x except 1, sketch the graph of $f(x)$. Find $f^{-1}(x)$, where f^{-1} is the inverse of the function f, and state the domain of f^{-1}.

2 The functions f and g are defined by

$$f : x \mapsto \cos x \quad (0 \leqslant x \leqslant \pi),$$
$$g : x \mapsto \tan x \quad (0 \leqslant x < \tfrac{1}{2}\pi).$$

Sketch separate graphs of each of f, g and f^{-1}. State, giving your reasons, whether $f^{-1}g$ and $g^{-1}f$ exist. Solve the equation $f(x) = g(x)$, giving two decimal places in your answer. (C)

3 Find the ranges of the following functions:
(i) $f : x \mapsto x^2 - x$, $(x \in \mathbb{R})$,
(ii) $g : x \mapsto \dfrac{1}{x^2 - x}$, $(x \in \mathbb{R}, x \neq 0, x \neq 1)$.

Sketch, on separate axes, the graphs of f and g.   (C)

4   The functions f and g are defined by

$$f:x \mapsto 1-x^2, \ x \in \mathbb{R};$$
$$g:x \mapsto 2/(3-4x), \ x \in \mathbb{R} \text{ but } x \neq \tfrac{3}{4}.$$

(a) Find a formula for gf(x). What is the largest possible domain for the function gf?

(b) Find a formula for $g^{-1}(x)$ for $x \neq 0$.   (SMP)

5   For each of the following functions determine whether it has the same sign for all values of x, in which case state the sign. Give reasons for your results.

$$f(x) = 3x^2 - 7x + 5,$$
$$g(x) = 5 + 4x - x^2,$$
$$h(x) = 2x^2 - x - 10.$$

For each function which does not have the same sign for all values of x determine the range or ranges of values of x for which it is positive.   (C)

6   The function f from $\mathbb{R}$ to $\mathbb{R}$ is such that $f(x) = px^2 + qx + r$, where p, q and r are real constants.

(i) Find the range of f given that $p = q = r = -1$.

(ii) Find the possible values of q given that $p = 1, r = 3$ and the range of f is $\{y : y \geqslant -1\}$.   (C)

7   The functions f, g and h are defined by

$$f:x \mapsto 1/\sqrt{(1+x^2)}, \ x \in \mathbb{R},$$
$$g:x \mapsto \sin x, \ x \in \mathbb{R},$$
$$h:x \mapsto \sqrt{(1-x^2)}, \ x \in \mathbb{R}, \ |x| \leqslant 1.$$

(a) For each function, state whether it is even, odd or neither. State also whether or not it is periodic, giving the period where appropriate. (All your statements should be justified.)

(b) Find the value of hg($\pi/3$).

8   A function f has domain the set of real numbers. For $0 \leqslant x \leqslant 1$ it is given by the equation

$$f(x) = 1 - x.$$

Given also that f is an even function with period 2, draw its graph over the interval $-3 \leqslant x \leqslant 3$. Write down equations for the function for (i) $-1 \leqslant x \leqslant 0$, (ii) $2 \leqslant x \leqslant 3$.   (SMP)

9   The functions f and g have for domain the real numbers. What is meant by saying that (i) f is an odd function, (ii) g is an even function?

Assuming that neither function is zero for all x, which of the following statements is true of the function

$$h:x \mapsto f(x) + g(x)?$$

(a) h is an odd function.

(b) h is an even function.

(c) h is neither odd nor even.

(d) You cannot tell between (a), (b) or (c).

Justify your answer.   (SMP)

9 Indices and Logarithms

9.1 Powers of a number

The number formed by multiplying 2 by itself n times is denoted by 2^n, so that $2^1 = 2$, $2^2 = 4$, $2^3 = 8$, and so on. This means that we can define a function f, with domain equal to the set $\mathbb{N}$ of natural numbers, by $f(x) = 2^x$, for $x \in \mathbb{N}$. We tabulate the values of $f(x)$ for a number of values of x:

x	1	2	3	4	5	6
$f(x)$	2	4	8	16	32	64

The graph of f is a set of points with coordinates $(x, 2^x)$ and if we attempt to draw a smooth curve through these points, we obtain a curve which can be interpreted as the graph of a real function g, with $g(x) = 2^x$ (Fig. 9.1).

In this chapter, we shall extend the definition of a^x, for a positive number a, from the domain where x is a natural number to a domain where x is a rational number. Since any real number can be approximated

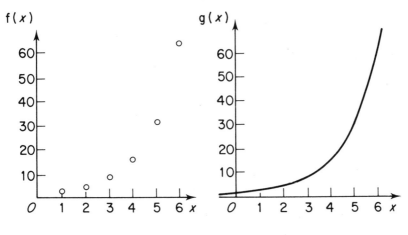

(a) Graph of f, domain $\mathbb{N}$,
$f(x) = 2^x$

(b) Graph of g, domain $\mathbb{R}$,
$g(x) = 2^x$

Fig. 9.1

by a rational number (by using a terminating decimal as an approximation) the definition of a^x can then be extended to the domain $\mathbb{R}$, by continuity.

9.2 Rules of indices

Consider the simple rules of indices, when the index (or power) is a positive integer. These are all proved by counting the number of occurrences of a. For all positive real numbers a and b, and for positive integers n and m,

$$a^n = a \times a \times a \times \ldots \times a \text{ } n \text{ times,}$$
$$a^n \times a^m = a^{n+m},$$
$$(a^n)^m = a^{nm},$$
$$(a^n)/(a^m) = a^{n-m}, \text{ providing that } m < n, \text{ (by cancellation of } m\,a\text{'s).}$$
$$(ab)^n = a^n b^n.$$

Note $ab^3 = a \times b \times b \times b$,　whereas　$(ab)^3 = (ab) \times (ab) \times (ab) = aaabbb$ $= a^3 b^3$, using the associativity and commutativity of multiplication.

Consider how we may fit a value for a^0 into the above. Putting $m = n$, we need the equation $1 = (a^n)/(a^n) = a^{n-n} = a^0$, and so we *define*

$$a^0 = 1.$$

We then find that all the above rules hold for all natural numbers n and m.

EXERCISE 9.2

1　By writing out the powers as products and quotients of the appropriate number of a's, verify that:
　　(i) $a^2 a^3 = a^5$,　(ii) $a^4 a^5 = a^9$,　(iii) $a^2 a^3 a^4 = a^9$,　(iv) $a^4 a^4 = a^8$,
　　(v) $(a^2)^4 = a^8$,　(vi) $a^8/a^3 = a^5$,　(vii) $a^2 a^3/a^5 = a^0$,　(viii) $a^2/a^2 = a^0$.
2　What would you expect to be the meaning of:
　　(i) a^{3-4},　(ii) a^{5-8},　(iii) a^{-1},　(iv) a^{-4}?
3　Prove that $\left(\dfrac{a}{b}\right)^3 = \dfrac{a^3}{b^3}$, where a and b are positive real numbers.

9.3 Extension to negative indices

The above rules suggest that we would require that

$$a^{-1}a = a^{-1+1} = a^0 = 1, \quad a^3 a^{-3} = a^{3-3} = a^0 = 1,$$

so that
$$a^{-1} = \frac{1}{a}, \quad a^{-3} = \frac{1}{a^3},$$

so we extend the domain of a^x to the whole of the integers by defining

$$a^{-n} = \frac{1}{a^n}, \text{ for positive integers } n.$$

EXERCISE 9.3A

1 Using the rules of indices for positive integers, prove that:
(i) $a^2 a^{-4} = a^{-2}$, (ii) $a^{-5} a^4 = a^{-1}$, (iii) $a^6 a^{-4} = a^2$, (iv) $(a^3)^{-2} = a^{-6}$,
(v) $(a^{-2})^4 = a^{-8}$, (vi) $(a^{-3})^{-2} = a^6$, (vii) $a^2/a^{-3} = a^5$,
(viii) $a^{-5}/a^3 = a^{-8}$, (ix) $a^{-4}/a^{-7} = a^3$.

2 Using the rules of indices for positive integers, prove that
(i) $a^n a^m = a^{n+m}$, (ii) $a^n/a^m = a^{n-m}$, (iii) $(a^n)^m = a^{nm}$, where n and m are any integers, by considering separately the cases: (a) $0 \leqslant n \leqslant m$, (b) $n < 0 \leqslant m$,
(c) $m < 0 \leqslant n$, (d) $n \leqslant m \leqslant 0$, (e) $m < n \leqslant 0$.

3 Tabulate the values of 2^x for all integer values of x, with $-6 \leqslant x \leqslant 6$, and plot the graph of the function f with domain equal to
$\{-6, -5, -4, -3, -2, -1, 0, 1, 2, 3, 4, 5, 6\}$, where $f(x) = 2^x$.
   By drawing a smooth curve through the points of this graph, draw the curve which could be the graph of 2^x for real values of x between -6 and 6. Estimate, from the graph, the values of $2^{\frac{1}{2}}, 2^{-\frac{1}{2}}, 2^{\frac{3}{8}}, 2^{-\frac{7}{8}}$. Can you guess anything about the sign of 2^x for all real values of x?

4 Simplify the following, for example, $(a^3 a^5)^2 = a^{16}$, $(a^2 b^{-3})^{-2} = a^{-4} b^6$:
(i) $10^3 \times 10^4$, (ii) $10^5 \times 10^{-3}$, (iii) $x^{-2} x^3$, (iv) $x^2 x^3 x^4$, (v) $10^4 \div 10^7$,
(vi) $2^5 \div 2^3$, (vii) $a^6 \div a^2$, (viii) $x^2 \div x^{-4}$, (ix) $(2^2 \times 3^{-1})^3$, (x) $(2^3)^4$,
(xi) $a^0 \times a^7$, (xii) $(2^{-4})^3$, (xiii) $(2^{-4})^{-3}$, (xiv) $(2^{-4})^0$,
(xv) $(2^2 \times 3^{-1})^{-1}$, (xvi) $(9^2 \times 3^{-5})^{-2}$, (xvii) $(10^{-2})^3/(10^{-3})^2$,
(xviii) $(a^2 b^3)^2$, (xix) $a^3(b^{-2}a)^3$, (xx) $(a^{-2} \times b^{-3})^2$, (xxi) $(a^{-3} b^{-2})^{-4}$.

Scientific notation

By using a multiplier, which consists of the base 10 raised to a positive or negative index, we can express every positive real number in the form $a \times 10^n$, where $1 \leqslant a < 10$ and $n \in \mathbb{Z}$. This is then called the *standard form* of the number. For example, $24\,600 = 2.46 \times 10^4$ and $0.002\,46 = 2.46 \times 10^{-3}$. This is the *scientific notation* of number in standard form and it enables us to express very large or very small numbers conveniently. It is used in some pocket calculators to handle and display numbers between 10^{99} and 10^{-99}. The standard form may be used to indicate the intended number of significant figures in a number, which is important since it shows the accuracy. The number between 1 and 10 in the standard form is assumed to be as accurate as the number of digits it displays. Thus 2.46×10^4 indicates $24\,600$, correct to three significant figures, whereas 2.4600×10^4 indicates $24\,600$, correct to 5 significant figures.
   The index of 10 in the standard form of a number is called its *characteristic index*, and it is equal to the number of digits between the position of the decimal point in the standard form and in the decimal form of the number, positive for numbers greater than one and negative for numbers less than one.

EXERCISE 9.3B

1   Write in scientific notation:
   (i) 27, (ii) 270, (iii) 0·270, (iv) 0·027, (v) 3456, (vi) 34000, (vii) 34·56,
   (viii) 3456000, (ix) 0·00003456.
2   Write in decimal notation:
   (i) $2·7 \times 10^3$, (ii) $2·789 \times 10^4$, (iii) $1·234 \times 10^{-3}$, (iv) $1·2 \times 10^{21}$,
   (v) $2·5 \times 10^{-10}$, (vi) $3·45 \times 10^6$.

9.4 Extension to rational numbers

The rational numbers $\mathbb{Q}$ consist of all fractions m/n, where $m \in \mathbb{Z}$ and
$n \in \mathbb{Z}^+$. The rational number $m/1$, with denominator 1, is identified with
the integer m. Also $\frac{1}{2} = \frac{2}{4} = \frac{3}{6}$; and so on, and, therefore, in order to have a
single fraction to represent the rational number m/n, we assume that m and
n have no common factor.

For rational indices of the real number a, we shall always assume that
$a > 0$. We first consider $a^{\frac{1}{2}}$. The rules of indices require that

$$a^{\frac{1}{2}}a^{\frac{1}{2}} = a^{\frac{1}{2}+\frac{1}{2}} = a^1 = a, \text{ and so } a^{\frac{1}{2}} = \sqrt{a}.$$

Since a is a positive number, it has two square roots, one positive and one
negative. We avoid any ambiguity by the following definition.

Definition $a^{\frac{1}{2}} = \sqrt{a} =$ the positive square root of a.

In a similar manner, for any natural number n, the product of n terms,
each equal to $a^{1/n}$ must be

$$a^{1/n} \times a^{1/n} \times a^{1/n} \times \ldots \times a^{1/n} = a^{(1/n + 1/n + 1/n + \cdots + 1/n)} = a^{n/n} = a^1 = a,$$

and so

Definition $a^{1/n} = \sqrt[n]{a}$, the positive nth root of a.

Since the nth root of a product of numbers is equal to the product of
their nth roots, for $m \in \mathbb{Z}$ and $n \in \mathbb{Z}^+$,

$$(a^m)^{1/n} = (a \times a \times a \times \ldots \times a)^{1/n} = a^{1/n} \times a^{1/n} \times a^{1/n} \times \ldots \times a^{1/n} = (a^{1/n})^m.$$

We, therefore, satisfy the rules of indices by the

Definition $a^{m/n} = (a^m)^{1/n} = (a^{1/n})^m$

and then $\sqrt[n]{(a^m)} = (\sqrt[n]{a})^m = a^{m/n}.$

It is then easy, but tedious, to show that, for such rational indices, all the
rules of indices hold. That is, for all positive numbers a and b and all

rational numbers p and q:

$$a^p \times a^q = a^{p+q},$$

$$a^{-p} = \frac{1}{a^p},$$

$$(a^p)/(a^q) = a^{p-q},$$

$$(a^p)^q = a^{pq},$$

$$a^p \times b^p = (ab)^p,$$

$$\frac{a^p}{b^p} = \left(\frac{a}{b}\right)^p.$$

We have now extended the domain of the function a^x to $\mathbb{Q}$. The graph of 2^x is the graph you drew in Exercise 9.3A, question 3. From this graph, the values of such numbers as $2^{\frac{1}{2}}$, $2^{-\frac{1}{2}}$, $2^{\frac{3}{8}}$ were estimated.

EXAMPLE *Simplify:* (i) $(\frac{4}{9})^{-\frac{1}{2}}$, (ii) $(3\frac{1}{2})^3 (27\frac{1}{3})^2 (81)^{-1}$.

(i) $(\frac{4}{9})^{-\frac{1}{2}} = 1/(\frac{4}{9})^{\frac{1}{2}} = 1/\sqrt{(\frac{4}{9})} = 1/(\frac{2}{3}) = \frac{3}{2}$,

(ii) $(3\frac{1}{2})^3 (27\frac{1}{3})^2 (81)^{-1} = (\sqrt{3})^3 (3)^2 / 3^4 = 3\sqrt{3}/9 = 1/\sqrt{3}$.

EXERCISE 9.4

1 Write down the value of:
(i) 3^3, (ii) $27^{\frac{1}{3}}$, (iii) $64^{\frac{1}{6}}$, (iv) $(\frac{4}{9})^{\frac{1}{2}}$, (v) $(2 \cdot 25)^{\frac{1}{2}}$, (vi) 7^0, (vii) 3^{-1}, (viii) 6^{-2}, (ix) $(\frac{1}{8})^{\frac{1}{3}}$, (x) $(\frac{1}{4})^{-\frac{1}{2}}$, (xi) $(\frac{81}{16})^{\frac{1}{4}}$, (xii) $(\frac{16}{81})^{-\frac{1}{4}}$.

2 Simplify the following:
(i) $8^{\frac{2}{3}}$, (ii) $4^{-\frac{3}{2}}$, (iii) $25^{\frac{3}{2}}$, (iv) $5^{\frac{1}{2}} 5^{\frac{3}{2}}$, (v) $4^{\frac{1}{4}} 4^{\frac{1}{6}}$, (vi) $6^{\frac{1}{2}} 24^{\frac{1}{2}}$, (vii) $12^{\frac{1}{3}} 6^{\frac{2}{3}}$,

(viii) $\dfrac{12^{\frac{1}{3}} 3^{\frac{1}{3}}}{2^{\frac{2}{3}}}$, (ix) $12^{\frac{1}{3}} 6^{\frac{1}{3}} 81^{-\frac{1}{6}}$, (x) $3^n \div 27^{\frac{1}{3}n}$, (xi) $(\frac{1}{32})^{\frac{1}{3}} (64)^{\frac{5}{6}}$.

3 By squaring, verify the following special cases of rules of indices:

(i) $\sqrt{x}\sqrt{y} = \sqrt{(xy)}$, (ii) $\dfrac{\sqrt{x}}{\sqrt{y}} = \sqrt{\left(\dfrac{x}{y}\right)}$.

4 Express in the form a^p the following (remember that $x^{-\frac{1}{n}} = \dfrac{1}{x^{1/n}} = \dfrac{1}{\sqrt[n]{x}}$, and

that this is quite different from $-x^{1/n}$, which is $-(\sqrt[n]{x})$):
(i) $3^{\frac{1}{2}} \times 3^{\frac{3}{2}}$, (ii) $4^{\frac{1}{4}} \times 4^{\frac{1}{2}}$, (iii) $(5^{\frac{1}{2}})^3$, (iv) $(5^5)^{\frac{1}{2}}$, (v) $a^{\frac{3}{4}} a^{-\frac{1}{4}}$, (vi) $x^{-\frac{2}{3}} x$, ?
(vii) $a^{\frac{4}{3}} a^{\frac{2}{3}}$, (viii) $x^{1 \cdot 2} x^{0 \cdot 8}$, (ix) $a^{-1 \cdot 5} \times a^{3 \cdot 5}$, (x) $a^{-\frac{1}{2}} a^{\frac{3}{4}}$, (xi) $2^{-5} \div 2^{-7}$,
(xii) $\sqrt{(a^4)}$, (xiii) $x^{-\frac{2}{3}} x^{\frac{1}{4}}/x^{\frac{1}{6}}$, (xiv) $3^{-n} 8^n / 27^{n/3}$, (xv) $2^4 4^{-3} 8^2$,
(xvi) $(4\frac{1}{2})^3 (32\frac{1}{3})^2 (256)^{-1}$.

5 Complete the following table of values of the function $f : x \mapsto 16^x$.

x	-2	$-1\frac{1}{2}$	-1	$-\frac{1}{2}$	$-\frac{1}{4}$	0	$\frac{1}{4}$	$\frac{1}{2}$	$\frac{3}{4}$	1	$1\frac{1}{2}$	2
16^x			$1/16$			1				16		

Sketch a graph of this function and state whether you think that the following statements are true or false:

(i) f is a monotonic increasing function, that is, if $x < y$ then $f(x) < f(y)$;

(ii) $f(x)$ is always positive and tends to zero as x tends to $-\infty$.

9.5 Diversion

Even if a is a positive rational number, fractional powers of a, such as $a^{\frac{1}{2}}$, $a^{\frac{7}{8}}$, are usually not rational numbers, and are then called *surds*.

EXAMPLE   *Prove that* $2^{\frac{1}{2}} = \sqrt{2}$ *is not rational.*

The proof is by the method of contradiction. That is, we assume that $2^{\frac{1}{2}}$ is a rational number and show that this leads to a contradiction, and so our assumption was false and $2^{\frac{1}{2}}$ is not rational.

Suppose that m and n are natural numbers with no common factors and that $2^{\frac{1}{2}} = m/n$. Then $n\,2^{\frac{1}{2}} = m$, so that $2n^2 = m^2$. Now the square of an odd integer is odd and, since m^2 is even, m is also even. Hence $m = 2p$ for some natural number p. But then $m^2 = 2n^2 = 4p^2$, which implies $n^2 = 2p^2$. As with m, n must be even because n^2 is even, but then m and n have a common factor 2 which contradicts our assumption. This assumption must, therefore, be false and hence $2^{\frac{1}{2}}$ is not rational.

Any real number can be thought of as an infinite decimal, where integers and finite decimals are regarded as infinite decimals ending in recurring zero. When an integer m is divided by an integer n, there can only be at most n different remainders so any rational number m/n will be represented by a recurring decimal with at most n digits recurring. Conversely, it can be shown (see §26.2) that a recurring decimal represents a rational number, so that the non-recurring decimals are real numbers which are not rational, and are, therefore, called irrational. Irrational numbers include surds such as $2^{\frac{1}{2}}$ and other numbers such as π.

In practice, we approximate to a real number by a finite decimal. A number may be given to four decimal places in a table or to six decimal places by a calculator. For example, we might use $3 \cdot 1415926$ for π, accurate to 8 significant figures, or $1 \cdot 414$ for $\sqrt{2}$, accurate to three decimal places. This means that we are, in fact, using rational approximations, namely $\dfrac{31415926}{10000000}$ or $\dfrac{1414}{1000}$. In practice, we use rational approximations to real numbers and, by using more and more decimal places, we can achieve greater and greater accuracy of approximation. In this way we can define a^x, for any real number x, as a limit of approximations.

9.6 The power function 2^x and the logarithmic function $\log_2 x$

The graph of 2^x is shown in Fig. 9.2 and, from this graph, it is seen that 2^x is monotonic increasing, that is,

$$\text{if } x_1 < x_2 \quad \text{then} \quad 2^{x_1} < 2^{x_2}.$$

The domain of 2^x is the set $\mathbb{R}$ of all real numbers and its range is $\mathbb{R}^+$, the set of all positive real numbers.

$$\text{As } x \to +\infty, \quad 2^x \to +\infty, \quad \text{as} \quad x \to -\infty, \quad 2^x \to 0.$$

Since 2^x takes as its value each positive real number just once, we see that

$$2^x \text{ is a one-one function of } \mathbb{R} \text{ on to } \mathbb{R}^+.$$

As a result, we can introduce an inverse function to 2^x, with domain $\mathbb{R}^+$

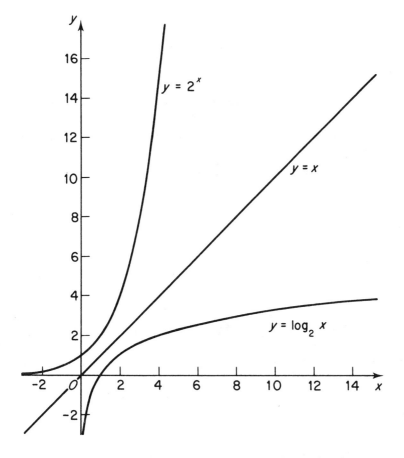

Fig. 9.2 Graphs of the power, identity and logarithmic functions.

and range $\mathbb{R}$. This function is called

$$\log_2 x = \text{the } logarithm \text{ of } x \text{ to the } base \text{ 2.}$$

Logarithm is another name for index or power, since $\log_2 x$ is the index of 2 which gives that power of 2 equal to x.

Definition $y = \log_2 x \Leftrightarrow 2^y = x$

and then we have the two functions, which are functional inverses of each other.

$$\text{Power function} \qquad\qquad \text{Logarithmic function}$$
$$2^x : \mathbb{R} \to \mathbb{R}^+ \qquad\qquad \log_2 x : \mathbb{R}^+ \to \mathbb{R}$$
$$x \mapsto 2^x \qquad\qquad\qquad\qquad x \mapsto \log_2 x$$

The graphs of these two functions have been drawn in Fig. 9.2, using the following tables of values:

x	-2	-1	0	1	2	3	4
2^x	$\frac{1}{4}$	$\frac{1}{2}$	1	2	4	8	16
x	$\frac{1}{4}$	$\frac{1}{2}$	1	2	4	8	16
$\log_2 x$	-2	-1	0	1	2	3	4

Note how these tables have the entries in the two rows interchanged, so that the two graphs are reflections of one another in the line $y = x$, the graph of the identity function. This is a property of all inverse functions.

EXERCISE 9.6

1 Write down:
   (i) $\log_2 4$, (ii) $\log_2 8$, (iii) $\log_2 32$, (iv) $\log_2 2$, (v) $\log_2 1$, (vi) $\log_2 \frac{1}{2}$,
   (vii) $\log_2 \frac{1}{4}$, (viii) $\log_2 \sqrt{2}$, (ix) $\log_2 \sqrt[3]{2}$.
2 Sketch the graphs with equations
   (i) $y = (\frac{1}{2})^x$, (ii) $y = \log_2 x$.
   Find a transformation of the Cartesian plane which takes the second graph into the first graph.

9.7 The logarithmic function $\log_a x$

In §9.6, the base of the logarithmic function was 2. We now generalise and use any fixed positive number a as the base. As before, we have the power function

$$a^x : \mathbb{R} \to \mathbb{R}^+, \quad x \mapsto a^x$$

and the logarithmic function

$$\log_a x : \mathbb{R}^+ \to \mathbb{R}, \quad x \mapsto \log_a x.$$

Definition $y = \log_a x \Leftrightarrow a^y = x$, for all $x, a \in \mathbb{R}^+, y \in \mathbb{R}$.

Thus, $\log_a x$, the logarithm of x to the base a, is the power to which a must be raised in order to give x. It follows immediately from the definition that

$$a^{\log_a x} = x = \log_a(a^x),$$

which is the usual property of inverse functions.

The logarithm is the functional inverse of the power function and this is why on some calculators the $\log_a x$ key is named $(\text{INV})(a^x)$.

EXERCISE 9.7

1 Simplify:
   (i) $\log_5 5$, (ii) $\log_{10} 100$, (iii) $\log_5 125$, (iv) $\log_7 343$, (v) $\log_3 81$,
   (vi) $\log_{13}(13)^2$, (vii) $\log_2 1024$, (viii) $\log_4 2$, (ix) $\log_4 8$, (x) $\log_4 32$,
   (xi) $\log_8 32$, (xii) $\log_{10} 0{\cdot}0001$, (xiii) $\log_{16} 4$, (xiv) $\log_a \sqrt{a}$, (xv) $\log_b b^3$,
   (xvi) $\log_c c^{\frac{1}{4}}$, (xvii) $\log_{27} 9$, (xviii) $\log_4 1$, (xix) $\log_{0{\cdot}1} 10$.
2 Express in index notation the equation:
   (i) $\log_t s^2 = 2$, (ii) $\log_3 (\frac{1}{9}) = -2$, (iii) $\log_x y = z$.
3 Express in logarithmic notation, (for example, $3^4 = 81 \Rightarrow \log_3 81 = 4$):
   (i) $10^6 = 1\,000\,000$, (ii) $125 = 5^3$, (iii) $1024 = 2^{10}$, (iv) $\frac{1}{2} = 16^{-\frac{1}{4}}$,
   (v) $9^{\frac{3}{2}} = 27$, (vi) $a = b^c$.
4 In compound interest, the amount £A which is in the account at the beginning of a year is increased by an interest of $x\%$ at the end of the year, the interest being added to the account. Prove that an initial principal of £P will increase to an amount £A after n years, where $A = P\left(1 + \dfrac{x}{100}\right)^n$. Express n in terms of A, P and x, using logarithms to the base 10.

9.8 Rules for manipulating logarithms

The rules for indices give rise to corresponding rules for logarithms. Suppose that

$$a^x = b \quad \text{so that} \quad x = \log_a b$$
$$a^y = c \quad \text{so that} \quad y = \log_a c.$$

Then $a^{x+y} = a^x a^y = bc$

so that $x + y = \log_a (bc)$

and thus $\log_a b + \log_a c = \log_a (bc)$.

Also $a^{x-y} = a^x a^{-y} = a^x/a^y = b/c$

so $x - y = \log_a (b/c)$

and $\log_a b - \log_a c = \log_a (b/c)$.

Consider $$b^d = (a^x)^d = a^{xd} = a^{dx}$$

and so $$\log_a(b^d) = dx = d\log_a b.$$

Also, from the definitions of logarithms, $\log_a a = 1$ and

$$\log_a(a^b) = b = a^{\log_a b}.$$

These rules are summarised:

$$\log_a b + \log_a c = \log_a(bc)$$
$$\log_a b - \log_a c = \log_a(b/c)$$
$$\log_a(b^d) = d\log_a b$$
$$\log_a a = 1$$
$$\log_a(a^b) = b = a^{\log_a b}.$$

EXAMPLE 1   *Solve for x the equation $4 \times 3^x = 7$, leaving your answer in logarithmic form.*

Taking logarithms of both sides to the base 3,

$$\log_3(4 \times 3^x) = \log_3 4 + \log_3(3^x) = \log_3 7.$$

Hence, $x = \log_3(3^x) = \log_3 7 - \log_3 4 = \mathbf{log_3(7/4)}.$

EXERCISE 9.8

1 Express, in terms of $\log_a x$, $\log_a y$ and $\log_a z$:

(i) $\log_a\left(\dfrac{xy}{z}\right)$, (ii) $\log_a(xyz)$, (iii) $\log_a(x^2 y^3 z^4)$, (iv) $\log_a\sqrt{(xz)}$,

(v) $\log_a(1/\sqrt[3]{y})$.

2 Express as a single logarithm to the base a:

(i) $\log_a 18 - \log_a 9$, (ii) $\log_a x + \log_a y - \log_a z$, (iii) $3\log_a y - \log_a x$,

(iv) $1 + \log_a 3$, (v) $5 - \log_a 5$.

3 Simplify:

(i) $\frac{1}{2}\log_3 81$, (ii) $\log_4(\frac{1}{8})$, (iii) $\log_{25}(\frac{1}{5})$, (iv) $3\log_9 3 - \log_4\frac{1}{4}$,

(v) $\log_8 16 + \log_{27} 9$, (vi) $\log_{100} 10 - \log_{1000} 100$, (vii) $\log_5 45 - \log_5 9$,

(viii) $\log_a(b^2) + \log_a(b^3) - \log_a(b^4)$, (ix) $\log_a(b/c) + \log_a(c/b)$.

4 Find a value of x satisfying the equation:

(i) $\log_x 3 = \log_4 4$, (ii) $\log_3 x = 3$, (iii) $\log_x 16 = 2$, (iv) $\log_x 16 = 8$,

(v) $\log_2 x = 3\log_2 5 - 2\log_2 3$, (vi) $\log_{10} x = \log_{10} 4 - 2\log_{10} 5 + 3\log_{10} 6$.

5 Solve, in terms of logarithms, the equation:

(i) $3^x = 7$, (ii) $10^x = 4$, (iii) $(0.1)^x = 7$, (iv) $5^{1-x} = 3$, (v) $5 \times 2^x = 120$.

6 Solve the equations:

(i) $3^{x-1} = 3^{2x+1}$, (ii) $3^{2x+1} = 9^{2x}$, (iii) $2^{2x+6} = 4^{5-x}$.

9.9 Change of base

To see the effect of changing the base of a logarithm, suppose that $b = a^x$ and $c = b^y = (a^x)^y = a^{xy}$. Then $x = \log_a b$, $y = \log_b c$ and $xy = \log_a c$.

Hence, we have proved that

$$\log_a b \times \log_b c = \log_a c.$$

This can be used in order to change logarithms from one base a to another base b, since

$$\log_b c = \log_a c \times \frac{1}{\log_a b},$$

so $\dfrac{1}{\log_a b}$ is a common scale factor for changing logarithms to the base a into logarithms to the base b.

In particular,

$$\log_a b = \frac{1}{\log_b a}$$

since $\log_a a = 1$.

EXERCISE 9.9

1   Simplify:
    (i) $\log_a b \times \log_b c \times \log_c a$,   (ii) $\log_a b / \log_a c + \log_c (b^2)$.
2   Solve the equation $\log_9 2 = \log_3 x$.
3   Given that $\log_{10} 2 = 0 \cdot 3010$, $\log_{10} 5 = 0 \cdot 6990$, solve the equation $5 = 2^x$.

Other notations

The above rules of logarithms together with tables of logarithms to the base 10, can be used to perform the arithmetical operations of multiplication and division in terms of addition and subtraction. Such tables were commonly used before the advent of electronic calculators and the logarithms to the base 10 are called common logarithms. As a notation, the base 10 is often omitted in common logarithms, and the letter 'o' can also be omitted, thus

$$\log_{10} x = \log x = \lg x.$$

In calculus (Chapter 23), logarithms to another base are used. The logarithms are called natural logarithms and the base is denoted by e. The number $e \approx 2 \cdot 7182818$ and can be defined as that base such that the function $\log_e x$ has unit gradient when $x = 1$. The notation for $\log_e x$ is

$$\log_e x = \ln x.$$

The function $\ln x$ has domain $\mathbb{R}^+$ and is called the *logarithmic* function; $\ln x$ has range $\mathbb{R}$ and is a one-one function. Its inverse function is called the *exponential* function and is denoted by e^x. The exponential function has domain $\mathbb{R}$ and range $\mathbb{R}^+$. Values of the two functions $\ln x$ and e^x are available in tables and on scientific calculators. Their properties will be discussed in detail in Chapter 23. The only property of these functions, which we use at present, is that

$$y = \ln x \Leftrightarrow x = e^y, \text{ or } x = \ln y \Leftrightarrow y = e^x,$$

and that e^x satisfies the usual rules of indices.

EXAMPLE 1 *Simplify* $\dfrac{e^{2x} - \ln e}{e^x - e^{\ln 1}}.$

Since $e = e^1$, $\ln e = 1$. Also $\ln 1 = 0$ so that $e^{\ln 1} = e^0 = 1$.

Hence $\dfrac{e^{2x} - \ln e}{e^x + e^{\ln 1}} = \dfrac{e^{2x} - 1}{e^x + 1} = \dfrac{(e^x)^2 - 1}{e^x + 1} = \dfrac{(e^x + 1)(e^x - 1)}{e^x + 1} = \mathbf{e^x - 1}.$

EXAMPLE 2 *Solve the equation* $5e^x - 2e^{-x} + 3 = 0.$

Let $e^x = y$ so that $e^{-x} = \dfrac{1}{y}$ and the equation becomes $5y - \dfrac{2}{y} + 3 = 0$, or $5y^2 + 3y - 2 = 0$. On factorising, this becomes $(5y - 2)(y + 1) = 0$ so $y = -1$ or $y = \frac{2}{5}$. However, $y = e^x > 0$ for all x, so there is only one solution, $e^x = y = \frac{2}{5}$, that is, $\mathbf{x = \ln \frac{2}{5}}.$

MISCELLANEOUS EXERCISE 9

1 Use the substitution $y = 5^x$ to solve $25^x = 5^{x+1} - 6$.
2 Given that $\log 2 = 0{\cdot}301$, $\log 3 = 0{\cdot}477$, $\log 5 = 0{\cdot}699$, find: (i) $\log_2 3$; (ii) $\log_3 2$; (iii) $\log_2 5$; (iv) $\log_2 6$; (v) $\log (2{\cdot}4)$.
3 Find the value of $\log_4 (2\sqrt{2})$. *(L)*
4 Solve the equation $\log_2 x + 4\log_x 2 = 5$. *(L)*
5 Solve the equation

$$e^{\ln x} + \ln e^x = 8. \qquad (L)$$

6 Given that $\lg y = 3 - \frac{3}{4}\lg x$, express y in terms of x in a form not involving logarithms.

$$[\lg \equiv \log_{10}.] \qquad (L)$$

7 Find, without using tables or a calculator, the value of x given that

$$\frac{4^{3+x}}{8^{10x}} = \frac{2^{10-2x}}{64^{3x}}. \qquad (L)$$

8 Solve, for real x, the equation $\log_2 (x + 4) = 2 - \log_2 x$. *(L)*

9 Simplify $\dfrac{e - (e^{(x+\frac{1}{2})} \div e^{-2x})^2}{e^{3x} + \ln e}.$ *(L)*

10 If $\log_a 45 + 4\log_a 2 - \frac{1}{2}\log_a 81 - \log_a 10 = \frac{3}{2}$, find the base a. *(L)*
11 Find the real solution of the equation $e^{3x} - 2e^x - 3e^{-x} = 0$. *(L)*
12 Solve the equation $2^{2x} - 5(2^{x+1}) + 16 = 0$. *(L)*
13 You are given that positive variables x, y are related by the equation

$$2\ln y = c - \ln x,$$

where c is constant, and that $y = 3$ when $x = 4$. Find, in as simple a form as possible (and not involving logarithms), an expression for y in terms of x. *(SMP)*

14 Given that
$$\ln y = 1 - 3\ln x,$$
write an equation, expressing y in terms of x, which does not involve logarithms. *(SMP)*

15 (i) Solve the equation $10^{x-3} = 2^{10+x}$ giving your answer correct to two significant figures. *(L)*

16 Given that $2e^x - 2e^{-x} = 3$, find the value of x. *(L)*

17 (a) Solve the equation $2^{2/x} = 32$.
(b) Solve the equation $\log_x 2 \times \log_x 3 = 5$,
giving your answers correct to two decimal points. *(L)*

18 Establish the formula $\log_y x = \dfrac{1}{\log_x y}$.

Solve the simultaneous equations
$$\log_x y + 2\log_y x = 3,$$
$$\log_9 y + \log_9 x = 3. \qquad (JMB)$$

19 If x and y are positive numbers, prove that $(\log_x y)(\log_y x) = 1$.

Find the possible values of $\log_x y$ such that $\log_x y = 1 + 2\log_y x$.

Hence, or otherwise, solve the simultaneous equations
$$\log_x y = 1 + 2\log_y x,$$
$$x + y = 12. \qquad (JMB)$$

20 If
$$2\log_y x + 2\log_x y = 5,$$
show that $\log_y x$ is either $\frac{1}{2}$ or 2. Hence find all pairs of values of x and y which satisfy simultaneously the equation above and the equation
$$xy = 27. \qquad (JMB)$$

21 (a) Given that $\log 2 = 0\cdot301\,030\,0$ and $\log 3 = 0\cdot477\,121\,3$, find, without using tables or calculators,

(i) $\log 16$,   (ii) $\log\left(\dfrac{1}{9}\right)$,   (iii) $\log \sqrt[3]{12}$.

(b) Without using tables or calculators, find the value of

(i) $\dfrac{\log 125}{\log 5}$,   (ii) $(\log_7 7) \times (\log_7 49)$.

(c) Given that $\log(x^3 y^2) = 9$ and $\log\left(\dfrac{x}{y}\right) = 2$, find $\log x$ and $\log y$ without using tables or calculators.

(d) Solve the equation $3^x.3^{2x+3} = 10$, giving the answer correct to two decimal places. *(JMB)*

10 Linear laws

10.1 Linear relations (revision)

It often happens in scientific experiments that two variables are proportional to each other. For example, if the pressure P and the temperature T of a fixed volume of a gas are measured (in appropriate units) and if (P_1, T_1) and (P_2, T_2) are two pairs of measurements, then it is found that P and T are proportional, that is, $P_1/T_1 = P_2/T_2$. This result is modelled mathematically by saying that P is a *function* of T, given by $P = aT$, for some constant a, where $a = P_1/T_1 = P_2/T_2$. More generally, two variables may be directly related by a linear relation. If the length L of an elastic string is measured when the string is stretched by a force F, it is found that L is related to F by an equation $L = aF + b$, where a and b are constants.

In both these examples, one variable, say y, is a *linear function* of another variable, x, given by the equation

$$y = ax + b, \quad \text{where } a \text{ and } b \text{ are constants.}$$

The special case of proportional variables occurs when $b = 0$ and $y = ax$. The relation holds for the particular units in which the quantities are measured, and this determines the units of a and b. However, the question of units will not be considered here. The values of x, y, a and b will be regarded as real numbers. At the end of any calculations, the units can be considered and put into the answers, if this is needed.

When $y = ax + b$, the graph of y as a function of x is a straight line, with gradient a, passing through the point $(0, b)$. If a number of pairs of values of x and y are obtained by measurements, the corresponding points (x, y) may be plotted on a Cartesian graph and these points should lie on a straight line. The points may not lie exactly on a line, due to experimental error or to rounding off of numbers. However, a ruler may be used to draw the best possible line through (or near) the points. Then, by using this line, the values of the constants a and b can be estimated. Finally the relation (or *law* as it is called), $y = ax + b$, can be used to estimate a value of y for a given value of x.

EXAMPLE *The quantities x and y are related by the linear law $y = ax + b$. Use the given data to estimate the values of a and b by drawing a straight line graph, approximately passing through the set of points $\{(x, y)\}$:*

x	2·0	4·0	6·0	8·0	10·0
y	2·8	4·3	5·7	7·2	8·8

Plot the five points on a graph and use a ruler to draw the best straight line through these points (see Fig. 10.1).

The line meets the y-axis at $(0, 1\cdot3)$, so $b = 1\cdot3$. Also the line passes through $(10, 8\cdot7)$ and hence $8\cdot7 = 10a + 1\cdot3$, so that $a = 0\cdot74$.

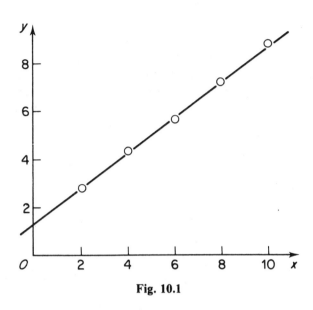

Fig. 10.1

EXERCISE 10.1

1 Plot the following sets of points, draw the best straight line through or near them, then fit the given data to the linear law $y = mx + c$:

(i)

x	0·8	2·0	3·2	4·2	5·6	6·8
y	3·6	4·0	4·2	4·6	5·0	5·4

(ii)

x	3	13	22	31	37
y	0·22	0·18	0·14	0·11	0·08

(iii)

x	3·0	3·1	3·2	3·3	3·4	3·5
y	81	82	83·5	85	86	88

10.2 Mathematical models and linear laws

When mathematics is used to solve a problem, the problem must first be translated into a mathematical form. This is called making a *mathematical model* of the problem, and will usually involve a number of variables and various relations between them. Certain assumptions will be made which will often involve approximations. Mathematical arguments and processes are then used to solve the mathematical problem of the model, and finally the results are translated back into a solution of the original problem. Thus, the steps are:

 I state the original problem,
 II translate into a mathematical model,
III solve the mathematical problem,
IV translate back to solve the original problem.

In science generally, the model uses information previously obtained in order to predict the results of future measurements or experiments. If these predictions agree with the results (within experimental error), then the model is satisfactory. If later experiments produce results which differ from the predictions, then the model must be improved and modified until its predictions are satisfactory.

The relations used in a scientific theory may be referred to as *laws* of the particular science and such laws often contain constants which have to be determined from experimental data. This may be difficult unless the relations concerned are linear. Therefore, it is necessary to convert a functional relationship into a linear form. This may often be done by means of a change of variables.

10.3 Conversion of a law to a linear form

Once a given law has been converted to a linear form, a graph may be plotted using the new variables, which are linearly related, and this graph should be a straight line. The equation of the line may then be obtained as in §10.1 and, from this, the values of the constants in the original law are determined.

EXAMPLE 1   *The e.m.f. of a cell is E volts and its internal resistance is r ohms. When the cell has a load of R ohms, its external voltage is V volts. These quantities are related by the equation*

$$ER = V(R + r).$$

For various loads, the voltage V is measured, with the following results:

R :	120	180	270	410	2200
V :	1·591	1·604	1·613	1·619	1·629

Convert the relationship between R and V to a linear form, by a suitable change of variables, and hence determine E and r.

Divide the equation of the law by ERV, so that it becomes

$$\frac{1}{V} = \frac{r}{ER} + \frac{1}{E} \quad \text{or} \quad y = \frac{r}{1000E}x + \frac{1}{E}$$

if we put $x = \dfrac{1000}{R}$ and $y = \dfrac{1}{V}$.

Using the given data, the corresponding values of x and y are

$$\frac{1000}{R} = x: \qquad 8\cdot33 \qquad 5\cdot55 \qquad 3\cdot70 \qquad 2\cdot44 \qquad 0\cdot455$$

$$\frac{1}{V} = y: \qquad 0\cdot6285 \qquad 0\cdot6234 \qquad 0\cdot6200 \qquad 0\cdot6177 \qquad 0\cdot6139.$$

These points (x, y) are plotted in Fig. 10.2 and a line is drawn through them. Reading from the graph, we see that, when $x = 0$, $y = 0\cdot6132$ (with some doubt about the last digit) so $1/E = 0\cdot6132$ and $E = 1/0\cdot6132 = \mathbf{1\cdot631}$.

In order to find the slope m of the graph, where $y = mx + 0\cdot6132$, we note that, when $x = 5$, $y = 0\cdot6224$, again with some doubt about the last digit. From these figures,

$$m = \frac{r}{1000E} = \frac{0\cdot6224 - 0\cdot6132}{5} = \frac{0\cdot0092}{5}$$

and so $r = 200 \times 0\cdot0092E$ giving $r = \mathbf{3\cdot001}$.

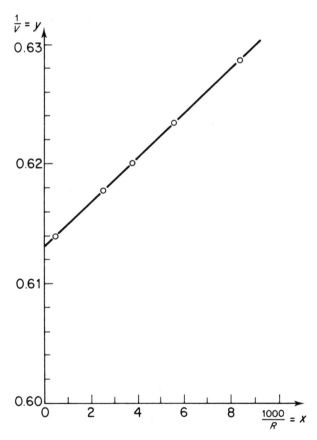

Fig. 10.2 Graph for Example 1 $y = \dfrac{1}{V}$ and $x = \dfrac{1000}{R}$.

Accuracy   The above figures have doubtful accuracy, and this needs investigating. In calculating E, we noted that the value of y for $x = 0$ had some doubt in the last digit. In fact, the most accurate value that we can read from the graph for $y(0)$ is 0·613 which gives $E = 1·63$, indicating accuracy to two decimal places. Then, in calculating m, we read two numbers from the graph, and each had at most three figure accuracy, so we take them as 0·622 and 0·613. This gives

$$m = \frac{0·622 - 0·613}{5} = \frac{0·009}{5} = 0·0018,$$

with considerable doubt in the last digit. Finally,

$$r = 1000 \times 0·0018 \times 1·63 = 2·9,$$

accurate to at most one digit. We, therefore, find that the e.m.f. of the cell is E volts, that is, 1·63 volts and its internal resistance is r ohms, that is, 3 ohms.

These calculations indicate the need to consider accuracy in numerical results. There is no objection to performing a calculation to a large number of significant figures, and on a calculator it is convenient to use the full range of the calculator's display. However, at the end of the calculation, care must be taken to study the accuracy and the number of significant figures at every stage of the calculation. As we saw in the above example, most of the significance of a number may be lost in the calculation because of the subtraction of two numbers which are nearly equal. One way to test the accuracy is to do what we did in the case of r, namely, to repeat the calculation with a small change in the initial figures and see the effect upon the answer. In our case the change of 2 in the fourth significant figure was a change of 0·03 % and this caused r to change from 3·001 to 2·9, a change of 3 %.

EXAMPLE 2   *The number, n, of cells in a given volume of a growing medium is assumed to vary with time, t, according to the relation $n = a10^{bt}$. Find a suitable change of variable to convert this relation to a linear law. Explain how a graph, drawn from experimental data, can be used to find the values of a and b.*

Since the variable t occurs in an exponent, we take common logarithms of the equation, that is, take logarithms to the base 10, obtaining

$$\log n = \log(a10^{bt}) = \log a + \log 10^{bt} = \log a + bt,$$

which gives $\log n$ as a linear function of t. Let $y = \log n$ and plot points with coordinates (t, y) from the experimental data. Draw the best line to fit these points and this line has equation $y = \log a + bt$. When $t = 0$, the line meets the y-axis at $(0, y_o)$ so $y_o = \log a$ and a can then be found, from tables or calculator, as the antilog of y_o, that is, $a = 10^{y_o}$. The gradient of the line is the other required constant b, so, if the line also meets the t-axis at $(t_o, 0)$, then $b = -y_o/t_o$.

10.4 Summary of substitutions

Some of the substitutions, that is, changes of variable, which are useful to convert a given relation into linear form, are listed under the types of relations concerned.

(i) **Products**   Suppose that $xy = a$, then two types of substitution are possible:

(a) let $X = \dfrac{1}{x}$, $Y = y$, so that $Y = aX$;

(b) let $X = \log x$, $Y = \log y$, so that $Y + X = \log a$, assuming that x, y and a are all positive, using logarithms to any convenient base.

(ii) **Sums of functions of x and of y**   Some examples are:

(a) if $ax^2 + by^2 = c$, let $X = x^2$, $Y = y^2$, then $aX + bY = c$;

(b) if $\dfrac{a}{x} + \dfrac{b}{y} = c$, let $X = \dfrac{1}{x}$, $Y = \dfrac{1}{y}$, then $aX + bY = c$;

(c) if $y = \sqrt{\{a + b \sin x\}}$, let $X = \sin x$, $Y = y^2$, then $Y = a + bX$.

(iii) **Products involving powers or exponents**

(a) if $yx^q = p$, let $Y = \log y$, $X = \log x$, then $Y + qX = \log p$;

(b) if $y^2 10^{kx} = a$, let $Y = \log y$, $X = x$, then $2Y + kX = \log a$;

(c) if $s = a 10^{-bt}$, let $Y = \log s$, $X = t$, then $Y = \log a - bX$;

(d) if $2Lf = \sqrt{(T/M)}$, where L and M are constants, let $Y = f^2$, $X = T$, then $X = 4L^2 M Y$.

EXERCISE 10.4

1   Given that $ax + by = 1$, use the following approximate values of x and y to estimate the values of a and b graphically.

x	0·10	0·20	0·30	0·40	0·50
y	0·42	0·36	0·29	0·24	0·18

2   The variables x and y are related by the equation $xy = c + dx$, and five measurements gave the following results:

x	1·2	2·1	3·3	4·6	6·1
y	8·8	5·3	3·5	2·7	2·1

Using a new variable $X = 1/x$, plot an X–y graph to find c and d.

3   A mathematical model assumes that x and y are related by the equation $\dfrac{a}{x} + \dfrac{b}{y} = 1$, for some constants a and b. By converting to new variables $X = 1/x$ and $Y = 1/y$ and drawing a straight line graph, estimate the values of a

and *b* from the data:

x	12·5	14·5	18·0	22·0	32·5
y	14·9	16·5	18·5	20·5	24·5

4 Assuming that $s = ut + \frac{1}{2}ft^2$ and by changing to a new variable $y = s/t$, find the values of *u* and *f*, given the data:

s	4·8	15·6	37·1	59	99
t	1	2	3	4	5

5 The concentrations *C* of an acid in water and *D* of the acid in another solvent are related by the equation $D = kC^n$, for a constant *k* and an integer *n*. By finding a corresponding linear law and drawing a straight line graph, find the values of *n* and *k* from the data, where both *C* and *D* are numbers of grams per litre:

C	245	332	447	681	900
D	13·2	23·5	44·7	82·2	148

6 The concentration *C* (in 10^{-3} mols per litre) at time *t* (in seconds) of a gas during its thermal decomposition was found to be:

C	22·9	12·29	6·89	3·68	2·16
t	0	20	40	60	80

Given that *C* and *t* are related by the equation $C = ae^{-bt}$, find a corresponding linear law, draw a graph from the data, and estimate the values of the constants *a* and *b*. (Use natural logarithms, base e.)

7 Using the ideal gas law, $PV = RT$, estimate the value of *R* from the following set of values of *P* and *V*, measured for $T = 273$:

V	28·4	23·7	17·9	16·2
P	80	100	120	140

8 Assume that *r* is proportional to s^n, where *n* is a positive integer, use the given values to draw a straight line graph and find *n*. Deduce the function f, where $r = f(s)$.

s	1·2	1·3	1·4	1·5
r	4·1	5·3	6·6	8·1

9 Given that $y = ab^x$, use the data to find estimates of *a* and *b*.

x	2·0	2·4	2·8	3·2	3·6
y	69	88	101	131	138

MISCELLANEOUS EXERCISE 10

1 A relation of the form $y = ae^x + b$ is known to exist between two variables x and y. By plotting y against e^x, use the following table of experimental values of x and y to estimate the constants a and b to 1 significant figure.

x	1	2	3	4
y	24	56·7	145·6	387·2

(L)

2

x	1·5	2·5	3	4	5
y	−6·0	11·0	6·2	4·1	3·3

The table shows values of a variable y corresponding to certain values of another variable x. By drawing a suitable linear graph relating the reciprocals of x and y, verify that the values of x and y satisfy approximately a relationship of the form

$$\frac{1}{x} + \frac{1}{y} = \frac{1}{a},$$

where a is a constant. Use your graph to estimate the value of a to one decimal place. Estimate also the value of x when $y = 5\cdot1$.   (L)

3 The values of x and y given in the table below satisfy approximately the relationship $e^y = Kx^a$. By drawing a suitable linear graph determine the values of the constants a and K.

x	1	2	3	4	5	6	7
y	2	8·9	13·0	15·9	18·1	19·9	21·5

(L)

4 Given that the values of x and y in the table below are experimental values of variables that satisfy $y = ax + b$, estimate graphically the constants a and b.

x	2	4	7	8	10
y	1·8	1·2	0·5	0·3	−0·2

(L)

5 A relation of the form $y = ax^n$ is known to exist between x and y. By plotting $\ln y$ against $\ln x$, or otherwise, use the following table of approximate values to estimate the constants a and n to 2 significant figures.

x	0·3	0·5	1	1·5	2
y	1·4	6·3	50	169	401

(L)

6

x	0	1	2	3	4	5
y	2·28	3·45	5·17	7·76	11·65	17·46

The table shows approximate values of a variable y corresponding to certain values of another variable x. By drawing a suitable linear graph, verify that the values of x and y satisfy approximately a relationship of the form $y = ab^x$.

Use your graph to estimate values of a and b, giving answers to one decimal place.

(L)

7 In an experiment to find the focal length f of a lens, the following object distances u and image distances v were recorded:

u	15	20	25	30	35
v	59	31	23	20	18

By plotting the reciprocal of u against the reciprocal of v estimate a value for f from the formula

$$\frac{1}{u}+\frac{1}{v}=\frac{1}{f}.$$

(L)

8 Rewrite the following equations in suitable form to display a linear relationship in each case between two of the variables, x, $\ln x$, y, and $\ln y$.

(a) $\dfrac{2}{x}+\dfrac{3}{y}=\dfrac{4}{xy}$,

(b) $5x = 6^y$.

(L)

9 Two variables are related by the law $y = a + b \ln x$. Using the measured values of x and y given in the table draw a suitable graph and use it to estimate, to the nearest whole number, the values of a and b.

x	2	3	4	5	6	7
y	57	98	127	149	167	183

(L)

10 An experiment to estimate constants a and b in a relationship of the form $y = ab^x$ produced the following results:

x	5	15	25	30	35	40
y	2·4	6·3	16·3	26·2	42·2	67·9

By plotting $\lg y$ against x, using suitable scales, estimate a and b correct to 2 significant figures. [$\lg y \equiv \log_{10} y$.]

(L)

11

x	0·5	1·5	2·5	3·5	4·0	4·5
y	3	10	31	92	162	280

The table shows approximate values of a variable y corresponding to certain known values of another variable x. It is believed that the values of x and y satisfy a relationship of the form $y = ab^x$. By taking logarithms and by drawing a suitable linear graph, estimate values of a and b to one decimal place.

Estimate also the value of y when $x = 4·2$.

(L)

12

x	1	2	3	4	5
y	3	21	59	110	178

The table shows approximate values of a variable y corresponding to certain values of another variable x. The equation $y = ax + bx^2$, where a and b are constant integers, is an approximation to the relation between x and y. By plotting a graph of y/x against x, estimate the values of a and b. (*L*)

13 The table below gives approximate values for y corresponding to the given values for x. Assuming that x and y satisfy an equation of the form $y = ab^x$, estimate, by drawing a straight line graph relating x and $\log_{10} y$, values for a and b, giving two places of decimals in your answers.

x	0·2	0·4	0·7	0·9	1·3
y	0·4885	0·5967	0·8055	0·9838	1·4677

Estimate the value of y when $x = 0.82$. (*L*)

14 The table below gives values of the variables u and v, which are related by an equation of the form $v = au + b/u$. Find values of the constants a and b by drawing a straight-line graph relating uv and u^2.

u	1	2	3	4	5	
v	12·5	7·0	5·5	5·0	4·9	(*L*)

11 Sketch Graphs

One method of drawing a graph of a function is to calculate the value of the function at a large number of points of its domain and to plot the corresponding points. The graph is then obtained by joining these points by a curve. This can be very laborious, and the object of this chapter is to find methods of *graph sketching* involving less calculation, and yet to retain all the important features of the graph. We begin by recalling some results.

11.1 Revision

Linear functions (Chapter 1)

The graph of a linear function is a straight line and is fixed when two points on it are fixed. The straight line graph with equation:

(i) $y = mx + c$ passes through $(0, c)$ and has gradient m, for example, Fig. 11.1(a);

(ii) $\dfrac{y}{b} + \dfrac{x}{a} = 1$ passes through the points $(a, 0)$ and $(0, b)$, for example, Fig. 11.1(b).

$$(a)\ y = \tfrac{4}{3}x + \tfrac{2}{3} \qquad\qquad (b)\ 5y + 8x = 20$$

Fig. 11.1 Graphs of linear functions.

Quadratic functions (Chapter 2)

The graph of a quadratic function is a parabola with its axis parallel to the y-axis, and the sign of the coefficient of x^2 determines the orientation: coefficient of x^2 positive, curve is $\cup$ shaped with minimum at the vertex; coefficient of x^2 negative, curve is $\cap$ shaped with maximum at the vertex.

The equation may be given in factorised form or may be rearranged by completing the square. If the equation of the graph is:

(i) $y = a(x - \alpha)(x - \beta)$, $\alpha < \beta$, then the graph crosses the axis at $(\alpha, 0)$ and $(\beta, 0)$ and between these points the graph is below the x-axis if $a > 0$ and above the x-axis if $a < 0$, the vertex is at $((\alpha + \beta)/2, -\frac{1}{4}a(\alpha - \beta)^2)$, Fig. 11.2(a);

(ii) $y = a(x - d)^2 + c$, then the vertex is at (d, c), Fig. 11.2(b). In Fig. 11.2, we have shown one parabola (a) with $a > 0$ and one (b) with $a < 0$.

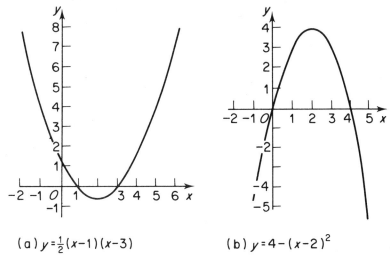

(a) $y = \frac{1}{2}(x-1)(x-3)$ (b) $y = 4 - (x-2)^2$

Fig. 11.2 Graphs of quadratic functions.

EXERCISE 11.1

1 Sketch the graph of the function f, given that:
   (i) $f(x) = 2x - 1$,   (ii) $f(x) = 2(x - 1)(x - 2)$,   (iii) $f(x) = -3(x - 1)^2 + 4$.
2 Sketch the graph with equation:
   (i) $3y + 2x = 6$, (ii) $2y = 5$, (iii) $y = (3 - x)(x + 2)$,
   (iv) $y - 2x^2 - 3x + 1 = 0$.

11.2 The graph of a cubic function

Suppose that we wish to sketch the graph with equation

$$y = x^3 - x^2 - 6x + 1.$$

We begin by calculating the values of y for a number of values of x, and show the calculation in a table, thus:

x	-4	-3	-2	-1	0	1	2	3	4	5
x^3	-64	-27	-8	-1	0	1	8	27	64	125
$-x^2$	-16	-9	-4	-1	0	-1	-4	-9	-16	-25
$-6x$	24	18	12	6	0	-6	-12	-18	-24	-30
y	-55	-1	1	5	1	-5	-7	1	25	70.

Note The formula $y = \{(x-1)x-6\}x+1$ can be useful to calculate y on a calculator or computer. It involves fewer multiplications and does not need the storage of intermediate results, compared with the method of calculating the separate terms and adding. This saves computing time. Expand the expression to see that it gives the correct form for y. Check the results in the table by using this formula with a calculator.

Fig. 11.3 Graph: $y = x^3 - x^2 - 6x + 1$

The points (x, y), found from the table, are plotted in Fig. 11.3 and the graph is drawn as a curve through these points. What are the general features of the graph and could they have been discovered without having to do the above calculations?

Large values of $|x|$

As x (or $-x$) becomes large, the term in x^3 becomes the most important term because the higher powers of x become larger much faster than the lower powers do. We say that x^3 is the *dominant term* and, for large values of x, and of $-x$, the shape of the graph will be similar to the graph of x^3. In a polynomial of degree n, the dominant term will be the term $a_n x^n$. Therefore, it is useful to know the shape of the graph of x^n, for different values of n, and we consider these graphs in §11.4.

Intersections with the axes

Obviously, by putting $x = 0$, we see that the graph of $y = f(x)$ crosses the y-axis at $(0, f(0)) = (0, 1)$ and this point on a graph can always be found. It is seen in Fig. 11.3 that the graph crosses the x-axis near to the points where $x \in \{-2, 0, 3\}$. If the expression for $f(x)$ can be factorised, then the factorised form can indicate where the graph meets the x-axis. For example, the graph of the function g where

$$g(x) = x^3 - x^2 - 6x = x(x + 2)(x - 3)$$

crosses the x-axis at $(-2, 0)$, $(0, 0)$, $(3, 0)$, giving three useful points of the graph.

Small values of x

When x is very small (either positive or negative), the higher powers of x will be very small and the dominant terms will be the linear terms. In the general polynomial these are the terms $a_1 x + a_0$. In our example, this means that, for small values of x, the graph will approximate to the graph of the linear function $-3x + 1$, which is the tangent to the polynomial graph when $x = 0$. Thus the graph crosses the y-axis at the point $(0, 1)$, as we noted before, but now we also know that, at this point, the gradient of the graph is -3.

Turning points

The graph in Fig. 11.3 clearly has a peak and a trough, and these are called *turning points* of the graph, since at these points the graph turns over, either from rising to falling, or from falling to rising, as x increases. Near the peak, the values of the function are less than the values at the peak and so this peak is called a *(local) maximum* of the graph. Similarly, near the trough, the function takes larger values than the value at the turning point and so this trough is called a *(local) minimum* of the graph. Of course, at other parts of the graph, y may take values which are greater than the maximum and other values which are less than the minimum. That is why the word 'local' has been used, but it has been written in parentheses because it is usually omitted and we just refer to maxima and minima.

The gradient f' of the function f can be used to find the turning points on the graph $y = f(x)$. At such a point, the tangent is parallel to Ox and so the gradient is zero. At a maximum, the gradient changes from positive to negative as x increases and at a minimum it changes from negative to positive. This is easily seen by considering the shape of the graph on each side of the turning point. The gradient may vanish at a point without changing sign on passing through that point. In this case, the point is a *point of inflexion* (Chapter 22). The maximum and minimum points and the points of inflexion are collectively called *stationary points* since, at all such points, the tangent to the graph is parallel to Ox and the rate of change of the value of the function is zero.

In the case of our cubic example where $f(x) = x^3 - x^2 - 6x + 1$ the gradient f' is given by $f'(x) = 3x^2 - 2x - 6$. The stationary points are given by $f'(x) = 0$, and we may solve the quadratic equation by means of the formula, which gives the turning points when $x = -1.09$ and when $x = 1.78$. These values agree with the position of the turning points seen on the graph in Fig. 11.3.

11.3 Useful ideas for graph sketching

We summarise the ideas that arose in §11.2, when we considered the cubic function. Not all these ideas will be useful in every case, but many of them will be found useful when graph sketching the graph $y = f(x)$.

1 Use the dominant terms in $f(x)$ to find the shape of the graph for large values of x and of $-x$.

2 When $f(x)$ is a polynomial, the linear terms in $f(x)$ give the tangent to the graph at $(0, f(0))$ and so this gives the intersection with the y-axis and the gradient at this point.

3 Any zeros of f will give the points of intersection with the x-axis, and these will easily be spotted if $f(x)$ factorises.

4 Any zeros of f' will give stationary points on the graph, and consideration of the sign of $f'(x)$ on each side of such stationary points will distinguish between a maximum, a minimum or an inflexion.

Note: In the example of §11.2, the cubic graph has a maximum and a minimum but this may not always be so for a cubic graph. It is possible for $f'(x)$ to have only one zero (equal roots of the quadratic equation) when the maximum and the minimum coincide at a point of inflexion (where $f'(x) = 0$ but $f'(x)$ has the same sign each side of the point). It is also possible that the quadratic equation $f'(x) = 0$ has no solution. In that case, $f'(x)$ is either always positive or always negative and the graph of f has no turning points.

EXERCISE 11.3

1   By calculating a number of points on the graph and plotting them, draw the graph with the equation:
    (i) $y = x$,   (ii) $y = 5 - 3x$,   (iii) $y = -x^2$,   (iv) $y = x^2 + x + 1$,
    (v) $y = -x^3$,   (vi) $y = 3 - x^3$,   (vii) $y = 2x^3$.
2   Use the hints to graph sketching to sketch the graph of the function f, where f(x) is:
    (i) $x^3 + x$,   (ii) $x^3 + 3x^2 + 3x + 1$,   (iii) $x^3 - 4x$,   (v) $(x-1)(x-2)(x-3)$,
    (v) $2x^3 - 9x^2 + 12x - 5$.

11.4 The graph with equation $y = x^n$, $n \in \mathbb{N}$

The graph of f, where $f(x) = x^n$, $n \in \mathbb{N}$, takes one of two forms depending on whether n is odd or even.

n odd   In this case, $f(-x) = (-x)^n = -x^n = -f(x)$, so f is an odd function and its graph is unaltered by a rotation of a half turn about the origin O. For every point (x, y) on the graph, there is another point $(-x, -y)$. The graph passes through $(-1, -1)$, $(0, 0)$ and $(1, 1)$. For $n = 1$, the graph is the line $y = x$. For $n > 1$, the gradient $f'(x)$ is nx^{n-1}, which is always positive except at the origin, since $n - 1$ is even. Thus, the curve touches the x-axis at the origin, where there is a point of inflexion.

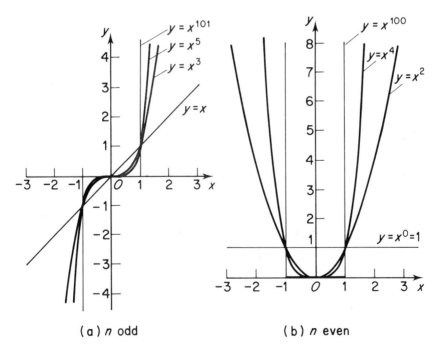

(a) *n* odd   (b) *n* even

Fig. 11.4 Graphs of $y = x^n$

For increasing values of n, the graph becomes steeper for $x > 1$ and $x < -1$ and it approaches the x-axis for $-1 < x < 1$. In Fig. 11.4(a), these features are shown for the cases $n = 1, 3, 5, 101$.

n even $f(x) = x^n = (-x)^n = f(-x)$, so f is an even function with a graph which is unaltered by a reflection in the y-axis. The graph passes through $(-1, 1)$ and $(1, 1)$ and, except for $n = 0$, through $(0, 0)$, where it touches the x-axis at a minimum point. The effect of increasing n is to make the graph steeper for $|x| > 1$ and nearer to the x-axis for $|x| < 1$. In Fig. 11.4(b) the graphs are shown for $n = 0, 2, 4, 100$.

EXERCISE 11.4

1   State the degree of $f'(x)$ if $f(x)$ is a polynomial of degree:
    (i) 3,   (ii) 4,   (iii) n.
    In each case, state the largest possible number of maxima and of minima that the graph of f can have.

2   Indicate in a rough sketch a graph of a polynomial of degree n, with r maxima and s minima:
    (i) $n = 2, r = 1$;   (ii) $n = 2, r = 0$;   (iii) $n = 3, r = 0 = s$,
    (iv) $n = 3, r = 1 = s$, (a) coefficient of x^3 positive, (b) coefficient of x^3 negative;
    (v) $n = 4, r = 1, s = 0$; (vi) $n = 4, r = 1, s = 2$;   (vii) $n = 4, r = 0, s = 1$;
    (viii) $n = 4, r = 2, s = 1$.

3   By plotting points, using the factors of $f(x)$, and using any other of our methods, sketch the graph of f, given that
    (i) $f(x) = x - x^3$,   (ii) $f(x) = (x - 1)(x + 2)(x - 3)$,
    (iii) $(x + 1)(x + 2)(x - 1)(x - 2) = f(x)$,   (iv) $f(x) = (x - 2)^2(x + 3)^3$,
    (v) $f(x) = x^3 - x^5$, (vi) $f(x) = x^4 - x^2$,   (vii) $f(x) = x^4 + x^2 + 1$,
    (viii) $f(x) = x^4 + x^3 + x^2 + x + 1$.

4   Trace the graph of $y = x^3$, using Fig. 11.4, and then sketch the graphs with equation:
    (i) $y = (x + 1)^3$,   (ii) $y = (x - 2)^3$,   (iii) $y = -x^3$,   (iv) $y = \frac{1}{2}x^3$.

5   Repeat question 4 with the index 3 replaced by an index 4.

11.5 The graph of $(x-h)^n$

Questions 4 and 5 of Exercise 11.4 lead to the next results. In these two questions, the graphs of (i) and (ii) are the graphs of x^3 and x^4 translated parallel to the x-axis. Consider the table of values of x^3 and $(x - 2)^3$:

x	-2	-1	0	1	2	3	4
x^3	-8	-1	0	1	8	27	64
$(x-2)^3$	-64	-27	-8	-1	0	1	8

The effect of subtracting 2 from x, to give $f(x-2)$ instead of $f(x)$ is to translate (shift) the graph along the x-axis by 2 units, so that the centre of the graph is at $(2, 0)$ instead of $(0, 0)$.

Generally, if the graph of $f(x)$ is translated a distance h along the x-axis, that is, a distance h parallel to Ox, then the new curve will be the graph of $f(x-h)$. This was explained in terms of the composition of functions in §8.3.

Summary The graph of $(x-h)^n$ is the same as the graph of x^n translated a distance h parallel to Ox, with the sign of h taken into account.

For odd n, the graph of x^n is symmetrical about the origin $O(0,0)$, and the corresponding point of symmetry of the graph of $(x-h)^n$ is $(h, 0)$.

For even n, the graph of x^n is symmetrical about the axis $x = 0$, and the corresponding axis of symmetry of the graph of $(x-h)^n$ is $x = h$.

Note: There is a sign change in the correspondence. The graph of $(x-2)^5$ is symmetrical about $(2,0)$ but the graph of $(x+2)^5$ is symmetrical about $(-2,0)$.

11.6 Scale change and the graph of $y = a(x-h)^n$, $n \in \mathbb{N}$

The graph of $y = \frac{1}{2}x^3$ can be obtained from the graph of $y = x^3$ by halving the distance of all the points on the graph from the x-axis, which can be described by applying to the graph a one-way stretch with factor $\frac{1}{2}$ parallel

(a) $y = x^2$ (b) $y = (x+4)^2$ (c) $y = 3(x+4)^2$

Fig. 11.5 Change of origin and scale.

to the axis Oy. Similarly the graph of $3x^4$ is obtained from the graph of x^4 by a one-way stretch with factor 3 parallel to Oy. We may superimpose the transformations of §11.5 and scale change to obtain a sketch of the graph of $a(x-h)^n$, as we saw in §8.6.

EXAMPLE   *Sketch the graph with equation* $y = 3(x+4)^2$.

We obtain the required graph in three steps, as shown in Fig. 11.5. Start, in (a), with the graph of x^2 and shift the whole graph a distance of 4 units to the left, in the *negative x*-axis direction, to give the graph with equation $y = (x+4)^2$. This means that the vertex of the graph is shifted from $(0, 0)$ to $(-4, 0)$ because $x = -4$ makes $(x+4) = 0$. Finally, the scale is changed in the *y*-axis direction by a one way stretch of factor 3 to give the graph $y = 3(x+4)^2$, shown in Fig. 11.5(c).

Summary   The graph of $a(x-h)^n$ is obtained from the graph of x^n by
(i) a translation through a (signed) distance h parallel to Ox, to give the graph of $(x-h)^n$ followed by
(ii) a one way stretch parallel to Oy with factor a.

EXERCISE 11.6

1 Sketch the graph with equation:
   (i) $y = 2(x-1)^2$, (ii) $y = -3x^3$, (iii) $y = 3(x+2)^3$, (iv) $y = -2(x+3)^4$,
   (v) $y = 4(3-x)^3$.
2 Explain the transformation which takes the graph $y = x^n$ into the graph:
   (i) $y = 2x^n$, (ii) $y = x^n - 2$, (iii) $y = x^n + 3$, (iv) $y = 3 - x^n$,
   (v) $y = (x-3)^n$, (vi) $y = (x+2)^n$, (vii) $y = 2x^n + 5$, (viii) $y = 4 - 3x^n$,
   (ix) $y = 4(x-3)^n$, (x) $y = 4(x+1)^n$, (xi) $y = 4 + (x+1)^n$.
3 Draw the graph of x^3 and, using your results for question 2, sketch the graphs given in question 2 with $n = 3$.

11.7 Negative powers of x

We tabulate some values of x^{-1} and use these to draw the graph $y = x^{-1}$, Fig. 11.6. Note that x^{-1} is not defined at $x = 0$, so the function x^{-1} has domain $\mathbb{R}\backslash\{0\}$.

x	-4	-2	-1	$-\frac{1}{2}$	-0.1	0	0.1	$\frac{1}{2}$	1	2	4
x^{-1}	$-\frac{1}{4}$	$-\frac{1}{2}$	-1	-2	-10	$-$	10	2	1	$\frac{1}{2}$	$\frac{1}{4}$

If we look at the values of x^{-1} as x approaches zero, by taking small x, we obtain the following values:

x	0·001	0·000 001	$-0·001$	$-0·000\,000\,001$
x^{-1}	1 000	1 000 000	$-1 000$	$-1\,000\,000\,000.$

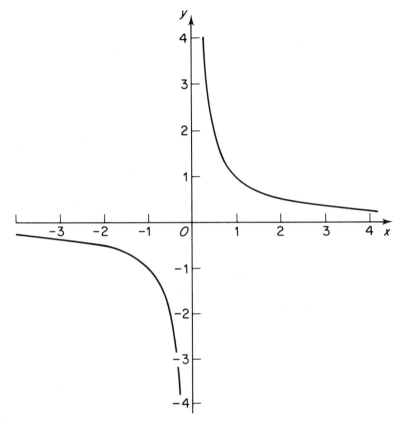

Fig. 11.6 Graph of $y = x^{-1}$

If we choose a number N, however large, we can find a small value h of x so that h^{-1} is larger than N. Similarly, if we choose M to be large and negative, we can find a negative number $-h$ such that $(-h)^{-1} < M$. This manner in which the graph behaves near to $x = 0$ is described by saying

as x tends to zero from above x^{-1} tends to infinity
as x tends to zero from below x^{-1} tends to negative infinity.

This is a description of the behaviour of x^{-1} and must not be interpreted as meaning that a number infinity (or negative infinity) exists. It does not! In symbols, we write:

$$x^{-1} \to \infty \text{ as } x \to 0+, \quad \text{and} \quad x^{-1} \to -\infty \text{ as } x \to 0-.$$

Note that the graph is not continuous, in the sense that it can not be drawn without lifting pen from paper, but it consists of two branches. The lines $x = 0$ and $y = 0$, which the graph approaches 'at infinity' are called *asymptotes* of the graph.

Using the methods of §11.6, the graph of ax^{-1} can be drawn from the graph of x^{-1}, by means of a one-way stretch with factor a, parallel to the y-axis; the graph of $(x-h)^{-1}$ is the graph of x^{-1} translated a distance h parallel to Ox; and the graph of $a(x-h)^{-1}$ is the graph of x^{-1} first translated a distance h parallel to Ox and then stretched by a factor a parallel to Oy.

EXERCISE 11.7

1 Sketch the graphs of
   (i) x^{-2}, (ii) x^{-4}, (iii) x^{-100}, (iv) x^{-3}, (v) x^{-5}, (vi) x^{-101}; cf. Fig. 11.4.
2 Suggest the general shape of the graph of the function f, given by $f(x) = x^n$:
   (a) for n positive and even, (b) for n positive and odd, (c) for n negative and even, (d) for n negative and odd.
3 Discuss the behaviour of x^n as x becomes large and positive or large and negative, distinguishing between the four cases used in question **2**.
4 Sketch the graphs of the functions:

   (i) $\dfrac{2}{x^2}$, (ii) $\dfrac{-3}{x^3}$, (iii) $\dfrac{1}{(x-1)^3}$, (iv) $\dfrac{2}{(x+3)^3}$, (v) $\dfrac{-3}{(x-2)^4}$.

11.8 Rational powers of x

The graphs of the functions x^3 and $x^{1/3}$ are reflections of each other in the line $y = x$, since they are inverse functions (see §8.8). We illustrate this in

(a) $y = x^{1/3}$ (b) $y = x^{1/2}$ and $y = x^{1/4}$

Fig. 11.7

Fig. 11.7(a). A similar situation holds for x^n and $x^{1/n}$ for any odd integer n. For even n, the function x^n is not one-one so we restrict its domain to $\mathbb{R}^+ \cup \{0\}$ and then it has an inverse function $x^{1/n}$ with the same domain, where

$$x^{1/n} = \sqrt[n]{x} = \text{the positive } n\text{th root of } x.$$

The graphs for $n = 2$ and $n = 4$ are shown in Fig. 11.7(b).

If the domain of the functions is limited to the positive real numbers then the graphs of the functions x^n all pass through $(1, 1)$ and are spaced out according to the size of n, as can be seen from Figs. 11.4 and 11.7. The graphs for $n > 0$ all have increasing gradient, and those with $n < 0$ have decreasing gradient, with increasing x. A graph may be drawn for any rational value of n, for instance, the graph for $n = 3/2$ lies between the graphs for $n = 1$ and $n = 2$.

MISCELLANEOUS EXERCISE 11

1 Sketch the graph of the function f, with domain $\mathbb{R}^+$, where $f(x)$ is given by:
   (i) $\sqrt[4]{x}$, (ii) $x^{2/3}$, (iii) $\frac{1}{4}x^{5/2}$, (iv) $\sqrt{(x+1)}$.
2 Draw, on the same graph the curves with equation $y = x^n$ for:
   (i) $n = 0$, (ii) $n = \frac{1}{4}$, (iii) $n = \frac{1}{2}$, (iv) $n = 1$, (vi) $n = 1\frac{1}{2}$, (vii) $n = 2$.
3 Repeat question 2 for the corresponding negative values of n.
4 Sketch the graph:
   (i) $y = 1 - x^3$, (ii) $y = -2\sqrt{x}$, (iii) $y = -x^4/6$, (iv) $y = 3x^2 - 1$,
   (v) $y = -\frac{1}{4}\sqrt[3]{x}$, (vi) $y = 2/(1+x)$, (vii) $y = 1/(2+3x)$.
5 The function f is periodic with period 2 and

$$f(x) = 4/x \qquad \text{for } 1 < x \leqslant 2,$$
$$f(x) = 2(x-1) \quad \text{for } 2 < x \leqslant 3.$$

Sketch the graph of f when $-3 \leqslant x \leqslant 3$.   (L)

12 Vectors II

12.1 Column vectors in the plane

In Chapter 5 we considered vectors in terms of displacements. We now extend the definitions, referring to Cartesian axes $O(x, y)$ in the plane. A point P, with coordinates (x, y), has position vector $\mathbf{r}$, which we write as a column vector,

$$\mathbf{r} = \overrightarrow{OP} = \begin{pmatrix} x \\ y \end{pmatrix}.$$

The length OP of the vector $\mathbf{r}$ is called the *magnitude* or *modulus* of $\mathbf{r}$. We denote this by means of the modulus sign, and if OP is of length r,

$$OP = r = |\mathbf{r}| = |\overrightarrow{OP}| = \left| \begin{pmatrix} x \\ y \end{pmatrix} \right|.$$

By Pythagoras' theorem,

$$OP^2 = x^2 + y^2 \quad \text{so} \quad r = |\mathbf{r}| = \sqrt{(x^2 + y^2)} = \left| \begin{pmatrix} x \\ y \end{pmatrix} \right|.$$

For example, $\left| \begin{pmatrix} 1 \\ 1 \end{pmatrix} \right| = \sqrt{2}$ and $\left| \begin{pmatrix} 3 \\ -4 \end{pmatrix} \right| = 5.$

Note For every vector $\mathbf{a}$, $|\mathbf{a}| \geqslant 0$ and $|\mathbf{a}| = 0$ only when $\mathbf{a} = \mathbf{0} = \begin{pmatrix} 0 \\ 0 \end{pmatrix}.$

Unit vector

A vector of unit modulus is called a *unit vector*. Thus

$$\mathbf{u} \text{ is a vector} \Leftrightarrow |\mathbf{u}| = 1.$$

For example, $\begin{pmatrix} \frac{1}{\sqrt{2}} \\ \frac{1}{\sqrt{2}} \end{pmatrix}$ and $\begin{pmatrix} \frac{3}{5} \\ -\frac{4}{5} \end{pmatrix}$ are unit vectors.

The unit vector $\mathbf{u}$ in the direction of the vector $\mathbf{a}$ is given by $\mathbf{u} = \dfrac{\mathbf{a}}{|\mathbf{a}|}.$

Clearly $\mathbf{u}$ is parallel to $\mathbf{a}$ and

$$|\mathbf{u}| = \left| \frac{\mathbf{a}}{|\mathbf{a}|} \right| = \frac{1}{|\mathbf{a}|} |\mathbf{a}| = 1.$$

We use a special notation for the Cartesian unit vectors, parallel to the axes Ox and Oy, namely

$$\begin{pmatrix} 1 \\ 0 \end{pmatrix} = \mathbf{i}, \quad \begin{pmatrix} 0 \\ 1 \end{pmatrix} = \mathbf{j}.$$

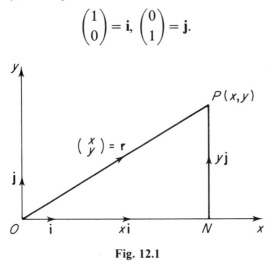

Fig. 12.1

In Fig. 12.1, let P be the point (x, y), so that $\overrightarrow{OP} = \mathbf{r} = \begin{pmatrix} x \\ y \end{pmatrix}$. Let N be the foot of the perpendicular from P on to Ox, then $ON = x$, $PN = y$ and, so, $\overrightarrow{ON} = x\mathbf{i}$ and $\overrightarrow{NP} = y\mathbf{j}$. Therefore,

$$\mathbf{r} = \overrightarrow{OP} = \begin{pmatrix} x \\ y \end{pmatrix} = x\mathbf{i} + y\mathbf{j} = x\begin{pmatrix} 1 \\ 0 \end{pmatrix} + y\begin{pmatrix} 0 \\ 1 \end{pmatrix}.$$

The properties of vector addition and of multiplication by a scalar, and the fact that the unit vectors $\mathbf{i}$ and $\mathbf{j}$ are not parallel, immediately lead to the following rules for manipulating column vectors.

Theorem 12.1 Let the point $P(x, y)$ have position vector $\mathbf{r}$, with $\mathbf{r} = \begin{pmatrix} x \\ y \end{pmatrix}$. Then

$$\begin{pmatrix} x_1 \\ y_1 \end{pmatrix} = \begin{pmatrix} x_2 \\ y_2 \end{pmatrix} \Leftrightarrow x_1 = x_2 \quad \text{and} \quad y_1 = y_2,$$

$$\begin{pmatrix} x_1 \\ y_1 \end{pmatrix} + \begin{pmatrix} x_2 \\ y_2 \end{pmatrix} = \begin{pmatrix} x_1 + x_2 \\ y_1 + y_2 \end{pmatrix},$$

$$\lambda \begin{pmatrix} x \\ y \end{pmatrix} = \begin{pmatrix} \lambda x \\ \lambda y \end{pmatrix}.$$

EXAMPLE   *Given that* $\mathbf{a} = \begin{pmatrix} 2 \\ 3 \end{pmatrix}$ *and* $\mathbf{b} = \begin{pmatrix} -1 \\ 5 \end{pmatrix}$, *write down:*

(i) $\mathbf{a} + \mathbf{b}$,   (ii) $\mathbf{a} - \mathbf{b}$,   (iii) $2\mathbf{a}$,   (iv) $3\mathbf{a} - 2\mathbf{b}$.

(i) $\begin{pmatrix} 2 \\ 3 \end{pmatrix} + \begin{pmatrix} -1 \\ 5 \end{pmatrix} = \begin{pmatrix} 2-1 \\ 3+5 \end{pmatrix} = \begin{pmatrix} 1 \\ 8 \end{pmatrix}$,

(ii) $\begin{pmatrix} 2 \\ 3 \end{pmatrix} - \begin{pmatrix} -1 \\ 5 \end{pmatrix} = \begin{pmatrix} 2-(-1) \\ 3-5 \end{pmatrix} = \begin{pmatrix} 3 \\ -2 \end{pmatrix}$,

(iii) $2\begin{pmatrix} 2 \\ 3 \end{pmatrix} = \begin{pmatrix} 4 \\ 6 \end{pmatrix}$,

(iv) $3\begin{pmatrix} 2 \\ 3 \end{pmatrix} - 2\begin{pmatrix} -1 \\ 5 \end{pmatrix} = \begin{pmatrix} 3 \times 2 + 2 \times 1 \\ 3 \times 3 - 2 \times 5 \end{pmatrix} = \begin{pmatrix} 8 \\ -1 \end{pmatrix}$.

EXERCISE 12.1

1   By expressing each vector in terms of the Cartesian unit vectors, prove theorem 12.1.

2   Write down:

(i) $\begin{pmatrix} 1 \\ -2 \end{pmatrix} + \begin{pmatrix} 2 \\ -1 \end{pmatrix}$,   (ii) $2\begin{pmatrix} -1 \\ 2 \end{pmatrix} - \begin{pmatrix} 2 \\ 1 \end{pmatrix}$,   (iii) $4\begin{pmatrix} 3 \\ -2 \end{pmatrix} - 3\begin{pmatrix} 3 \\ 1 \end{pmatrix}$,

(iv) $a\begin{pmatrix} 1 \\ 2 \end{pmatrix} - b\begin{pmatrix} 2 \\ 1 \end{pmatrix}$,   (v) $3\begin{pmatrix} x \\ y \end{pmatrix} - 4\begin{pmatrix} -x \\ y \end{pmatrix}$,   (vi) $a\begin{pmatrix} x \\ y \end{pmatrix} + b\begin{pmatrix} u \\ v \end{pmatrix}$.

3   Verify that:

(i) $\begin{pmatrix} 2 \\ 1 \end{pmatrix} + \begin{pmatrix} 3 \\ 4 \end{pmatrix} = \begin{pmatrix} 3 \\ 4 \end{pmatrix} + \begin{pmatrix} 2 \\ 1 \end{pmatrix}$,   (ii) $2\left\{ 3\begin{pmatrix} 1 \\ 2 \end{pmatrix} \right\} = 6\begin{pmatrix} 1 \\ 2 \end{pmatrix}$,

(iii) $\begin{pmatrix} 1 \\ 2 \end{pmatrix} + \left\{ \begin{pmatrix} 4 \\ 3 \end{pmatrix} + \begin{pmatrix} 2 \\ 5 \end{pmatrix} \right\} = \left\{ \begin{pmatrix} 1 \\ 2 \end{pmatrix} + \begin{pmatrix} 4 \\ 3 \end{pmatrix} \right\} + \begin{pmatrix} 2 \\ 5 \end{pmatrix}$.

4   Verify that column vectors satisfy the rules of §5.2, by using $\mathbf{a} = \begin{pmatrix} x \\ y \end{pmatrix}$,
$\mathbf{b} = \begin{pmatrix} u \\ v \end{pmatrix}$, $\mathbf{c} = \begin{pmatrix} w \\ z \end{pmatrix}$ in the following:

(i) commutativity of addition $\mathbf{a} + \mathbf{b} = \mathbf{b} + \mathbf{a}$;

(ii) zero multiplication $0\mathbf{a} = \mathbf{0} = \begin{pmatrix} 0 \\ 0 \end{pmatrix}$;

(iii) associativity of addition $(\mathbf{a} + \mathbf{b}) + \mathbf{c} = \mathbf{a} + (\mathbf{b} + \mathbf{c})$;

(iv) associativity of products $(hk)\mathbf{a} = h(k\mathbf{a})$;

(v) distributivity $h\mathbf{a} + k\mathbf{a} = (h + k)\mathbf{a}$;

(vi) distributivity $h(\mathbf{a} + \mathbf{b}) = h\mathbf{a} + h\mathbf{b}$.

12.2 Linear combinations of vectors

The splitting of **r** into the sum of *x***i** and *y***j** is called *resolving* **r** into *vector components* *x***i** and *y***j**, and *x* and *y* are called the *Cartesian components* of **r**.

Any vector can be resolved into Cartesian component vectors. These components are represented by the sides of a rectangle, parallel to the axes $O(x, y)$, with the given vector represented by the diagonal of the rectangle.

Using the language of §5.5, the pair of Cartesian unit vectors $\{i, j\}$ forms a basis for the set of all vectors in the plane.

Definition   A *linear combination* of a set of vectors is a sum of scalar multiples of the vectors.

Theorem 5.5 may be restated: every vector in the plane is uniquely expressed as a linear combination of a pair of given basis vectors. For example, using the basis $\{i, j\}$, the vector $\begin{pmatrix} 5 \\ 12 \end{pmatrix}$ is a unique linear combination $5i + 12j$ of the basis vectors. The modulus of this vector is given in terms of the multiples of the basis vectors, namely $\sqrt{(5^2 + 12^2)}$, by Pythagoras' theorem. This is because the basis vectors i and j are perpendicular unit vectors. The same is not always true. Consider the basis $\{a, b\}$, where $a = \begin{pmatrix} 1 \\ 0 \end{pmatrix}$, $b = \begin{pmatrix} 1 \\ 2 \end{pmatrix}$, which are not perpendicular unit vectors. Then

$$\begin{pmatrix} 5 \\ 12 \end{pmatrix} = -a + 6b \quad \text{and} \quad 1^2 + 6^2 \neq 5^2 + 12^2.$$

EXAMPLE 1   *Express the vector* $\begin{pmatrix} 3 \\ 4 \end{pmatrix}$: (i) *as a linear combination of the Cartesian unit vectors* i *and* j, (ii) *as a linear combination of the two vectors* $\begin{pmatrix} 2 \\ 1 \end{pmatrix}$ *and* $\begin{pmatrix} 1 \\ -2 \end{pmatrix}$.

(i) $a = \begin{pmatrix} 3 \\ 4 \end{pmatrix} = 3\begin{pmatrix} 1 \\ 0 \end{pmatrix} + 4\begin{pmatrix} 0 \\ 1 \end{pmatrix} = 3i + 4j$.

(ii) Suppose that $a = \begin{pmatrix} 3 \\ 4 \end{pmatrix} = sb + tc = s\begin{pmatrix} 2 \\ 1 \end{pmatrix} + t\begin{pmatrix} 1 \\ -2 \end{pmatrix}$, then we have to solve two simultaneous equations in s and t,

$$3 = 2s + t \quad \text{and} \quad 4 = s - 2t.$$

Eliminate t by adding twice the first equation to the second,

$$6 + 4 = 4s + 2t + s - 2t = 5s, \quad \text{or} \quad 10 = 5s,$$

so $s = 2$ and then

$$t = 3 - 2s = 3 - 4 = -1.$$

Thus $a = 2b - c$, Fig. 12.2(a).

EXAMPLE 2   *Find the unit vector which bisects the angle between the vectors* $\begin{pmatrix} 4 \\ 3 \end{pmatrix}$ *and* $\begin{pmatrix} -3 \\ 4 \end{pmatrix}$.

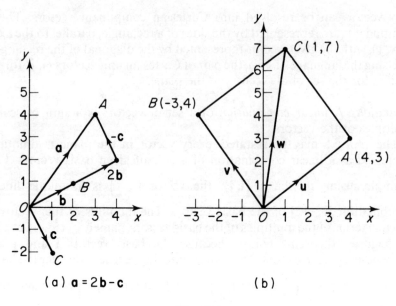

(a) a = 2b − c   (b)

Fig. 12.2

The unit vectors **u** and **v** in the given directions are given by $\mathbf{u} = \begin{pmatrix} \frac{4}{5} \\ \frac{3}{5} \end{pmatrix}$ and $\mathbf{v} = \begin{pmatrix} -\frac{3}{5} \\ \frac{4}{5} \end{pmatrix}$. The parallelogram with sides **u** and **v** is a rhombus and its diagonal **u** + **v** bisects the angle between the sides. Hence, the required vector **w** is in the direction of (**u** + **v**). So

$$\mathbf{w} = k(\mathbf{u} + \mathbf{v}) = \frac{k}{5}\begin{pmatrix} 1 \\ 7 \end{pmatrix}.$$

This vector has modulus $\dfrac{k}{5}\sqrt{(1 + 49)}$, so $k = \dfrac{5}{\sqrt{50}}$ and $\mathbf{w} = \dfrac{1}{5\sqrt{2}}\begin{pmatrix} 1 \\ 7 \end{pmatrix}$. This method of solution is a general one, which would apply to other problems of this type. However, in this particular example, the initial vectors are perpendicular and equal in length, and so another method of solution is possible. In Figure 12.2(b), let A and B be the points with position vectors given by $\mathbf{a} = \begin{pmatrix} 4 \\ 3 \end{pmatrix}$ and $\mathbf{b} = \begin{pmatrix} -3 \\ 4 \end{pmatrix}$ respectively. Then it will be seen that the point C, with position vector given by $\mathbf{c} = \mathbf{a} + \mathbf{b} = \begin{pmatrix} 1 \\ 7 \end{pmatrix}$, is the fourth vertex of the square $OACB$. Hence OC bisects the angle between OA and OB and the required unit vector

$$\mathbf{w} = \frac{\overrightarrow{OC}}{|OC|} = \frac{1}{5\sqrt{2}}\begin{pmatrix} 1 \\ 7 \end{pmatrix}.$$

EXERCISE 12.2

1 Find the modulus of the vector:

(i) $\begin{pmatrix} -3 \\ -4 \end{pmatrix}$, (ii) $\begin{pmatrix} 5 \\ 12 \end{pmatrix}$, (iii) $\begin{pmatrix} 1 \\ 1 \end{pmatrix}$, (iv) $\begin{pmatrix} -8 \\ 6 \end{pmatrix}$, (v) $3\mathbf{i} - 4\mathbf{j}$, (vi) $\mathbf{i} + 2\mathbf{j}$,

(vii) $3\mathbf{j}$.

2 For each of the vectors in question 1, find a unit vector in that direction.

3 Given the four points $A(1, 3)$, $B(4, 5)$, $C(5, 3)$, $D(2, 1)$, find the column vectors representing $\overrightarrow{AB}$ and $\overrightarrow{CD}$ and prove that $ABCD$ is a parallelogram.

4 Express as a linear combination of the vectors $\mathbf{a}$ and $\mathbf{b}$, where $\mathbf{a} = \begin{pmatrix} 2 \\ 1 \end{pmatrix}$ and $\mathbf{b} = \begin{pmatrix} -3 \\ 4 \end{pmatrix}$, the vectors:

(i) $\begin{pmatrix} -1 \\ 5 \end{pmatrix}$, (ii) $\begin{pmatrix} 6 \\ 3 \end{pmatrix}$, (iii) $\begin{pmatrix} 0 \\ 1 \end{pmatrix}$, (iv) $\begin{pmatrix} 1 \\ 0 \end{pmatrix}$, (v) $\begin{pmatrix} x \\ y \end{pmatrix}$, (vi) $\mathbf{i} + 2\mathbf{j}$,

(vii) $11\mathbf{j}$.

5 Express as a linear combination of $\mathbf{a}$ and $\mathbf{b}$, where $\mathbf{a} = \mathbf{i} - 2\mathbf{j}$ and $\mathbf{b} = 2\mathbf{i} + \mathbf{j}$, the vectors:

(i) $\mathbf{i} + 4\mathbf{j}$, (ii) $\mathbf{i}$, (iii) $\mathbf{j}$, (iv) $\mathbf{i} + \mathbf{j}$, (v) $\mathbf{i} - \mathbf{j}$, (vi) $x\mathbf{i} + y\mathbf{j}$,

(vii) $\begin{pmatrix} 2 \\ 5 \end{pmatrix}$, (viii) $\begin{pmatrix} s \\ t \end{pmatrix}$.

6 Write down the ratio theorem, §5.4, in terms of Cartesian vectors, using $\mathbf{r} = \begin{pmatrix} x \\ y \end{pmatrix}$, $\mathbf{a} = \begin{pmatrix} p \\ q \end{pmatrix}$, $\mathbf{b} = \begin{pmatrix} s \\ t \end{pmatrix}$. Rewrite the theorem in terms of the Cartesian coordinates (x, y), (p, q), (s, t) of the points concerned.

7 The coordinates of the points A and B are $(3, 4)$ and $(12, 5)$ respectively. If O is the origin, find the coordinates of the point on the line-segment AB which is equidistant from the lines OA and OB. (L)

8 Points A, B, C have coordinates $(1, 3)$, $(3, -1)$, $(5, 7)$ respectively. The triangle ABC has medians AD, BE, CF. Write down, as column vectors, the position vectors of A, B, C, D, E, F.

Given that $3\overrightarrow{OG} = \overrightarrow{OA} + \overrightarrow{OB} + \overrightarrow{OC}$, find the position vector of G. Prove that DA, EB, FC intersect at G, and, by using the ratio theorem, prove that G is the point of trisection of each of these line segments.

9 Find unit vectors in the directions of $\overrightarrow{OA}$ and $\overrightarrow{OB}$, where A and B are points $(4, 3)$ and $(3, -4)$. Use the sum and difference of the unit vectors to find points on the unit circle, centre O, equidistant from the diameters through A and B.

10 The points A and B have position vectors $3\mathbf{i} + 2\mathbf{j}$ and $-\mathbf{i} + 4\mathbf{j}$ respectively, referred to O as origin. The point D has position vector $11\mathbf{i} - 2\mathbf{j}$ and is such that

$$\overrightarrow{OD} = m\overrightarrow{OA} + n\overrightarrow{OB}.$$

Calculate the values of m and n. (L)

11 Given that $\overrightarrow{OA} = (-2\mathbf{i} - 3\mathbf{j})$ and $\overrightarrow{OB} = (5\mathbf{i} + t\mathbf{j})$, where t is a constant, determine the value of t when the points O, A and B are collinear. (L)

12 The vectors $\overrightarrow{OP}$ and $\overrightarrow{OQ}$ are given by

$$\overrightarrow{OP} = (\lambda\mathbf{i} + \mu\mathbf{j}), \quad \overrightarrow{OQ} = (-\mu\mathbf{i} + \lambda\mathbf{j}),$$

where λ and μ are non-zero constants. Show that the angle between $\overrightarrow{OP}$ and $\overrightarrow{OQ}$ is $\pi/2$ and find the length of PQ in terms of λ and μ.

Given that R is the mid-point of PQ, express $\overrightarrow{OR}$ in terms of λ, μ, **i** and **j**.　　　　　　　　　　　　　　　　　　　　(L)

12.3　Cartesian coordinates in three dimensions

In two dimensions, we use two Cartesian coordinates (x, y) to fix the position of a point relative to axes $O(x, y)$. In three-dimensional space, we need a third coordinate, giving us coordinates (x, y, z) to fix the position of a point, relative to axes $O(x, y, z)$. The third axis Oz is perpendicular to Ox and to Oy, so it is perpendicular to the plane $O(x, y)$. There are two directions perpendicular to this plane and we choose Oz such that, on looking along Oz, a clockwise rotation of one right-angle will bring the axis Ox into the position of Oy. This is shown in Fig. 12.3, in (a) where the axis Oz is 'going into the paper', and in (b) where the axis Oz is 'coming out of the paper'. Note that, in each case, Ox is brought into the position of Oy by a rotation through 90° clockwise when looking along Oz. In (b), the axes $O(x, y)$ are drawn in the usual position for plane coordinates, and it appears that an anti-clockwise rotation is needed to bring Ox to Oy. However, this anticlockwise rotation is about an axis going *into* the paper and this is clockwise about Oz which is coming *out* of the paper.

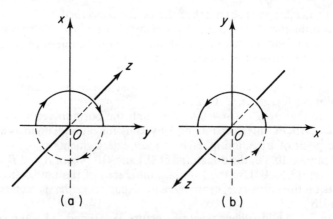

Rotation Ox to Oy is clockwise about Oz

Fig. 12.3　Three-dimensional axes $O(x, y, z)$.

Fig. 12.4, shows how the position of a point P is fixed by its coordinates (x, y, z), so that we can identify P with (x, y, z).

Choose unit vectors **i**, **j**, **k**, along Ox, Oy, Oz respectively. Let OP be the diagonal of a rectangular box, which has vertices A, B, C on Ox, Oy, Oz respectively and L, M, N in the planes $O(y, z)$, $O(z, x)$, $O(x, y)$ respectively.

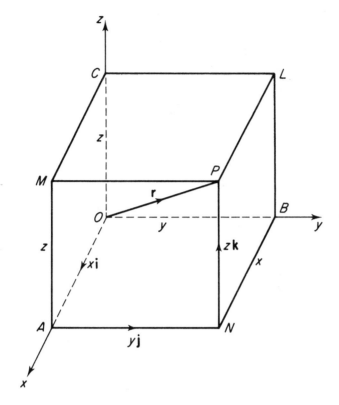

P has coordinates x, y, z, all positive
The arrows show the positive directions of Ox, Oy, Oz.

Fig. 12.4 Three-dimensional coordinates

Then
$$\overrightarrow{OP} = \overrightarrow{OA} + \overrightarrow{AN} + \overrightarrow{NP} = x\mathbf{i} + y\mathbf{j} + z\mathbf{k}.$$

We introduce three-dimensional column vectors, extending the ideas of §12.1. For the point $P(x, y, z)$ the position vector of P is $\overrightarrow{OP}$ where

$$\overrightarrow{OP} = \mathbf{r} = \begin{pmatrix} x \\ y \\ z \end{pmatrix} = x\begin{pmatrix} 1 \\ 0 \\ 0 \end{pmatrix} + y\begin{pmatrix} 0 \\ 1 \\ 0 \end{pmatrix} + z\begin{pmatrix} 0 \\ 0 \\ 1 \end{pmatrix},$$

so that $\mathbf{i} = \begin{pmatrix} 1 \\ 0 \\ 0 \end{pmatrix}, \mathbf{j} = \begin{pmatrix} 0 \\ 1 \\ 0 \end{pmatrix}, \mathbf{k} = \begin{pmatrix} 0 \\ 0 \\ 1 \end{pmatrix}$, and $\mathbf{r} = x\mathbf{i} + y\mathbf{j} + z\mathbf{k}$.

By two applications of Pythagoras' theorem,
$$OP^2 = ON^2 + NP^2 = OA^2 + AN^2 + NP^2,$$
so
$$|\mathbf{r}|^2 = r^2 = OP^2 = x^2 + y^2 + z^2$$

and the modulus of the column vector

$$\left|\begin{pmatrix} x \\ y \\ z \end{pmatrix}\right| = \sqrt{(x^2 + y^2 + z^2)}.$$

As in the case of two dimensions, $\mathbf{r}$ is a linear combination of $\mathbf{i}, \mathbf{j}, \mathbf{k}$. We say that $\mathbf{r}$ is resolved into vector components $x\mathbf{i}, y\mathbf{j}, z\mathbf{k}$ and that x, y, z are the components of $\mathbf{r}$. For example,

$$2\mathbf{i} + 3\mathbf{j} + 4\mathbf{k} = \begin{pmatrix} 2 \\ 3 \\ 4 \end{pmatrix} \text{ has components 2, 3, 4.}$$

Corresponding to theorem 12.1, we have the rules for combining column vectors in three dimensions, which follow from the properties of vector addition and multiplication by a scalar, and the fact that the unit vectors $\mathbf{i}, \mathbf{j}$ and $\mathbf{k}$ do not lie in one plane. We state the results as a theorem, without proof, which we leave as an exercise.

Theorem 12.3   Let the point $P(x, y, z)$ have position vector $\mathbf{r}$, with $\mathbf{r} = \begin{pmatrix} x \\ y \\ z \end{pmatrix}$. Then

$$\begin{pmatrix} x_1 \\ y_1 \\ z_1 \end{pmatrix} = \begin{pmatrix} x_2 \\ y_2 \\ z_2 \end{pmatrix} \Leftrightarrow x_1 = x_2 \text{ and } y_1 = y_2 \text{ and } z_1 = z_2,$$

$$\begin{pmatrix} x_1 \\ y_1 \\ z_1 \end{pmatrix} + \begin{pmatrix} x_2 \\ y_2 \\ z_2 \end{pmatrix} = \begin{pmatrix} x_1 + x_2 \\ y_1 + y_2 \\ z_1 + z_2 \end{pmatrix},$$

$$\lambda \begin{pmatrix} x \\ y \\ z \end{pmatrix} = \begin{pmatrix} \lambda x \\ \lambda y \\ \lambda z \end{pmatrix}.$$

Other bases in three dimensions

More generally, a vector can be resolved into components in any three non-coplanar directions. *Non-coplanar* means not parallel to one plane and so (in particular) non-parallel. This corresponds to the resolution of a vector into components in two directions in the plane (§5.5). Let $\overrightarrow{OP} = \mathbf{r}$, and let $\mathbf{u}, \mathbf{v}$ and $\mathbf{w}$ be any three non-coplanar unit vectors. Construct three planes through O, each containing two of the three vectors $\mathbf{u}, \mathbf{v}, \mathbf{w}$, and three more parallel planes through P, Fig. 12.5.

Then these six planes form the faces of a parallelepiped, with edges parallel to $\mathbf{u}, \mathbf{v}, \mathbf{w}$ and diagonal $\overrightarrow{OP}$. Let the three edges $\overrightarrow{OA} = a\mathbf{u}, \overrightarrow{AF} = b\mathbf{v}, \overrightarrow{FP} = c\mathbf{w}$, then

$$\mathbf{r} = \overrightarrow{OP} = a\mathbf{u} + b\mathbf{v} + c\mathbf{w}.$$

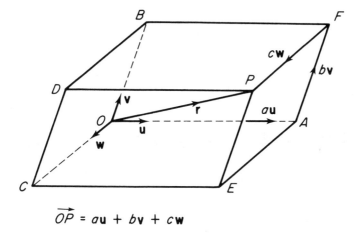

$$\overrightarrow{OP} = a\mathbf{u} + b\mathbf{v} + c\mathbf{w}$$

Fig. 12.5

In this way, $\overrightarrow{OP}$ is resolved into three unique components $a\mathbf{u}$, $b\mathbf{v}$, $c\mathbf{w}$, in the directions of $\mathbf{u}$, $\mathbf{v}$, $\mathbf{w}$, and $\overrightarrow{OP}$ is called the resultant of $a\mathbf{u}$, $b\mathbf{v}$, $c\mathbf{w}$. This means that $\mathbf{u}$, $\mathbf{v}$, $\mathbf{w}$ is a basis for vectors in space. Algebraically, a, b and c are found by solving three simultaneous equations, which is beyond the scope of our present study.

EXERCISE 12.3

1 State which of the alternatives (a) or (b) is true in each case:
   (i) Oz is vertically (a) up, (b) down, when Ox is North and Oy is East;
   (ii) Ox is vertically (a) up, (b) down, when Oy is West and Oz is South;
   (iii) If O is at the centre of the Earth and Oz is its axis pointing to the North Pole, then the rotation of the Earth is (a) positive, (b) negative, about Oz.

2 Find the magnitudes of $\mathbf{a}$ and $\mathbf{b}$, where $\mathbf{a} = \begin{pmatrix} 1 \\ 2 \\ -2 \end{pmatrix}$ and $\mathbf{b} = \begin{pmatrix} 3 \\ -4 \\ 5 \end{pmatrix}$, and of $\mathbf{a} + \mathbf{b}$, $2\mathbf{a} - 3\mathbf{b}$. Write down the unit vectors in the directions of each of these four vectors.

3 Given the two points $A(1, -2, 3)$ and $B(-1, 3, 4)$, find the column vector $\overrightarrow{AB}$ and, hence, find the distance between A and B.

4 Given that $\mathbf{a} = \begin{pmatrix} 3 \\ 2 \\ 1 \end{pmatrix}$, $\mathbf{b} = \begin{pmatrix} -2 \\ 1 \\ -1 \end{pmatrix}$, $\mathbf{c} = \begin{pmatrix} 4 \\ 2 \\ -1 \end{pmatrix}$, write down the vectors:
   (i) $\mathbf{a} + \mathbf{b} - \mathbf{c}$, (ii) $2\mathbf{a} + 3\mathbf{b}$, (iii) $-\mathbf{b} + 3\mathbf{c}$, (iv) $3\mathbf{a} + 2\mathbf{b} + \mathbf{c}$.

5 For the following sets of coordinates for the four points A, B, C, D, respectively, find the column vectors $\overrightarrow{AB}$ and $\overrightarrow{CD}$ and determine whether or not the four points lie at the vertices of a parallelogram:
   (i) $(1, 0, 2)$, $(2, 2, 5)$, $(-1, -1, -1)$, $(0, 1, 2)$;
   (ii) $(2, -3, 5)$, $(0, -1, 2)$, $(1, 0, 1)$, $(-1, 1, -2)$;
   (iii) $(1, -2, 3)$, $(3, -1, -1)$, $(4, 0, 1)$, $(2, -1, 5)$.

6   The coordinates of *P, Q, R, S* are $(1, 2, -1)$, $(2, 4, 2)$, $(-1, 2, 1)$, $(0, 3, 2)$, respectively. Write down the column vectors $\overrightarrow{PQ}$, $\overrightarrow{PR}$, $\overrightarrow{PS}$, $2\overrightarrow{PQ} + 3\overrightarrow{PR}$, and deduce that *P, Q, R* and *S* lie in one plane.

7   The position vectors of the points *A* and *B* relative to an origin *O* are $5\mathbf{i} + 4\mathbf{j} + \mathbf{k}$, $-\mathbf{i} + \mathbf{j} - 2\mathbf{k}$ respectively. Find the position vector of the point *P* which lies on *AB* produced such that $AP = 2BP$.   (L)

12.4 The equation of a line in two dimensions

In §5.3, we found that, if **a** is the position vector of *A* and if **b** is any non-zero vector, then the equation $\mathbf{r} = \mathbf{a} + t\mathbf{b}$ is the equation of a line, with a parameter *t*. In the Cartesian plane, let $\mathbf{a} = \begin{pmatrix} 2 \\ 1 \end{pmatrix}$ and $\mathbf{b} = \begin{pmatrix} 4 \\ 3 \end{pmatrix}$, then we have the equation

$$\mathbf{r} = \begin{pmatrix} x \\ y \end{pmatrix} = \begin{pmatrix} 2 \\ 1 \end{pmatrix} + t\begin{pmatrix} 4 \\ 3 \end{pmatrix} = \begin{pmatrix} 2 + t4 \\ 1 + t3 \end{pmatrix}$$

giving a pair of scalar equations for the line, with one parameter *t*,

$$x = 2 + 4t,$$
$$y = 1 + 3t.$$

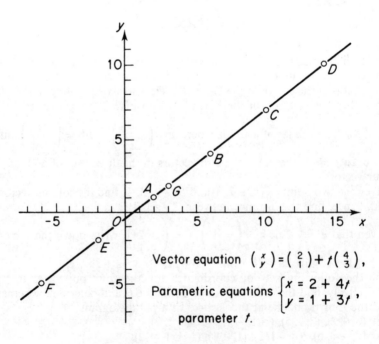

Vector equation $\begin{pmatrix} x \\ y \end{pmatrix} = \begin{pmatrix} 2 \\ 1 \end{pmatrix} + t\begin{pmatrix} 4 \\ 3 \end{pmatrix}$,

Parametric equations $\begin{cases} x = 2 + 4t \\ y = 1 + 3t \end{cases}$,

parameter *t*.

Fig. 12.6 Equations of a line.

For example, in Fig. 12.6, if we give t the values $0, 1, 2, 3, \ldots$, we obtain points A, $(2, 1)$, B, $(6, 4)$, C, $(10, 7)$, D, $(14, 10)$, $\ldots$. Similarly, taking t equal to $-1, -2, \ldots$ gives points E, $(-2, -2)$, F, $(-6, -5)$, $\ldots$, and all these points lie on the line through A with gradient $\frac{4}{3}$. Positive values of t give points on the line 'above' A and negative values give points 'below' A. Any real value of t can be used, for instance $t = \frac{1}{4}$ gives the point G, $(3, 1\frac{3}{4})$. Each point on the line corresponds to one, and only one, value of t.

If we eliminate t from the parametric equations of the line, by equating the values of t found from the two equations,

$$t = \frac{x-2}{4} = \frac{y-1}{3}$$

we obtain

$$y - 1 = \tfrac{3}{4}(x - 2),$$

the standard equation of the line through $(2, 1)$ with gradient $\frac{3}{4}$.

On the other hand, the equation of the line through (a, b) with gradient m is $y - b = m(x - a)$ (see §1.3), and this may be written

$$\frac{y-b}{m} = \frac{x-a}{1} = t$$

so the line has parametric equations, and a vector equation,

$$\begin{matrix} x = a + t \\ y = b + mt \end{matrix}, \qquad \mathbf{r} = \begin{pmatrix} x \\ y \end{pmatrix} = \begin{pmatrix} a \\ b \end{pmatrix} + t \begin{pmatrix} 1 \\ m \end{pmatrix}.$$

EXERCISE 12.4

1   Find parametric equations and a Cartesian equation for the line:

(i) $\mathbf{r} = \begin{pmatrix} 2 \\ 3 \end{pmatrix} + t \begin{pmatrix} 5 \\ 1 \end{pmatrix}$,   (ii) $\mathbf{r} = \begin{pmatrix} 1 \\ -3 \end{pmatrix} + t \begin{pmatrix} -2 \\ 5 \end{pmatrix}$,   (iii) $\mathbf{r} = \mathbf{i} + t(\mathbf{j} - 2\mathbf{i})$.

2   Find the vector equation and the Cartesian equation of the line through:
(i) A, $(4, -3)$ and B, $(3, 5)$; (ii) P and Q, with position vectors $\overrightarrow{OP}$ and $\overrightarrow{OQ}$, where $\overrightarrow{OP} = 2\mathbf{i} + 3\mathbf{j}$ and $\overrightarrow{OQ} = -\mathbf{i} + \mathbf{j}$.

3   Find a vector equation of the line L which passes through $(\frac{5}{8}, \frac{3}{4})$ and has gradient $\frac{1}{2}$.

4   The line L has equation $\mathbf{r} = \begin{pmatrix} 3 \\ 1 \end{pmatrix} + t \begin{pmatrix} -4 \\ 3 \end{pmatrix}$. Find a unit vector in the direction of L and hence find the coordinates of the points on L whose distance from $\begin{pmatrix} 3 \\ 1 \end{pmatrix}$ is 15 units.

5   Find the vector equation of a line through O parallel to $y + 3x = 10$.

6   The points $A(2, 3)$, $B(-1, 2)$, $C(0, 5)$ are vertices of a rhombus $ABCD$. Find:
(i) the coordinates of D, (ii) the vector equations of AC and of BD, (iii) the position vector of the point where AC meets BD.

12.5 The vector equation of a line in three dimensions

Consider the vector equation

$$\mathbf{r} = \begin{pmatrix} x \\ y \\ z \end{pmatrix} = \begin{pmatrix} 4 \\ 2 \\ 1 \end{pmatrix} + t \begin{pmatrix} 5 \\ 10 \\ 9 \end{pmatrix}. \qquad (12.5)$$

When $t = 0$, $\mathbf{r} = \mathbf{a} = \begin{pmatrix} 4 \\ 2 \\ 1 \end{pmatrix}$, corresponding to the point A, $(4, 2, 1)$. When t takes values $1, 2, \ldots$ the x, y, z components of $\mathbf{r}$ increase by $5, 10, 9$ respectively, for each increase of 1 in t, giving a succession of position vectors of the points $(9, 12, 10)$, $(14, 22, 19)$, ... Similarly the values -1, $-2, \ldots$ of t give the points $(-1, -8, -8)$, $(-6, -18, -17)$, . . . These points all lie on the line through $A(4, 2, 1)$, parallel to the vector $\begin{pmatrix} 5 \\ 10 \\ 9 \end{pmatrix}$. If B is the point $(9, 12, 10)$, then the line is the line AB, and equation 12.5 is the vector equation of AB. The vector $\begin{pmatrix} 5 \\ 10 \\ 9 \end{pmatrix}$, $= \mathbf{v}$, defines the direction of

Fig. 12.7

the line *AB* and it is called a *direction vector* of the line *AB* (see Fig. 12.7). Any other vector parallel to **v** is also a direction vector of the line.

The scalar form of the vector equation of the line *AB* gives us the parametric equations of the line; in terms of the parameter *t*.

$$x = 4 + 5t$$
$$y = 2 + 10t$$
$$z = 1 + 9t$$

Elimination of *t* from these three equations gives the two Cartesian equations of the line in standard form:

$$\frac{x-4}{5} = \frac{y-2}{10} = \frac{z-1}{9}.$$

Note that from this equation, the coordinates of *A*, $(4, 2, 1)$ can be read off from the numerators and the direction vector $\begin{pmatrix} 5 \\ 10 \\ 9 \end{pmatrix}$ can be read off from the denominators.

Note also that, in three dimensions, a line is given by one vector equation, or by three parametric equations, or by two Cartesian equations. The Cartesian equations of a line can not always be written in the above standard form. For example, the parametric equations

$$x = 3 + 4t, \quad y = 2, \quad z = 1 + 5t$$

become two Cartesian equations

$$\frac{x-3}{4} = \frac{z-1}{5}, \, y = 2.$$

In the general case, suppose that a line *L* passes through a point *A*, with position vector **a**. Then a general point *P*, with position vector **r**, lies on *L* if, and only if, $\overrightarrow{AP}$ is parallel to a direction vector of *L*. Let **v** be a direction

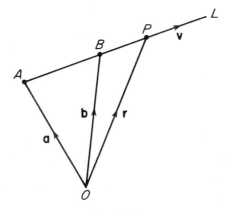

Fig. 12.8

vector of L (see Fig. 12.8), then

$$P \text{ lies on the line } L \Leftrightarrow \overrightarrow{AP} = t\mathbf{v}$$
$$\Leftrightarrow \overrightarrow{OP} = \mathbf{r} = \overrightarrow{OA} + t\mathbf{v} = \mathbf{a} + t\mathbf{v}$$

and the vector equation of L is $\mathbf{r} = \mathbf{a} + t\mathbf{v}$.

Let B be another point on the line L, with $\overrightarrow{OB} = \mathbf{b}$. Then B will be given by some value, say s, of the parameter t, and then $\mathbf{b} = \mathbf{a} + s\mathbf{v}$. Two points on L with parameters of the same sign will lie on the same side of A, and two points with parameters of opposite signs will lie on opposite sides of A.

Warning It is very important to distinguish between:
(i) the direction vector $\mathbf{v}$ of the line AB; and
(ii) the vector $\mathbf{r}$, which is the position vector $\mathbf{r} = \overrightarrow{OP}$ of a general point P on the line AB;
and also between
(iii) the vector $\overrightarrow{AB}$, parallel to $\mathbf{v}$, (since $\overrightarrow{AB} = \mathbf{b} - \mathbf{a} = s\mathbf{v}$); and
(iv) the vector equation of AB, namely $\mathbf{r} = \mathbf{a} + t\mathbf{v}$, which has direction vector $\mathbf{v}$.

In the example above, for the line L, the vector $\begin{pmatrix} 5 \\ 10 \\ 9 \end{pmatrix}$ is a direction vector, but so is $\begin{pmatrix} -10 \\ -20 \\ -18 \end{pmatrix}$ and so is $\begin{pmatrix} 2\frac{1}{2} \\ 5 \\ 4\frac{1}{2} \end{pmatrix}$.

Another point which is important to remember is that a vector equation is an equation, and both sides of the '=' sign must be present, and both sides must be vectors, even if one side of the equation is the zero vector $\mathbf{0}$.

EXAMPLE 1 *Determine whether or not the points $A(3, 1, 3)$ and $B(0, -5, 2)$ lie on the line L with equation* $\mathbf{r} = \begin{pmatrix} 2 \\ -1 \\ 4 \end{pmatrix} + t \begin{pmatrix} 1 \\ 2 \\ -1 \end{pmatrix}$.

For a point to lie on the line, its three coordinates must be given by the same value of t. We therefore find the value of t to make one coordinate correct and then check the value of the other two coordinates.

For the point A, we require $x = 3 = 2 + t$, which is given by $t = 1$. Then $y = -1 + 2t = 1$, $z = 4 - t = 3$, and so A **lies on** L.

For B, we require $x = 0 = 2 + t$, giving $t = -2$, $y = -1 + (-2)2 = -5$, which is correct, and $z = 4 + (-2)(-1) = 6 \neq 2$.

So B **does not lie on** L.

EXAMPLE 2 *Show that the points $A(1, 2, 3)$, and $B(3, 3, 2)$ both lie on the line L with equation* $\mathbf{r} = \begin{pmatrix} 1 \\ 2 \\ 3 \end{pmatrix} + t \begin{pmatrix} 2 \\ 1 \\ -1 \end{pmatrix}$. *Find the coordinates of the point C where L meets the coordinate plane $y = 0$. Write down the ratio of the lengths AB and AC.*

Clearly A is the point on L with parameter $t = 0$, and B is the point with parameter $t = 1$. When $y = 0$, $t = -2$, so $x = -3$, $z = 5$, and the coordinates of C are $(-3, 0, 5)$. The distances along L from A are proportional to the value of the parameter t. Hence B and C lie on opposite sides of A and $AB : AC = 1 : 2$. Note that had we been asked to find the ratio of the vectors $\overrightarrow{AB}$ and $\overrightarrow{AC}$, with direction counting, it would be $-1 : 2$.

EXAMPLE 3 *Write down a direction vector for the line AB, where* $\overrightarrow{OA} = -2\mathbf{i} + 3\mathbf{j} + \mathbf{k}$ *and* $\overrightarrow{OB} = 5\mathbf{k}$. *Find a vector equation for AB. Given that* $\overrightarrow{OC} = 2\mathbf{i} - 3\mathbf{j} + 9\mathbf{k}$ *and* $\overrightarrow{OD} = -4\mathbf{i} + 6\mathbf{j} - 3\mathbf{k}$, *use a similar method to find a vector equation of the line CD. Show that these two equations represent the same line and deduce that A, B, C, D are collinear.*

$\overrightarrow{AB} = \overrightarrow{OB} - \overrightarrow{OA} = 5\mathbf{k} - (-2\mathbf{i} + 3\mathbf{j} + \mathbf{k}) = 2\mathbf{i} - 3\mathbf{j} + 4\mathbf{k}$, which is a direction vector for the line AB. Therefore, the equation of AB is

$$\mathbf{r} = 5\mathbf{k} + t(2\mathbf{i} - 3\mathbf{j} + 4\mathbf{k}).$$

$\overrightarrow{CD} = \overrightarrow{OD} - \overrightarrow{OC} = -4\mathbf{i} + 6\mathbf{j} - 3\mathbf{k} - (2\mathbf{i} - 3\mathbf{j} + 9\mathbf{k}) = -6\mathbf{i} + 9\mathbf{j} - 12\mathbf{k}$, which is a direction vector for the line CD. Therefore the equation of CD is

$$\mathbf{r} = 2\mathbf{i} - 3\mathbf{j} + 9\mathbf{k} + s(-6\mathbf{i} + 9\mathbf{j} - 12\mathbf{k}).$$

Since $-6\mathbf{i} + 9\mathbf{j} - 12\mathbf{k} = -3(2\mathbf{i} - 3\mathbf{j} + 4\mathbf{k})$, the lines AB and CD are parallel. Also, for $s = \frac{1}{3}$,

$$\mathbf{r} = 2\mathbf{i} - 3\mathbf{j} + 9\mathbf{k} + \tfrac{1}{3}(-6\mathbf{i} + 9\mathbf{j} - 12\mathbf{k}) = 5\mathbf{k},$$

so B lies on CD. Thus the two lines are the same line and A, B, C, D are collinear.

EXERCISE 12.5

1 Find parametric and Cartesian equations of the line having a vector equation:

(i) $\mathbf{r} = \begin{pmatrix} 2 \\ 5 \\ 4 \end{pmatrix} + t \begin{pmatrix} -3 \\ 1 \\ -2 \end{pmatrix}$, (ii) $\mathbf{r} = \begin{pmatrix} 0 \\ 2 \\ -1 \end{pmatrix} + t \begin{pmatrix} 2 \\ 1 \\ 4 \end{pmatrix}$,

(iii) $\mathbf{r} = \begin{pmatrix} 4 \\ 1 \\ 2 \end{pmatrix} + t \begin{pmatrix} -3 \\ 12 \\ -5 \end{pmatrix}$, (iv) $\mathbf{r} = \begin{pmatrix} 2 \\ -2 \\ 3 \end{pmatrix} + s \begin{pmatrix} 1 \\ 1 \\ 1 \end{pmatrix}$.

2 Find a vector equation for the line:

(i) through $(3, -1, 4)$ in the direction $\begin{pmatrix} -1 \\ 3 \\ 2 \end{pmatrix}$;

(ii) through $(1, 1, -1)$ in the direction $\begin{pmatrix} 4 \\ 3 \\ 5 \end{pmatrix}$;

(iii) through the points $(2, -3, 4)$ and $(1, -3, 2)$;
(iv) through the points $(2, -4, 1)$ and $(1, -5, 7)$;
(v) through the points $(-7, 3, -1)$ and $(2, -3, 5)$.

3 Find a vector equation of the line with parametric equations:
(i) $x = 2 + t$, $y = -1 + 3t$, $z = 3 - 4t$;   (ii) $x = t$, $y = 2 - 3t$, $z = 4t$;
(iii) $x = 4 - 2t$, $y = t$, $z = 0$;   (iv) $x = 3$, $y = 2 - t$, $z = t$.

4 Use the parameter indicated to find a vector equation of the line:
(i) $y = 2x + 3$, $z = -4x - 2$, (parameter x);
(ii) $x = 3y - 7$, $z = 2y - 1$, (parameter y);
(iii) $x = 3z - 4$, $y = z$, (parameter z);
(iv) $x = 2y + 6$, $z = 2$, (parameter y);
(v) $x + y = 3$, $z - x = 2$, (parameter x);
(vi) $2y = 3x + 4$, $5z = 4 - x$, (parameter x).

5 Find a direction vector of the line with equations:

(i) $\dfrac{y-3}{2} = \dfrac{x-1}{4} = \dfrac{z-6}{3}$,   (ii) $\dfrac{x}{2} = \dfrac{2y-4}{3} = z$,

(iii) $\dfrac{3x+1}{7} = \dfrac{4-y}{5} = \dfrac{2z}{3}$,   (iv) $x = 2y - 6$, $z = 4 - 3y$,

(v) $x + 2y = 9$, $3 - z = x$,   (vi) $4x - 8 = y$, $x = 3z - 8$.

6 Find Cartesian equations of the line:

(i) with vector equation $\mathbf{r} = \begin{pmatrix} 2 \\ 4 \\ 3 \end{pmatrix} + t \begin{pmatrix} -3 \\ -14 \\ 9 \end{pmatrix}$;

(ii) through the origin O and the point $A(2, -3, 6)$;
(iii) with parametric equations $x = 3 - t$, $y = 5 + 2t$, $z = 7$;
(iv) through the points $A(5, 7, -3)$ and $B(2, 4, 5)$;
(v) with equation $\mathbf{r} = 3\mathbf{i} - \mathbf{k} + t(2\mathbf{j} - 4\mathbf{k})$.

7 Determine whether the point $A(-6, +5, -2)$ lies on the line L with

equation $\mathbf{r} = \begin{pmatrix} 2 \\ 3 \\ -5 \end{pmatrix} + t \begin{pmatrix} -4 \\ 1 \\ 2 \end{pmatrix}$.

8 Show that $A(3, -1, 4)$, $B(9, 11, -11)$ and $C(-5, -17, 24)$ all lie on the line $\mathbf{r} = 3\mathbf{i} - \mathbf{j} + 4\mathbf{k} + t(2\mathbf{i} + 4\mathbf{j} - 5\mathbf{k})$. State the corresponding values of t and find the ratio of the lengths of AB and AC.

9 The points A and B are given by $t = 0$ and $t = 1$, respectively, on the line L

with vector equation $\mathbf{r} = \begin{pmatrix} 2 \\ 7 \\ 3 \end{pmatrix} + t \begin{pmatrix} 1 \\ 3 \\ 6 \end{pmatrix}$. Determine the coordinates of the

point C on L such that A lies between B and C and $CA:AB = 2:1$.

10 Determine whether the pair of vector equations represent the same line:

(i) $\mathbf{r} = \begin{pmatrix} -3 \\ 2 \\ 5 \end{pmatrix} + t \begin{pmatrix} 1 \\ 3 \\ -4 \end{pmatrix}$ and $\mathbf{r} = \begin{pmatrix} 0 \\ 11 \\ 7 \end{pmatrix} + s \begin{pmatrix} -1 \\ -3 \\ 4 \end{pmatrix}$,

(ii) $\mathbf{r} = \begin{pmatrix} 2 \\ -1 \\ 4 \end{pmatrix} + t \begin{pmatrix} \frac{1}{2} \\ \frac{1}{3} \\ \frac{1}{4} \end{pmatrix}$ and $\mathbf{r} = \begin{pmatrix} 8 \\ 3 \\ 6 \end{pmatrix} + s \begin{pmatrix} 6 \\ 4 \\ 3 \end{pmatrix}$.

11 State a vector equation of the line passing through the points A and B whose position vectors are $\mathbf{i} - \mathbf{j} + 3\mathbf{k}$ and $\mathbf{i} + 2\mathbf{j} + 2\mathbf{k}$ respectively.
Determine the position vector of the point C which divides the line-segment AB internally such that $AC = 2CB$.   *(L)*

12 Two loci are given by Cartesian equations (i) $x + 2y + 3z = 18$, and (ii) $x = 2y = 3z$. Show that one locus is a line and that the other is not. State what you think the other locus might be. Find points which lie on both loci and interpret this result.

12.6 Scalar products

So far, we have dealt with linear combinations of vectors, using the operations of addition and multiplication by a scalar. If we wish to define some sort of product of two vectors, we could consider the product of their moduli. However, this would not take into account the directions of the vectors, and it is not very useful. What turns out to be useful is the product of the moduli of the two vectors multiplied by the cosine of the angle between them. This product takes into account their moduli and their directions. It is called the *scalar product* of the vectors and the notation is to place a dot between the two vectors, so it is also called 'the dot product'.

Definition Let the vectors **a** and **b** have moduli (lengths) a and b and let θ be the angle between **a** and **b**, then the *scalar product* of **a** and **b** is the real number **a** . **b**, where

$$\mathbf{a} . \mathbf{b} = |\mathbf{a}||\mathbf{b}| \cos \theta = ab \cos \theta.$$

If two vectors happen to be represented by line segments, which do not originate from the same point, then we define the angle between them as the angle between two position vectors (originating from O) which are equal to the given vectors. Thus, in Fig. 12.9, the vectors **a** and **b** are represented by $\overrightarrow{PQ}$ and $\overrightarrow{RS}$ and also by $\overrightarrow{OA}$ and $\overrightarrow{OB}$ and the angle between $\overrightarrow{PQ}$ and $\overrightarrow{RS}$, that is, the angle between **a** and **b** is $\theta = \angle AOB$. Note that, if θ is acute then **a** . **b** is positive, if θ is obtuse then **a** . **b** is negative.

We now show that many of the properties of products are satisfied by scalar products. The one property that cannot apply to scalar products is associativity since, because **a** . **b** is a scalar, (**a** . **b**) . **c** has no meaning,

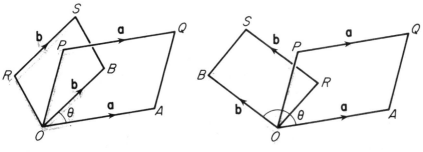

(a) θ acute, **a**.**b** = $ab\cos\theta > 0$ (b) θ obtuse, **a**.**b** = $ab\cos\theta < 0$

Fig. 12.9 Scalar product.

whereas $(\mathbf{a}.\mathbf{b})\mathbf{c}$ is the multiple of $\mathbf{c}$ by $\mathbf{a}.\mathbf{b}$ so the brackets can not be moved. The following shows that scalar products commute and distribute with addition. Let $|\mathbf{a}| = a$, $|\mathbf{b}| = b$, $|\mathbf{c}| = c$.

Commutativity

$$\mathbf{a}.\mathbf{b} = ab \cos \theta = ba \cos \theta = \mathbf{b}.\mathbf{a}.$$

Multiplication by scalars

Let k, l be scalars. Then if $k \geqslant 0, l \geqslant 0$,

$$(k\mathbf{a}).(l\mathbf{b}) = |k\mathbf{a}||l\mathbf{b}| \cos \theta = kl|\mathbf{a}||\mathbf{b}| \cos \theta = (kl)\mathbf{a}.\mathbf{b}.$$

If either, or both, of k and l is negative it still follows that

$$(k\mathbf{a}).(l\mathbf{b}) = (kl)\mathbf{a}.\mathbf{b}$$

on using two facts:

(i) if θ is the angle between $\mathbf{a}$ and $\mathbf{b}$, then $(\pi - \theta)$ is the angle between $\mathbf{a}$ and $(-\mathbf{b})$ and also between $(-\mathbf{a})$ and $\mathbf{b}$, and θ is the angle between $(-\mathbf{a})$ and $(-\mathbf{b})$ (see Fig. 12.10);
(ii) $\cos(\pi - \theta) = -\cos \theta$.

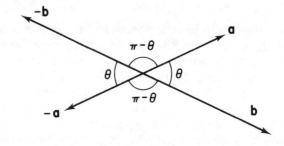

Fig. 12.10

Distributivity

$$\mathbf{a}.(\mathbf{b}+\mathbf{c}) = \mathbf{a}.\mathbf{b}+\mathbf{a}.\mathbf{c}$$

Proof In Fig. 12.11, let $\mathbf{a} = \overrightarrow{OA}$, $\mathbf{b} = \overrightarrow{OB}$ and $\mathbf{c} = \overrightarrow{BC}$, so that $(\mathbf{b}+\mathbf{c}) = \overrightarrow{OC}$. Let BL and CM be the perpendiculars from B and C on to OA, produced, if necessary, in either direction. Let $\overrightarrow{BD}$ be a line through B parallel to $\mathbf{a}$ and let CN be the perpendicular from C on to BD. Note that, because BND and $OLMA$ are both parallel to $\mathbf{a}$, these seven points all lie in one plane, but the point C may not lie in this plane. If it does, then, because CN and CM are both perpendicular to $\mathbf{a}$, C lies on NM and $BLMN$ is a rectangle. If C does not lie in the plane OAB, then, as shown in Fig. 12.11, since CN and CM are each perpendicular to $\mathbf{a}$, the plane CMN is

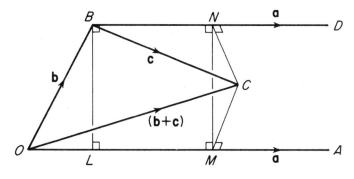

Fig. 12.11

perpendicular to **a** and again *BLMN* is a rectangle. Therefore, in each case, $\overrightarrow{BN} = \overrightarrow{LM}$. Now, with the signs taken into account,

$$\mathbf{a \cdot b} + \mathbf{a \cdot c} = a\,OB \cos \angle BOL + a\,BC \cos \angle CBN$$

$$= a\,OL + a\,BN = a\,OL + a\,LM = a\,OM$$

$$= a\,OC \cos \angle AOC = \mathbf{a}.\overrightarrow{OC}$$

$$= \mathbf{a \cdot (b + c)}.$$

Parallel vectors

If **a** and **b** are parallel, they can be in the same or in opposite directions to each other, corresponding to the angle between them being 0 or π.

> **a** and **b** in the same direction, $\theta = 0$, $\mathbf{a \cdot b} = ab$.

> **a** and **b** in opposite directions, $\theta = \pi$, $\mathbf{a \cdot b} = -ab$.

In particular, $\mathbf{a \cdot a} = aa = a^2$ and hence $|\mathbf{a}| = \sqrt{(\mathbf{a \cdot a})}$.

Perpendicular vectors

If **a** and **b** are perpendicular, $\theta = \frac{1}{2}\pi$, $\cos\theta = 0$, and so $\mathbf{a \cdot b} = 0$.
  Conversely, if $\mathbf{a \cdot b} = 0$, then either $\mathbf{a} = \mathbf{0}$, or $\mathbf{b} = \mathbf{0}$, or **a** and **b** are perpendicular.

EXERCISE 12.6A

1   Given vectors **a** and **b**, with moduli a and b, and with an angle θ between them, the projection of **a** along the direction of **b** is defined as $a\cos\theta$. Show that the scalar product $\mathbf{a \cdot b}$ is equal to b times the projection of **a** in the direction of **b** and is also equal to a times the projection of **b** in the direction of **a**.

2   The unit vector **n** is in the direction North. Vectors **a** and **b** have lengths 5 km and 2 km and are in the directions of bearings 60° and 330° respectively. Draw a diagram showing **n**, **a**, **b**, (**a** + **b**). Find **n.n**, **a.a**, **b.b**, **a.n**, **b.n**, **a.b**, (**a** + **b**).**n**.

3   Three vectors $\mathbf{p}$, $\mathbf{q}$ and $\mathbf{r}$ of magnitudes 5, 3 and 4 respectively, lie in one plane, with $\mathbf{q}$ and $\mathbf{r}$ on opposite sides of $\mathbf{p}$ and at angles $150°$ and $120°$ with $\mathbf{p}$ respectively. Find $\mathbf{p} \cdot \mathbf{q}$, $\mathbf{p} \cdot \mathbf{r}$, $\mathbf{q} \cdot \mathbf{r}$, $\mathbf{q} \cdot \mathbf{p}$, $\mathbf{p} \cdot (\mathbf{q} + \mathbf{r})$, and verify that $\mathbf{p} \cdot \mathbf{q} = \mathbf{q} \cdot \mathbf{p}$ and $\mathbf{p} \cdot \mathbf{q} + \mathbf{p} \cdot \mathbf{r} = \mathbf{p} \cdot (\mathbf{q} + \mathbf{r})$.

4   The vector $\mathbf{a}$ is resolved into two perpendicular components $\mathbf{a}_1$ and $\mathbf{a}_2$, such that $\mathbf{a} = \mathbf{a}_1 + \mathbf{a}_2$, $\mathbf{a}_1$ is parallel to a given vector $\mathbf{b}$ and $\mathbf{a}_2$ is perpendicular to $\mathbf{b}$.
Prove that $\mathbf{a}_1 = \dfrac{\mathbf{a} \cdot \mathbf{b}}{b^2}\,\mathbf{b}$ and $\mathbf{a}_2 = \mathbf{a} - \dfrac{\mathbf{a} \cdot \mathbf{b}}{b^2}\,\mathbf{b}$.

5   The vectors $\mathbf{a}$ and $\mathbf{b}$ are perpendicular and $|\mathbf{a}| = 15$, $|\mathbf{b}| = 8$. Calculate $|\mathbf{a} + \mathbf{b}|$ and $|\mathbf{a} - \mathbf{b}|$.   *(L)*

6   The vertices P, Q, R of a tetrahedron $OPQR$ have position vectors $\mathbf{a}$, $\mathbf{b}$ and $\mathbf{c}$ respectively relative to an origin O. If OP and QR are perpendicular, show that $\mathbf{a} \cdot (\mathbf{b} - \mathbf{c}) = 0$. If also OQ and RP are perpendicular, prove that OR and PQ are perpendicular.   *(L)*

7   The vectors $\mathbf{a}$ and $\mathbf{b}$ are such that $|\mathbf{a}| = 3$ and $|\mathbf{b}| = 5$. Calculate the magnitude of $\mathbf{a} + \mathbf{b}$ given that the angle between $\mathbf{a}$ and $\mathbf{b}$ is $\pi/3$.   *(L)*

Unit vectors

For any unit vector $\mathbf{u}$, $\mathbf{u} \cdot \mathbf{u} = 1 \times 1 \times \cos 0 = 1$.

For the Cartesian basis unit vectors, $\mathbf{i}$, $\mathbf{j}$, $\mathbf{k}$,

$$\mathbf{i} \cdot \mathbf{i} = \mathbf{j} \cdot \mathbf{j} = \mathbf{k} \cdot \mathbf{k} = 1,\ \mathbf{i} \cdot \mathbf{j} = \mathbf{j} \cdot \mathbf{k} = \mathbf{k} \cdot \mathbf{i} = \mathbf{j} \cdot \mathbf{i} = \mathbf{k} \cdot \mathbf{j} = \mathbf{i} \cdot \mathbf{k} = 0.$$

Cartesian components

Using the above and the distributive rule, if $\mathbf{a} = a_1\mathbf{i} + a_2\mathbf{j} + a_3\mathbf{k}$,

$$\mathbf{a} \cdot \mathbf{i} = a_1\mathbf{i} \cdot \mathbf{i} + a_2\mathbf{j} \cdot \mathbf{i} + a_3\mathbf{k} \cdot \mathbf{i} = a_1,\ \mathbf{a} \cdot \mathbf{j} = a_2,\ \mathbf{a} \cdot \mathbf{k} = a_3.$$

In two dimensions,

$$\mathbf{a} = a_1\mathbf{i} + a_2\mathbf{j},\ \mathbf{a} \cdot \mathbf{i} = a_1,\ \mathbf{a} \cdot \mathbf{j} = a_2.$$

The scalar product of $\mathbf{a}$ with a Cartesian unit vector is the component of $\mathbf{a}$ in that direction.

Component form

Again using the distributive rule and the results for unit vectors,

if $\mathbf{a} = a_1\mathbf{i} + a_2\mathbf{j} + a_3\mathbf{k}$, $\mathbf{b} = b_1\mathbf{i} + b_2\mathbf{j} + b_3\mathbf{k}$,

then $\mathbf{a} \cdot \mathbf{b} = (a_1\mathbf{i} + a_2\mathbf{j} + a_3\mathbf{k}) \cdot (b_1\mathbf{i} + b_2\mathbf{j} + b_3\mathbf{k}) = a_1 b_1 + a_2 b_2 + a_3 b_3$.

Vector form

$$\mathbf{a} \cdot \mathbf{b} = \begin{pmatrix} a_1 \\ a_2 \\ a_3 \end{pmatrix} \cdot \begin{pmatrix} b_1 \\ b_2 \\ b_3 \end{pmatrix} = a_1 b_1 + a_2 b_2 + a_3 b_3.$$

Thus, if θ is the angle between the vectors **a** and **b**, then $\mathbf{a}.\mathbf{b} = ab \cos \theta$ and

$$\cos \theta = \frac{a_1 b_1 + a_2 b_2 + a_3 b_3}{\sqrt{(a_1^2 + a_2^2 + a_3^2)} \sqrt{(b_1^2 + b_2^2 + b_3^2)}},$$

a very important result.

The scalar product can be used to establish geometrical properties such as distances from lines and angles between lines. The acute angle between two intersecting lines is either the angle, or the supplement of the angle, between their direction vectors (see Fig. 12.12). Also, the angle between two non-intersecting lines is defined in the same way, so that it is the angle between one line and a line which meets that first line and is parallel to the second line. This is also shown in Fig. 12.12. When two lines do not intersect, and are not parallel, they are called *skew*.

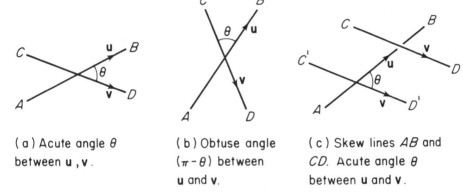

(a) Acute angle θ between **u**, **v**.

(b) Obtuse angle $(\pi - \theta)$ between **u** and **v**.

(c) Skew lines *AB* and *CD*. Acute angle θ between **u** and **v**.

Fig. 12.12 Angle θ between lines *AB*, *CD*

EXAMPLE 1   *Find the angle between the lines with equations*

$$\mathbf{r} = \begin{pmatrix} 3 \\ 1 \\ 2 \end{pmatrix} + t \begin{pmatrix} 3 \\ 5 \\ 4 \end{pmatrix}, \quad \text{and} \quad \mathbf{r} = \begin{pmatrix} 3 \\ 5 \\ 1 \end{pmatrix} + s \begin{pmatrix} -6 \\ 3 \\ 2 \end{pmatrix}.$$

The lines have direction vectors $\mathbf{v}_1 = \begin{pmatrix} 3 \\ 5 \\ 4 \end{pmatrix}$ and $\mathbf{v}_2 = \begin{pmatrix} -6 \\ 3 \\ 2 \end{pmatrix}$, and

$$\mathbf{v}_1 . \mathbf{v}_2 = -18 + 15 + 8 = 5 = |\mathbf{v}_1||\mathbf{v}_2| \cos \theta.$$

Also, $|\mathbf{v}_1| = \sqrt{(16 + 25 + 9)} = \sqrt{(50)}$, $|\mathbf{v}_2| = \sqrt{(36 + 9 + 4)} = \sqrt{(49)} = 7$, and so $\cos \theta = \dfrac{5}{7\sqrt{(50)}} = \dfrac{1}{7\sqrt{2}} = 0 \cdot 101$, giving $\theta \approx 1 \cdot 47$.

EXAMPLE 2   *Three lines L, L', L", have vector equations*

$$\mathbf{r} = \begin{pmatrix} 3 \\ 1 \\ 2 \end{pmatrix} + t \begin{pmatrix} 5 \\ 3 \\ 4 \end{pmatrix}, \; \mathbf{r} = \begin{pmatrix} -1 \\ 4 \\ -3 \end{pmatrix} + t \begin{pmatrix} -2 \\ -3 \\ 1 \end{pmatrix}, \; \mathbf{r} = \begin{pmatrix} -1 \\ 4 \\ -3 \end{pmatrix} + t \begin{pmatrix} -2 \\ -3 \\ -1 \end{pmatrix},$$

respectively. Find the common point of the lines, or show that the lines do not meet, in the case of the two lines:
(i) *L and L', (ii) L and L", (iii) L' and L".*

The same parameter t is used in the equations of the three lines. For a common point on two lines, the parameter will generally take different values for the two lines. Therefore, to avoid confusion, it is necessary to use different symbols for the parameters on the three lines. We shall therefore use parameters t for L, s for L', q for L''.

(i) Since the direction vectors are not multiples of each other, the lines L and L' are not parallel. For a common point, we need values of s and t satisfying the three equations

$$3 + 5t = -1 - 2s$$
$$1 + 3t = 4 - 3s$$
$$2 + 4t = -3 + s.$$

The first two equations give $t = -2$ and $s = 3$. These values do not satisfy the third equation, and hence **the lines are skew.**

(ii) Again L and L'' are not parallel, and for a common point

$$3 + 5t = -1 - 2q$$
$$1 + 3t = 4 - 3q$$
$$2 + 4t = -3 - q$$

and now all three equations are satisfied by $t = -2$ and $q = 3$, which give the coordinates of the common point as $(-7, -5, -6)$.

(iii) The lines L' and L'' are clearly not parallel and have a common point given by $s = 0$, $q = 0$, namely the point $(-1, 4, -3)$.

EXAMPLE 3   *Find the length of the perpendicular from the origin O on to the line*

with equation $\mathbf{r} = \begin{pmatrix} 4 \\ -1 \\ 0 \end{pmatrix} + t \begin{pmatrix} 1 \\ 0 \\ 1 \end{pmatrix}.$

Let P be the foot of the perpendicular OP, given by the parameter t. Then $\overrightarrow{OP} = \begin{pmatrix} 4+t \\ -1 \\ t \end{pmatrix}$ and this vector must be perpendicular to the direction vector

$\mathbf{v} = \begin{pmatrix} 1 \\ 0 \\ 1 \end{pmatrix}$, of the line. So $0 = \overrightarrow{OP}.\mathbf{v} = 4 + t + 0 + t$, whence $t = -2$ and the coordinates of P are $(2, -1, -2)$. The required perpendicular distance is $|\overrightarrow{OP}| = \sqrt{(4 + 1 + 4)} = 3$.

Resolution of vectors

Let $\mathbf{u}$ be a unit vector along a line L. Let $\mathbf{a} = \overrightarrow{QP}$ be a vector which makes an angle θ with $\mathbf{u}$. Let L' be the line parallel to L through Q. Let PN, QM, PN' be the perpendiculars from P, Q, P on to L, L, L' respectively (see Fig. 12.13). The diagram shows two cases (a) when θ is acute and (b) when θ is obtuse.

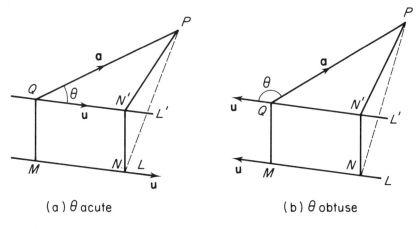

(a) θ acute (b) θ obtuse

Fig. 12.13

The projection of $\mathbf{a} = \overrightarrow{QP}$ on to the line L is $\overrightarrow{MN} = \overrightarrow{QN'}$ and this is called the resolved part of $\mathbf{a}$ in the direction $\mathbf{u}$. The length of MN is

$$MN = QN' = QP \cos \theta = \mathbf{a} \cdot \mathbf{u}$$

in case (a) and is

$$MN = QN' = -QP \cos \theta = -\mathbf{a} \cdot \mathbf{u}$$

in case (b). In case (a) $\overrightarrow{MN} = MN\mathbf{u} = (\mathbf{a} \cdot \mathbf{u})\mathbf{u}$. In case (b) $\overrightarrow{MN} = -MN\mathbf{u} = -(-\mathbf{a} \cdot \mathbf{u})\mathbf{u}$. So, in either case, the resolved part of $\mathbf{a}$ in the direction $\mathbf{u}$ is $(\mathbf{a} \cdot \mathbf{u})\mathbf{u}$.

EXAMPLE 4 *Find the resolved part of the vector $2\mathbf{i} + 3\mathbf{j} - 4\mathbf{k} = \mathbf{a}$ in the direction of the vector $\mathbf{i} - \mathbf{j} + \mathbf{k}$.*

The unit vector $\mathbf{u}$ in the required direction is $\mathbf{u} = \dfrac{1}{\sqrt{3}}(\mathbf{i} - \mathbf{j} + \mathbf{k})$ so the resolved part of $\mathbf{a}$ in this direction is

$$(\mathbf{a} \cdot \mathbf{u})\mathbf{u} = \left(2 \times \frac{1}{\sqrt{3}} + 3 \times \frac{-1}{\sqrt{3}} - 4 \times \frac{1}{\sqrt{3}} \right)\mathbf{u} = \frac{2-3-4}{\sqrt{3}}\mathbf{u} = \frac{-5}{\sqrt{3}}\mathbf{u}$$

$$= -\frac{5}{3}\mathbf{i} + \frac{5}{3}\mathbf{j} - \frac{5}{3}\mathbf{k}.$$

Direction cosines

Let the point D have coordinates (a, b, c) and position vector $\mathbf{d}$, where $\mathbf{d} = \overrightarrow{OD} = \begin{pmatrix} a \\ b \\ c \end{pmatrix}$; then $\mathbf{d}$ is a direction vector for the line $\overrightarrow{OD}$. Let this line $\overrightarrow{OD}$ make angles α, β, γ, with the Cartesian axes Ox, Oy, Oz, respectively.

Then these angles also define the direction of the line $\overrightarrow{OD}$. In fact, if $d = |\mathbf{d}| = \sqrt{(a^2 + b^2 + c^2)}$,

$$d \cos \alpha = \mathbf{d} \cdot \mathbf{i} = a,$$
$$d \cos \beta = \mathbf{d} \cdot \mathbf{j} = b,$$
$$d \cos \gamma = \mathbf{d} \cdot \mathbf{k} = c.$$

Definition

$(\cos \alpha, \cos \beta, \cos \gamma)$ are *direction cosines* for $\overrightarrow{OD}$,

(a, b, c) are *direction ratios* for $\overrightarrow{OD}$.

If we put $\cos \alpha = l, \cos \beta = m, \cos \gamma = n,$

then $a = ld, b = md, c = nd,$

and $l^2 + m^2 + n^2 = 1.$

EXAMPLE 5   *Find the direction cosines for the vector:* (i) $\begin{pmatrix} 2 \\ -1 \\ 2 \end{pmatrix}$, (ii) $3\mathbf{j} - 4\mathbf{k}$.

(i) The direction ratios for the given vector are $(2, -1, 2)$. The length of the vector is $\sqrt{(4 + 1 + 4)} = 3$. Hence the required direction cosines are $(\frac{2}{3}, -\frac{1}{3}, \frac{2}{3})$.
(ii) The direction ratios are $(0, 3, -4)$ and the vector has length 5. The direction cosines of the vector are $(0, \frac{3}{5}, \frac{4}{5})$.

EXERCISE 12.6B

1   Find the angle between:
   (i) the vectors $\mathbf{i} + \mathbf{j} - \mathbf{k}$ and $\mathbf{i} - 2\mathbf{j} - 2\mathbf{k}$;
   (ii) $\mathbf{i} + 2\mathbf{j} - 3\mathbf{k}$ and $\mathbf{k} - 2\mathbf{i} - 3\mathbf{j}$;
   (iii) the lines OA and OB, where A and B have coordinates $(2, -1, 2)$ and $(2, -2, 2)$;
   (iv) the lines PQ and RS, where the points P, Q, R, S have coordinates $(4, -3, 2), (3, 5, 6), (1, -1, -1), (-5, 2, 4)$;

   (v) the lines with equations: $\mathbf{r} = \mathbf{a} + t\mathbf{b}$ and $\mathbf{r} = 2\mathbf{b} - 3t\mathbf{a}$,

   where $\mathbf{a} = \begin{pmatrix} 1 \\ 3 \\ -2 \end{pmatrix}$ and $\mathbf{b} = \begin{pmatrix} 2 \\ 4 \\ 5 \end{pmatrix}$.

2   The co-ordinates of the points A, B and C are $(2, 3)$, $(4, 7)$, and $(5, 4)$ respectively. Calculate the acute angle between the lines AB and AC.   (*L*)
3   Expand the scalar product $(\mathbf{a} - \mathbf{b}) \cdot (\mathbf{a} - \mathbf{b})$. In the triangle ABC, $\overrightarrow{CA} = \mathbf{a}$, $\overrightarrow{CB} = \mathbf{b}$, use this scalar product to deduce the cosine formula for the triangle.
4   The vectors $\mathbf{a}$ and $\mathbf{b}$ are inclined to one another at an angle of $60°$ and $|\mathbf{a}| = 5$, $|\mathbf{b}| = 8$. Calculate $|\mathbf{a} - \mathbf{b}|$.   (*L*)
5   Find a unit vector $\hat{\alpha}$ parallel to the vector $\alpha = 2\mathbf{i} - \mathbf{j} - 3\mathbf{k}$. Determine the length of the resolved part of the vector $\beta = 2\mathbf{i} + 3\mathbf{j} - \mathbf{k}$ in the direction of α.   (*L*)
6   Determine whether the two lines, with the given equations, intersect. If they

do intersect, state the coordinates of the common point:

(i) $\mathbf{r} = \begin{pmatrix} 0 \\ 2 \\ -1 \end{pmatrix} + t \begin{pmatrix} 4 \\ -2 \\ 3 \end{pmatrix}$ and $\mathbf{r} = \begin{pmatrix} 4 \\ 1 \\ -2 \end{pmatrix} + s \begin{pmatrix} -1 \\ 3 \\ 4 \end{pmatrix}$,

(ii) $\mathbf{r} = \begin{pmatrix} 2 \\ -1 \\ 0 \end{pmatrix} + t \begin{pmatrix} -2 \\ 3 \\ 4 \end{pmatrix}$ and $\mathbf{r} = \begin{pmatrix} 4 \\ 1 \\ -2 \end{pmatrix} + s \begin{pmatrix} -1 \\ 4 \\ 3 \end{pmatrix}$,

(iii) $\mathbf{r} = \begin{pmatrix} 4 \\ 3 \\ -2 \end{pmatrix} + t \begin{pmatrix} 5 \\ 1 \\ 2 \end{pmatrix}$ and $\mathbf{r} = \begin{pmatrix} 2 \\ -5 \\ 2 \end{pmatrix} + t \begin{pmatrix} 3 \\ 2 \\ -1 \end{pmatrix}$.

7 Given that A and B are the points whose position vectors referred to the origin O are $(\mathbf{i} + 2\mathbf{j} + \mathbf{k})$ and $(3\mathbf{i} + 4\mathbf{j} + 2\mathbf{k})$ respectively, determine $|\overrightarrow{AB}|$ and direction cosines for the line AB. (L)

8 Find the length of the perpendicular from O to the line with the given equation. State the coordinates of the foot of the perpendicular:

(i) $\mathbf{r} = \begin{pmatrix} 6 \\ -2 \\ 1 \end{pmatrix} + t \begin{pmatrix} -4 \\ 3 \\ 5 \end{pmatrix}$; (ii) $\mathbf{r} = \begin{pmatrix} 4 \\ -2 \\ 3 \end{pmatrix} + t \begin{pmatrix} 2 \\ 1 \\ 1 \end{pmatrix}$.

9 Verify that the point A, $(1, 3, 4)$, is the foot of the perpendicular from O to the line L: $\mathbf{r} = \begin{pmatrix} 1 \\ 3 \\ 4 \end{pmatrix} + t \begin{pmatrix} 2 \\ 6 \\ -5 \end{pmatrix}$. Given that B is the reflection of O in L, write down the coordinates of B. Given that C and D are the points of L with parameters $t = 1$ and $t = -1$ respectively, calculate the area of the rhombus $OCBD$, giving the answer in surd form.

10 Using the fact that a diameter of a sphere subtends a right angle at a point on the surface, show that the equation of the sphere with diameter AB, where A and B are the points (a_1, a_2, a_3) and (b_1, b_2, b_3), is

$$(x - a_1)(x - b_1) + (y - a_2)(y - b_2) + (z - a_3)(z - b_3) = 0.$$

11 Find the coordinates of the foot of the perpendicular from $(1, 10, -2)$ to the line $\mathbf{r} = \begin{pmatrix} 4 \\ 1 \\ -3 \end{pmatrix} + t \begin{pmatrix} -3 \\ 2 \\ 5 \end{pmatrix}$.

12 Let $\mathbf{a} = \mathbf{i} - 2\mathbf{j} + \mathbf{k}$, $\mathbf{b} = 2\mathbf{i} + \mathbf{j} - \mathbf{k}$. Given that $\mathbf{c} = \lambda\mathbf{a} + \mu\mathbf{b}$ and that $\mathbf{c}$ is perpendicular to $\mathbf{a}$, find the ratio of λ to μ.

Let A, B be the points with position vectors $\mathbf{a}$, $\mathbf{b}$ respectively with respect to an origin O. Write down, in terms of $\mathbf{a}$ and $\mathbf{b}$, a vector equation of the line l through A, in the plane of O, A and B, which is perpendicular to OA.

Find the position vector of P, the point of intersection of l and OB. (JMB)

13 Given that the two lines

$$\frac{x-1}{p} = \frac{y+6}{5} = \frac{z-3}{-1} \quad \text{and} \quad \frac{x-2}{-2} = \frac{y-3}{4} = \frac{z-5}{3}$$

intersect, find the value of p and also the coordinates of their point of intersection. (JMB)

14   Show that the lines $L: \mathbf{r} = \begin{pmatrix} 3 \\ 2 \\ 1 \end{pmatrix} + t \begin{pmatrix} 5 \\ 4 \\ 3 \end{pmatrix}$ and $M: \mathbf{r} = \begin{pmatrix} 16 \\ -10 \\ 2 \end{pmatrix} + s \begin{pmatrix} 3 \\ 2 \\ -1 \end{pmatrix}$
are skew. Verify that both lines L and M are perpendicular to $\mathbf{n}$, where
$\mathbf{n} = \begin{pmatrix} 5 \\ -7 \\ 1 \end{pmatrix}$.

The point A on L has coordinates $(3, 2, 1)$. Write down a vector equation of the line N, through A with direction vector $\mathbf{n}$.

Show that the lines M and N intersect and find the coordinates at their point of intersection, B. Find, in surd form, the length AB.

15   The points P and Q are given by $t = p$ and $s = q$ on the lines

$$\mathbf{r} = \begin{pmatrix} 3 \\ 1 \\ 2 \end{pmatrix} + t \begin{pmatrix} 2 \\ -2 \\ 0 \end{pmatrix} \text{ and } \mathbf{r} = \begin{pmatrix} 1 \\ 0 \\ 3 \end{pmatrix} + s \begin{pmatrix} 3 \\ 4 \\ 7 \end{pmatrix},$$

respectively. If PQ is perpendicular to both lines, show that $\overrightarrow{PQ}$ may be written as $k \begin{pmatrix} 1 \\ 1 \\ -1 \end{pmatrix}$, where k is a scalar. Express $\overrightarrow{PQ}$ also in terms of p and q and deduce the value of k and the shortest distance between the lines.

(*JMB*)

16   The lines L_1 and L_2 have vector equations given by $\mathbf{r}_1 = 3\mathbf{i} + \mathbf{j} + t(2\mathbf{j} + \mathbf{k})$ and $\mathbf{r}_2 = 4\mathbf{k} + s(\mathbf{i} + \mathbf{j} - \mathbf{k})$ where t and s are parameters. Show that L_1 and L_2 intersect, and find in surd form the cosine of the angle between these lines.

(*JMB*)

12.7 Planes through the origin

Given a direction vector $\mathbf{n}$, there is just one plane Π through the origin O perpendicular to $\mathbf{n}$. The plane Π contains the set of all lines through O perpendicular to $\mathbf{n}$. Every line in Π, whether through O or not, is also perpendicular to $\mathbf{n}$, so we say that the direction of $\mathbf{n}$ is perpendicular, or normal, to the plane Π. This direction $\mathbf{n}$ is called

the direction *normal* to Π,

$\mathbf{n}$ is a *normal vector* to the plane Π.

Clearly, any non-zero multiple of $\mathbf{n}$ is also a normal vector to Π.

For example, with Cartesian axes $O(x, y, z)$, the axis Oz is normal to the x, y-plane, the plane on which $z = 0$. Thus any vector $\begin{pmatrix} 0 \\ 0 \\ k \end{pmatrix}$, $k \neq 0$, is a normal vector to the plane $z = 0$.

In the general case, if Π is a plane through O with normal $\mathbf{n}$, then a point P lies in Π if and only if its position vector $\overrightarrow{OP}$ is perpendicular to $\mathbf{n}$. Thus, if $\overrightarrow{OP} = \mathbf{r}$

$$P \text{ lies in } \Pi \Leftrightarrow \mathbf{r} \cdot \mathbf{n} = 0,$$

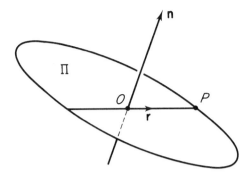

Fig. 12.14

so the equation of Π is $\mathbf{r} \cdot \mathbf{n} = 0$, (Fig. 12.14).

If $\mathbf{r} = \begin{pmatrix} x \\ y \\ z \end{pmatrix}$ and $\mathbf{n} = \begin{pmatrix} a \\ b \\ c \end{pmatrix}$, we obtain the Cartesian equation of Π,

$$ax + by + cz = 0.$$

EXAMPLE 1   *Find an equation of the plane through O with normal* $\mathbf{n} = \begin{pmatrix} 3 \\ -1 \\ 2 \end{pmatrix}$.

The point P (x, y, z) lies in the plane if $\mathbf{r}\, (= \overrightarrow{OP})$ is perpendicular to $\mathbf{n}$. So the equation of the plane is $\mathbf{r} \cdot \mathbf{n} = \mathbf{3x - y + 2z = 0}$.

EXAMPLE 2   *Find the equation of the plane Π, through the origin O and perpendicular to the two planes Π_1, $3x + 2y - z = 0$ and Π_2, $x - 2y + z = 0$.*

Let the normal to Π be $\mathbf{n}$, where $\mathbf{n} = \begin{pmatrix} a \\ b \\ c \end{pmatrix}$. Then $\mathbf{n}$ lies in each plane Π_1 and Π_2

and so $\mathbf{n}$ is perpendicular to the normals to each of these planes. Therefore,

$$\begin{pmatrix} a \\ b \\ c \end{pmatrix} \cdot \begin{pmatrix} 3 \\ 2 \\ -1 \end{pmatrix} = 0 \text{ and } \begin{pmatrix} a \\ b \\ c \end{pmatrix} \cdot \begin{pmatrix} 1 \\ -2 \\ 1 \end{pmatrix} = 0,$$

(see Fig. 12.15). Hence, $3a + 2b - c = 0$ and $a - 2b + c = 0$. On addition, $4a = 0$,

so $c = 2b$. As a possible vector $\mathbf{n}$, we take $b = 1, c = 2, a = 0$, and then $\mathbf{n} = \begin{pmatrix} 0 \\ 1 \\ 2 \end{pmatrix}$.

The equation of Π is

$$\mathbf{r} \cdot \mathbf{n} = \mathbf{y + 2z = 0}.$$

Note that the two equations we solved for a, b, c showed that the point A, (a, b, c) lies in both planes Π_1 and Π_2, so that these two planes intersect in the line OA, as shown in Fig. 12.15.

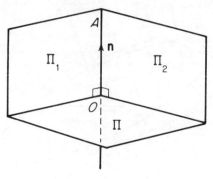

Fig. 12.15

EXERCISE 12.7

1   Find the equation of the plane through the origin O, perpendicular to:

(i) $\begin{pmatrix} 0 \\ 1 \\ 0 \end{pmatrix}$, (ii) $\begin{pmatrix} 2 \\ 3 \\ 4 \end{pmatrix}$, (iii) $\begin{pmatrix} 4 \\ -2 \\ 6 \end{pmatrix}$, (iv) $\mathbf{i} - \mathbf{j}$, (v) $5\mathbf{i} + 3\mathbf{j} - 2\mathbf{k}$.

2   Find a normal vector to the plane with equation:
(i) $x + 2y = 0$, (ii) $x + y + z = 0$, (iii) $3x - 4y + 2z = 0$.

3   Find the equation of the plane through the origin O such that the two points, $A\,(2, 0, 4)$ and $B\,(0, 4, -2)$, are reflections of each other in the plane.

4   Find normal vectors for the two planes through O with equations $2x + y - 3z = 0$ and $3y - 2x + z = 0$. Find the equations of the lines through O perpendicular to these planes. Find also the angle between these lines.

12.8 The vector equation of a general plane

For a given direction vector $\mathbf{n}$, there is a whole family of parallel planes for which $\mathbf{n}$ is a normal vector. One member of the family will pass through O (cf. §12.7), and the others are all parallel to this plane. Let the plane Π be the one member of the family which passes through a given point A. The position vector of A is $\overrightarrow{OA}\,(= \mathbf{a})$. Then Π is the plane through A, perpendicular to $\mathbf{n}$, as is shown in Fig. 12.16.

Let ON be the perpendicular from O on to Π. Two cases are shown in Fig. 12.16(a) and (b), differing in the side of Π on which O lies. In (a), $\overrightarrow{ON}$ is in the same direction as $\mathbf{n}$ and in (b) $\overrightarrow{ON}$ is in the opposite direction to $\mathbf{n}$.

Vector equation of Π

Let P be any point in Π with position vector $\mathbf{r}(= \overrightarrow{OP})$. Then $\overrightarrow{AP}$ is perpendicular to $\mathbf{n}$, so

$$0 = \overrightarrow{AP} \cdot \mathbf{n} = (\overrightarrow{OP} - \overrightarrow{OA}) \cdot \mathbf{n} = (\mathbf{r} - \mathbf{a}) \cdot \mathbf{n}.$$

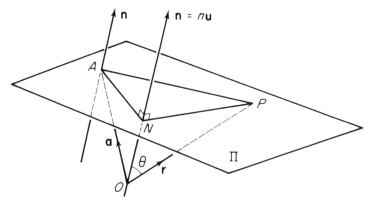

(a) $\overrightarrow{ON}.\mathbf{u} = p > 0$

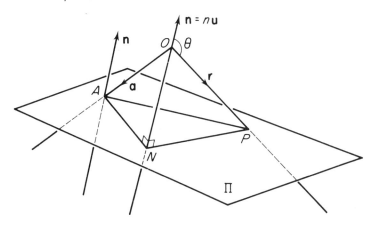

(b) $\overrightarrow{ON}.\mathbf{u} = p < 0$

Fig. 12.16

Conversely, if P is any point whose position vector $\mathbf{r}$ satisfies the equation $(\mathbf{r} - \mathbf{a}).\mathbf{n} = 0$, then

$$0 = (\mathbf{r} - \mathbf{a}).\mathbf{n} = \overrightarrow{AP}.\mathbf{n}$$

and so $\overrightarrow{AP}$ is perpendicular to $\mathbf{n}$ and P lies in Π. Hence the vector equation of Π is

$$(\mathbf{r} - \mathbf{a}).\mathbf{n} = 0.$$

Using the distributative rule for scalar products $(\mathbf{r} - \mathbf{a}).\mathbf{n} = \mathbf{r}.\mathbf{n} - \mathbf{a}.\mathbf{n}$, and, if we put $\mathbf{a}.\mathbf{n} = d$ then the equation of the plane Π is

$$\mathbf{r}.\mathbf{n} = \mathbf{a}.\mathbf{n} = d.$$

Note that in the particular case when $\mathbf{a} = \mathbf{0} = \begin{pmatrix} 0 \\ 0 \\ 0 \end{pmatrix}$, $d = 0$ and the equation of a plane through the origin is $\mathbf{r}.\mathbf{n} = 0$, as in §12.7.

Cartesian equation of Π

If $\mathbf{r} = \begin{pmatrix} x \\ y \\ z \end{pmatrix}$ and $\mathbf{n} = \begin{pmatrix} a \\ b \\ c \end{pmatrix}$, the equation becomes

$$ax + by + cz = d,$$

the Cartesian equation of Π.

To find a meaning for the scalar d, let $\mathbf{u}$ be the unit vector in the direction $\mathbf{n}$. Then $\mathbf{n} = n\mathbf{u}$, where $n = |\mathbf{n}| = \sqrt{(a^2 + b^2 + c^2)}$. Let the angle between $\mathbf{u}$ and $\mathbf{r}$ be θ, which is acute in case (a) and obtuse in case (b) in Fig. 12.16. Then

$$d = \mathbf{r} \cdot \mathbf{n} = \mathbf{r} \cdot (n\mathbf{u}) = n(\mathbf{r} \cdot \mathbf{u}) = nOP \cos \theta = np,$$

where $p = OP \cos \theta$, so that $\overrightarrow{ON} = p\mathbf{u}$.

Now $|p|$ is the length of the perpendicular ON from O on to Π, that is, the perpendicular distance from the origin O to Π.

The sign of p indicates on which side of Π the origin O lies.

Case (a): $p > 0$ and O lies on the opposite side of Π from $\mathbf{n}$.
Case (b): $p < 0$ and O lies on the same side of Π as $\mathbf{n}$.
If $p = 0$, then $N = O$ and P lies in the plane Π.

In conclusion,

$$p = \frac{d}{n} = \frac{d}{\sqrt{(a^2 + b^2 + c^2)}} = \mathbf{r} \cdot \frac{\mathbf{n}}{|\mathbf{n}|} = \mathbf{r} \cdot \mathbf{u},$$

so, in terms of the unit normal $\mathbf{u}$ and the distance p from O to the plane Π, measured positively in the direction $\mathbf{u}$, the equation of the plane is

$$\mathbf{r} \cdot \mathbf{u} = p.$$

General linear equation in three dimensions

Suppose that, instead of being given the plane Π, we wish to find the locus of a point $P(x, y, z)$ given by the equation

$$ax + by + cz = d. \tag{12.8}$$

Let $\mathbf{r} = \overrightarrow{OP} = \begin{pmatrix} x \\ y \\ z \end{pmatrix}$ and $\mathbf{n} = \begin{pmatrix} a \\ b \\ c \end{pmatrix} = n\mathbf{u}$, where $n = |\mathbf{n}| = \sqrt{(a^2 + b^2 + c^2)}$,

so that $\mathbf{u} \left(= \dfrac{1}{|\mathbf{n}|} \mathbf{n} \right)$ is the unit vector in the direction $\mathbf{n}$. Then equation 12.8 can be written

$$d = \mathbf{r} \cdot \mathbf{n} = \mathbf{r} \cdot (n\mathbf{u}) = n(\mathbf{r} \cdot \mathbf{u})$$

or

$$\mathbf{r} \cdot \mathbf{u} = p, \text{ where } p = \frac{d}{n}.$$

Let N be the point with position vector $p\mathbf{u}$, as is shown in Fig. 12.17, in case (a) with $p > 0$ and in case (b) with $p < 0$.

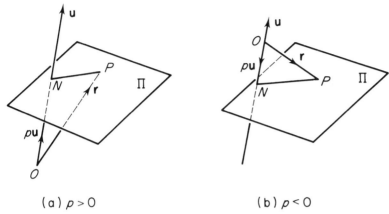

(a) $p > 0$ (b) $p < 0$

Fig. 12.17

Then   **r** satisfies equation $12.8 \Leftrightarrow \mathbf{r} \cdot \mathbf{u} = p = p\mathbf{u} \cdot \mathbf{u}$

$$\Leftrightarrow (\mathbf{r} - p\mathbf{u}) \cdot \mathbf{u} = 0$$

$$\Leftrightarrow (\overrightarrow{OP} - \overrightarrow{ON}) \cdot \mathbf{u} = \overrightarrow{NP} \cdot \mathbf{u} = 0$$

$$\Leftrightarrow \overrightarrow{NP} \text{ is perpendicular to } \mathbf{u}$$

$$\Leftrightarrow P \text{ lies in } \Pi,$$

where Π is the plane through N, perpendicular to **n**. Hence Π is the locus given by equation 12.8.

Summary $\mathbf{r} \cdot \mathbf{n} = ax + by + cz = d$ is the equation of the plane Π, perpendicular to **u**, the unit vector in the direction $\begin{pmatrix} a \\ b \\ c \end{pmatrix} (= \mathbf{n})$. The perpendicular $\overrightarrow{ON}$ from the origin O to Π is given by $\overrightarrow{ON} = p\mathbf{u}$, and Π is also given by the equation $\mathbf{r} \cdot \mathbf{u} = p$.

EXAMPLE 1   *Find a Cartesian equation for the plane Π, through A, $(5, -2, 4)$. with normal vector* $\begin{pmatrix} -1 \\ 2 \\ 3 \end{pmatrix}$.

The point P, (x, y, z), lies in $\Pi \Leftrightarrow \overrightarrow{AP}$ is perpendicular to $\begin{pmatrix} -1 \\ 2 \\ 3 \end{pmatrix}$

$$\Leftrightarrow \begin{pmatrix} x - 5 \\ y + 2 \\ z - 4 \end{pmatrix} \cdot \begin{pmatrix} -1 \\ 2 \\ 3 \end{pmatrix} = 0$$

$$\Leftrightarrow \begin{pmatrix} x \\ y \\ z \end{pmatrix} \cdot \begin{pmatrix} -1 \\ 2 \\ 3 \end{pmatrix} = \begin{pmatrix} 5 \\ -2 \\ 4 \end{pmatrix} \cdot \begin{pmatrix} -1 \\ 2 \\ 3 \end{pmatrix} = 3.$$

So the equation of Π is $-x + 2y + 3z = 3$.

EXAMPLE 2   *Find the coordinates of the point, P, of intersection of the line*

$$\mathbf{r} = \begin{pmatrix} 2 \\ 1 \\ 3 \end{pmatrix} + t \begin{pmatrix} -1 \\ 2 \\ 1 \end{pmatrix}, \text{ and the plane } \mathbf{r}.\begin{pmatrix} 1 \\ -1 \\ 1 \end{pmatrix} = -6.$$

Let P be the point on the line corresponding to $t = p$. Then

$$\overrightarrow{OP} = \begin{pmatrix} x \\ y \\ z \end{pmatrix} = \mathbf{r} = \begin{pmatrix} 2 - p \\ 1 + 2p \\ 3 + p \end{pmatrix},$$

and this vector satisfies the equation of the plane, if P is the point of intersection. Hence

$$-6 = \begin{pmatrix} 2 - p \\ 1 + 2p \\ 3 + p \end{pmatrix}.\begin{pmatrix} 1 \\ -1 \\ 1 \end{pmatrix} = 2 - p - (1 + 2p) + 3 + p = 4 - 2p,$$

so $p = 5$ and the coordinates of P are $(-3, 11, 8)$.

EXAMPLE 3   *Find the coordinates of N, the foot of the perpendicular from the*

origin O on to the plane $\mathbf{r}.\begin{pmatrix} 1 \\ -5 \\ 3 \end{pmatrix} = 5.$ *Deduce the coordinates of the reflection Q of*

O in this plane.

The normal to the plane is $\begin{pmatrix} 1 \\ -5 \\ 3 \end{pmatrix}$ $(= \mathbf{n})$ and so the equation of ON is $\mathbf{r} = t\mathbf{n}$. This

line meets the plane at N where $(t\mathbf{n}).\mathbf{n} = 5$, that is,

$$t = \frac{5}{\mathbf{n}.\mathbf{n}} = \frac{5}{1 + 25 + 9} = \frac{1}{7}.$$

Thus N is the point $(\frac{1}{7}, -\frac{5}{7}, \frac{3}{7})$.

Since $\overrightarrow{ON} = t\mathbf{n}$ and Q is the reflection of O in the plane, $\overrightarrow{OQ} = 2\overrightarrow{ON} = 2t\mathbf{n}$ and Q is the point $(\frac{2}{7}, -\frac{10}{7}, \frac{6}{7})$ (see Fig. 12.18).

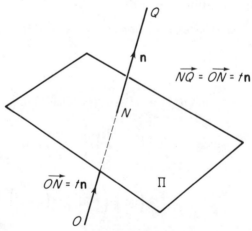

Fig. 12.18

EXERCISE 12.8

1 Find a Cartesian equation of the plane:

(i) through $(1, 2, 3)$ with normal vector $\begin{pmatrix} 1 \\ 0 \\ 1 \end{pmatrix}$,

(ii) through $(3, -4, 0)$ with normal vector $\begin{pmatrix} 2 \\ -1 \\ 3 \end{pmatrix}$,

(iii) through $(-5, 2, 1)$ with normal vector $3\mathbf{i} - 2\mathbf{j} + \mathbf{k}$.

2 Find a vector equation of the plane in the form $\mathbf{r} \cdot \mathbf{u} = p$, where $|\mathbf{u}| = 1$, given that the Cartesian equation of the plane is:
(i) $2x + y + 2z = 6$, (ii) $3x + 2y = 4$, (iii) $x - y + z = 1$,
(iv) $y - 4x + 5z + 7 = 0$.

3 Prove that the line $\mathbf{r} = \begin{pmatrix} 3 \\ 2 \\ -1 \end{pmatrix} + t \begin{pmatrix} 1 \\ 2 \\ -3 \end{pmatrix}$ is parallel to the plane
$x + y - z = 2$.

4 Find a vector equation of the plane described and its Cartesian equation:
(i) through the point $(2, 1, 0)$ parallel to the plane $x = y$,
(ii) through the point $(-1, 3, 1)$ parallel to the plane $2x - y + 3z = 6$,
(iii) through the point $(1, -2, 3)$ perpendicular to the vector $\mathbf{i} - \mathbf{j} + 2\mathbf{k}$,

(iv) through the point $(2, 1, 0)$ and perpendicular to the line

$\mathbf{r} = \begin{pmatrix} 1 \\ 3 \\ 2 \end{pmatrix} + t \begin{pmatrix} 4 \\ 2 \\ 3 \end{pmatrix}$,

(v) through the point $(3, -2, 1)$ and parallel to both the vectors $2\mathbf{i} + \mathbf{j} - 3\mathbf{k}$ and $3\mathbf{i} - \mathbf{j}$,

(vi) through the point $(1, 2, 1)$ and parallel to both the lines

$\mathbf{r} = \begin{pmatrix} 1 \\ 2 \\ 3 \end{pmatrix} + t \begin{pmatrix} 1 \\ -1 \\ -1 \end{pmatrix}$ and $\mathbf{r} = \begin{pmatrix} 4 \\ 3 \\ 2 \end{pmatrix} + t \begin{pmatrix} 0 \\ -1 \\ 1 \end{pmatrix}$,

(vii) through the line $\mathbf{r} = \begin{pmatrix} 0 \\ 1 \\ 4 \end{pmatrix} + t \begin{pmatrix} -1 \\ 2 \\ 1 \end{pmatrix}$ and parallel to the line

$\mathbf{r} = \begin{pmatrix} 2 \\ 1 \\ 4 \end{pmatrix} + t \begin{pmatrix} 1 \\ -2 \\ 1 \end{pmatrix}$.

5 Find the coordinates of the point of intersection of:

(i) the line $\mathbf{r} = \begin{pmatrix} 2 \\ 0 \\ 1 \end{pmatrix} + t \begin{pmatrix} 1 \\ 1 \\ 0 \end{pmatrix}$ and the plane $\mathbf{r} \cdot \begin{pmatrix} 1 \\ -1 \\ -1 \end{pmatrix} = 1$,

(ii) the line $\mathbf{r} = (1 + t)\mathbf{i} + (2 - t)\mathbf{j} + t\mathbf{k}$ and the plane $\mathbf{r} \cdot (\mathbf{i} - 3\mathbf{k}) = 5$.

6 Find the perpendicular distance from the origin to the plane:
(i) $x + 2y + 2z = 5$,   (ii) $3x + 4 = 2y - 6z$,   (iii) $\mathbf{r}.(3\mathbf{i} - 4\mathbf{j}) = 7$.

12.9 Parametric equation of a plane

Let $\mathbf{p}$ and $\mathbf{q}$ be non-parallel vectors, and let A be the point with position vector $\mathbf{a} = \overrightarrow{OA}$. Then there is one plane, Π, through A and parallel to both $\mathbf{p}$ and $\mathbf{q}$, Fig. 12.19.

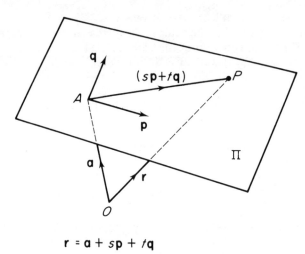

$$\mathbf{r} = \mathbf{a} + s\mathbf{p} + t\mathbf{q}$$

Fig. 12.19 Parametric equation of a plane.

A general point P in Π is given by $\overrightarrow{AP} = s\mathbf{p} + t\mathbf{q}$. The values of s and t are found by drawing a parallelogram with sides parallel to $\mathbf{p}$ and $\mathbf{q}$ and diagonal $\overrightarrow{AP}$ (theorem 5.5). Then

$$P \text{ lies in } \Pi \Leftrightarrow \mathbf{r} = \overrightarrow{OP} = \overrightarrow{OA} + \overrightarrow{AP} = \mathbf{a} + s\mathbf{p} + t\mathbf{q}$$

and so the equation of Π, in terms of two parameters s and t, is

$$\mathbf{r} = \mathbf{a} + s\mathbf{p} + t\mathbf{q}.$$

EXAMPLE 1   *Find a parametric equation of the plane $2x + 3y - z = 4$.*

In this case, we can use x and y as the parameters. Let $x = s$, $y = t$, then $2s + 3t - z = 4$ and so $z = 2s + 3t - 4$, and the equation of the plane is

$$\mathbf{r} = \begin{pmatrix} x \\ y \\ z \end{pmatrix} = \begin{pmatrix} s \\ t \\ 2s + 3t - 4 \end{pmatrix} = s \begin{pmatrix} 1 \\ 0 \\ 2 \end{pmatrix} + t \begin{pmatrix} 0 \\ 1 \\ 3 \end{pmatrix} + \begin{pmatrix} 0 \\ 0 \\ -4 \end{pmatrix}.$$

EXAMPLE 2   *Find a Cartesian equation of the plane, given by the parametric equation* $\mathbf{r} = \begin{pmatrix} 2 \\ 1 \\ 3 \end{pmatrix} + s \begin{pmatrix} 4 \\ -1 \\ 2 \end{pmatrix} + t \begin{pmatrix} 1 \\ -1 \\ 3 \end{pmatrix}.$

The vector equation is equivalent to three scalar equations,

$$x = 2 + 4s + t, \quad y = 1 - s - t \quad \text{and} \quad z = 3 + 2s + 3t.$$

We eliminate s and t from these equations. Add the first two equations to give

$$x + y = 3 + 3s, \quad \text{so} \quad s = \tfrac{1}{3}(x + y - 3).$$

Add four times the second equation to the first to give

$$x + 4y = 6 - 3t, \quad \text{so} \quad t = \tfrac{1}{3}(-x - 4y + 6).$$

Substitute these expressions for s and t into the third equation,

$$z = 3 + \tfrac{2}{3}(x + y - 3) + (-x - 4y + 6) = -\tfrac{1}{3}x - \tfrac{10}{3}y + 7,$$

giving as a Cartesian equation for the plane,

$$x + 10y + 3z = 21.$$

EXERCISE 12.9

1 Find a Cartesian equation and a vector equation for the plane given by the parametric equation:

(i) $\mathbf{r} = \begin{pmatrix} 4 \\ -1 \\ 2 \end{pmatrix} + s \begin{pmatrix} 1 \\ 2 \\ -3 \end{pmatrix} + t \begin{pmatrix} -1 \\ 2 \\ -1 \end{pmatrix}$,

(ii) $\mathbf{r} = \mathbf{i} - 2\mathbf{j} + s(2\mathbf{i} + \mathbf{j} - 3\mathbf{k}) + t(4\mathbf{j} - \mathbf{i} - \mathbf{k})$,

(iii) $\mathbf{r} = (2s + 3)\mathbf{i} + s\mathbf{j} + (t - s)\mathbf{k}$.

2 Find a parametric equation for the plane:

(i) $x = 0$, (ii) $x = z$, (iii) $2x - y + z = 3$, (iv) $y + 4 = 3z$,

(v) $2z = x + 2y + 3$.

3 Show that the vector $\begin{pmatrix} 2 \\ 6 \\ 5 \end{pmatrix}$ is normal to the plane

$\mathbf{r} = \begin{pmatrix} 1 \\ 1 \\ 0 \end{pmatrix} + s \begin{pmatrix} 2 \\ 1 \\ -2 \end{pmatrix} + t \begin{pmatrix} 1 \\ -2 \\ 2 \end{pmatrix}$. Hence, write down an equation of the plane

in the form $\mathbf{r} \cdot \mathbf{n} = p$ and deduce a Cartesian equation for the plane. Verify that, for all values of s and t, the coordinates given by the parametric equation of the plane satisfy the Cartesian equation.

4 A plane passes through a fixed point with position vector $\mathbf{k}$ relative to a given origin, and contains lines in the directions of two given non-parallel vectors $\mathbf{a}$ and $\mathbf{b}$. Write down an expression for the position vector, $\mathbf{r}$, of any point of the plane in terms of $\mathbf{k}$, $\mathbf{a}$, $\mathbf{b}$ and two scalar parameters s and t.

If $\mathbf{c}$ is a fixed vector at right angles to both $\mathbf{a}$ and $\mathbf{b}$, prove that the product $\mathbf{r} \cdot \mathbf{c}$ has a constant value at all points of the plane. *(SMP)*

12.10 Angles between lines and planes

Definition The angle between a line and a plane is the angle between the line and the projection of the line on to the plane.

Let $\overrightarrow{AB}$ be a line in the direction of a vector $\mathbf{u}$. Suppose that AB intersects a plane Π at A. Let $\mathbf{n}$ be a normal vector of Π. If $\overrightarrow{AB}$ is not perpendicular to Π, then $\mathbf{n}$ and $\mathbf{u}$ define a plane ABC, which intersects Π in the line AC. AC is the projection of AB on to Π, (Fig. 12.20).

Fig. 12.20

Then the angle θ between AB and Π is the angle BAC. Therefore, θ is the complement of the angle between $\mathbf{n}$ and $\mathbf{u}$. So

$$\mathbf{n}.\mathbf{u} = |\mathbf{n}||\mathbf{u}|\cos(90° - \theta) = |\mathbf{n}||\mathbf{u}|\sin\theta,$$

and θ can be found from this equation.

EXAMPLE 1   *Find the angle between the line* $\mathbf{r} = \begin{pmatrix} 4 \\ 3 \\ 1 \end{pmatrix} + t\begin{pmatrix} 1 \\ -1 \\ 2 \end{pmatrix}$ *and the*

plane $\mathbf{r}.\begin{pmatrix} 1 \\ 0 \\ 1 \end{pmatrix} = 5.$

The line is in the direction $\mathbf{u} = \begin{pmatrix} 1 \\ -1 \\ 2 \end{pmatrix}$ and the normal vector to the plane is

$\mathbf{n} = \begin{pmatrix} 1 \\ 0 \\ 1 \end{pmatrix}$. Hence, the angle θ between the line and the plane is given by

$$\sin\theta = \frac{|\mathbf{n}.\mathbf{u}|}{|\mathbf{n}||\mathbf{u}|} = \frac{1+0+2}{\sqrt{2}\sqrt{6}} = \frac{\sqrt{3}}{2}, \text{ so } \theta = 60°.$$

The angle between two planes

If the planes are parallel, the angle between them is zero. If they are not parallel, the two planes, say Π_1 and Π_2 will meet in a line L. The angle between Π_1 and Π_2 is then defined as the angle between two lines, one in each plane, each perpendicular to L.

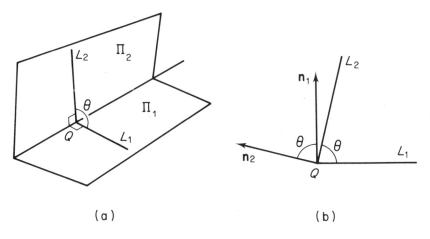

Fig. 12.21

Suppose that two such lines are L_1 and L_2 meeting at a point Q on L, (see Fig. 12.21(a)). Then L_1 and L_2 define a plane Π which is perpendicular to both Π_1 and Π_2. In Fig. 12.21(b) we show the cross-section of the three-dimensional figure of (a), in the plane Π. The line L is shown now as a single point Q and the planes Π_1 and Π_2 are shown by the lines L_1 and L_2. The normals $\mathbf{n}_1$ and $\mathbf{n}_2$ to Π_1 and Π_2, are perpendicular to L_1 and L_2 respectively. Therefore, the required angle θ between the planes Π_1 and Π_2, which is the angle between L_1 and L_2, is also the angle between $\mathbf{n}_1$ and $\mathbf{n}_2$. Therefore, θ may be found from the equation

$$|\mathbf{n}_1 . \mathbf{n}_2| = |\mathbf{n}_1||\mathbf{n}_2| \cos \theta.$$

EXAMPLE 2   *Find the angle between the two planes* $\mathbf{r}.\begin{pmatrix} -2 \\ 3 \\ 1 \end{pmatrix} = 5$ and

$\mathbf{r}.\begin{pmatrix} 4 \\ 2 \\ -1 \end{pmatrix} = 3.$

In this case $\mathbf{n}_1 . \mathbf{n}_2 = -8 + 6 - 1 = -3$, $|\mathbf{n}_1| = \sqrt{(14)}$, $|\mathbf{n}_2| = \sqrt{(21)}$, so $\cos \theta = \dfrac{3}{7\sqrt{6}}$, which gives $\theta \approx 79 \cdot 9°$.

12.11 Distance of a point from a plane

The shortest distance from a point $P(x_0, y_0, z_0)$ to a plane Π, $\mathbf{r}.\begin{pmatrix} a \\ b \\ c \end{pmatrix} = d$,

is the length of the perpendicular PN from P on to the plane. Let $Q, (x, y, z)$

be any point on Π so that $\begin{pmatrix} x \\ y \\ z \end{pmatrix} . \begin{pmatrix} a \\ b \\ c \end{pmatrix} = d$. The required length PN is

the magnitude of the resolved part of $\overrightarrow{PQ}$ in the direction $\mathbf{n}$. If p is this

resolved part, $p|\mathbf{n}| = \overrightarrow{PQ} . \mathbf{n} = \begin{pmatrix} x - x_0 \\ y - y_0 \\ z - z_0 \end{pmatrix} . \begin{pmatrix} a \\ b \\ c \end{pmatrix}$. Thus

$$p|\mathbf{n}| = \begin{pmatrix} x \\ y \\ z \end{pmatrix} . \begin{pmatrix} a \\ b \\ c \end{pmatrix} - \begin{pmatrix} x_0 \\ y_0 \\ z_0 \end{pmatrix} . \begin{pmatrix} a \\ b \\ c \end{pmatrix} = d - (ax_0 + by_0 + cz_0),$$

on using the equation satisfied by the position vector of Q.

Thus
$$p = \frac{d - (ax_0 + by_0 + cz_0)}{\sqrt{(a^2 + b^2 + c^2)}}.$$

If $p > 0$, then P is on the opposite side of the plane Π from the direction of its normal vector $\mathbf{n}$, as shown in Fig. 12.22. If $p < 0$, then P is on the same side of Π as $\mathbf{n}$. The required perpendicular distance PN is $|p|$.

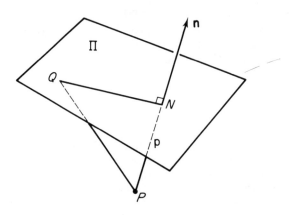

Fig. 12.22

EXAMPLE 1   *Find the perpendicular distance from the point $(-2, 1, -5)$ to the*

plane $\mathbf{r} . \begin{pmatrix} 2 \\ 6 \\ -3 \end{pmatrix} = 4$.

Using the notation of the theory above, $\mathbf{n} = \begin{pmatrix} 2 \\ 6 \\ -3 \end{pmatrix}$, and so $|\mathbf{n}| = 7$. Then

$7p = 4 - (-4 + 6 + 15) = -13$, so P is on the same side of the plane as the vector $\mathbf{n}$, and the perpendicular distance is $\frac{13}{7}$.

EXERCISE 12.11

1 Find, in surd form, the perpendicular distance of the point A from the plane Π, and state whether or not the point A is on the same side of Π as is the origin:

(i) A is the point $(1, 2, -3)$ and Π is the plane $\mathbf{r} \cdot \begin{pmatrix} 3 \\ -1 \\ 4 \end{pmatrix} = -5$,

(ii) A is the point $(5, -3, 2)$ and Π is the plane $\mathbf{r} \cdot \begin{pmatrix} 2 \\ 3 \\ 4 \end{pmatrix} = 7$.

2 The point B has coordinates $(-2, 3, -5)$. In each of the two cases in question **1** above, find (a) a vector equation, (b) Cartesian equations, of the line AB, and find also the angle between AB and the given plane Π.

3 For each of the following, find the angle between the two planes with the given equations and find also a vector equation of their common line:

(i) $\mathbf{r} \cdot \begin{pmatrix} -2 \\ 3 \\ 0 \end{pmatrix} = 4$ and $\mathbf{r} \cdot \begin{pmatrix} 3 \\ -2 \\ 1 \end{pmatrix} = 2$,

(ii) $\mathbf{r} \cdot \begin{pmatrix} -4 \\ 1 \\ 5 \end{pmatrix} = 5$ and $\mathbf{r} \cdot \begin{pmatrix} 3 \\ 5 \\ -2 \end{pmatrix} = 2$.

4 Show that
$$\mathbf{r} = \mathbf{a} + s(\mathbf{b} - \mathbf{a}) + t(\mathbf{c} - \mathbf{a})$$
is an equation of the plane which passes through the noncollinear points whose position vectors are $\mathbf{a}, \mathbf{b}, \mathbf{c}$, where $\mathbf{r}$ is the position vector of a general point on the plane and s and t are scalars. Find a Cartesian equation of the plane containing the points $(1, 1, -1)$, $(2, 0, 1)$ and $(3, 2, 1)$, and show that the points $(2, 1, 2)$ and $(0, -2, -2)$ are equidistant from, and on opposite sides of, this plane. *(L)*

5 Obtain equations of the straight line through the origin parallel to the straight line through the points $P(3, 2, 3)$ and $Q(-1, -2, 1)$. Find an equation of the plane which passes through both these two lines.

The line of intersection of a plane through P and a plane through Q is the y-axis. Find the angle between these two planes. *(L)*

6 The point O is the origin and points A, B, C, D have position vectors
$$\begin{pmatrix} 4 \\ 3 \\ 4 \end{pmatrix}, \begin{pmatrix} 6 \\ 1 \\ 2 \end{pmatrix}, \begin{pmatrix} 0 \\ 9 \\ -6 \end{pmatrix}, \begin{pmatrix} -1 \\ 1 \\ 1 \end{pmatrix},$$
respectively.
Prove that
(i) the triangle OAB is isosceles,
(ii) D lies in the plane OAB,
(iii) CD is perpendicular to the plane OAB,
(iv) AC is inclined at an angle of $60°$ to the plane OAB. *(C)*

MISCELLANEOUS EXERCISE 12

1   Find the angle between the vectors **a** and **b** given that $|\mathbf{a}| = 3$, $|\mathbf{b}| = 5$, $|\mathbf{a} - \mathbf{b}| = 7$. (L)

2   State a relation which exists between the vectors **p** and **q** when these vectors are (a) parallel, (b) perpendicular.
    The position vectors of the vertices of a tetrahedron $ABCD$ are
    $A: -5\mathbf{i} + 22\mathbf{j} + 5\mathbf{k}$, $B: \mathbf{i} + 2\mathbf{j} + 3\mathbf{k}$, $C: 4\mathbf{i} + 3\mathbf{j} + 2\mathbf{k}$, $D: -\mathbf{i} + 2\mathbf{j} - 3\mathbf{k}$.
    Find the angle CBD and show that AB is perpendicular to both BC and BD. Calculate the volume of the tetrahedron. If $ABDE$ is a parallelogram, find the position vector of E. (L)

3   Prove that if two pairs of opposite edges of a tetrahedron are perpendicular then the third pair of edges are also perpendicular.

4   $OABC$ is a tetrahedron such that $\overrightarrow{OA} = \mathbf{a}$, $\overrightarrow{OB} = \mathbf{b}$ and $\overrightarrow{OC} = \mathbf{c}$ where **a**, **b** and **c** are unit vectors. If angle $BOA = \cos^{-1}(2/5)$, angle $COB = \cos^{-1}(9/10)$ and OA is perpendicular to OC, find p and q such that the vector $\mathbf{r} = \mathbf{a} + p\mathbf{b} + q\mathbf{c}$ is perpendicular to the plane ABC. (JMB)

5   The position vectors of two points A and B relative to an origin O are **a** and **b**. You are given that **a** and **b** have unit length, and that the angle between these vectors is $60°$. Write down the values of the products $\mathbf{a} \cdot \mathbf{a}$, $\mathbf{b} \cdot \mathbf{b}$ and $\mathbf{a} \cdot \mathbf{b}$.
    The point C on the line-segment AB is such that $AC = 2CB$. If **c** is the position vector of C, express **c** in terms of **a** and **b**. Hence calculate
    (i) the length of **c**, (ii) the cosine of the angle between **a** and **c**. (SMP)

6   The position vectors of the points A, B, C relative to the origin O are **a**, **b**, **c** respectively. The point P is on BC such that $BP : PC = 2 : 3$; the point Q is on CA such that $CQ : QA = 1 : 4$. Find the position vector of the common point R of AP and BQ. (JMB)

7   The position vectors of points A, B, C relative to a fixed origin O are **a**, **b**, **c** respectively. If D is the mid-point of AB, and if E is the point which divides CB internally in the ratio $1 : 2$, write down the position vectors of D and E in terms of **a**, **b**, **c**.
    Show that the mid-point F of CD is on AE and find the ratio $AF : FE$. (JMB)

8   A tetrahedron $OABC$ with vertex O at the origin is such that $\overrightarrow{OA} = \mathbf{a}$, $\overrightarrow{OB} = \mathbf{b}$ and $\overrightarrow{OC} = \mathbf{c}$. Show that the line segments joining the mid-points of opposite edges bisect one another. Given that two pairs of opposite edges are perpendicular prove that $\mathbf{a} \cdot \mathbf{b} = \mathbf{b} \cdot \mathbf{c} = \mathbf{c} \cdot \mathbf{a}$ and show that the third pair of opposite edges is also perpendicular.
    Prove also that, in this case, $OA^2 + BC^2 = OB^2 + AC^2$. (L)

9   A plane passes through A, $(2, 2, 1)$, and is perpendicular to the line joining the origin to A. Write down a vector equation of the plane in the form $\mathbf{r} \cdot \mathbf{n} = p$, where **n** is a unit vector. (L)

10 Find the position vector of the point of intersection of the line

$$\mathbf{r} = \begin{pmatrix} 3 \\ 2 \\ 3 \end{pmatrix} + t \begin{pmatrix} 3 \\ 1 \\ 2 \end{pmatrix} \text{ and the plane } \mathbf{r} \cdot \begin{pmatrix} 4 \\ -3 \\ -2 \end{pmatrix} = 10.$$

11 The position vectors of A and C with respect to the origin O are $(4\mathbf{i} + 3\mathbf{j})$ and $(-3\mathbf{i} + 4\mathbf{j})$ respectively. Show that $|\overrightarrow{OA}| = |\overrightarrow{OC}|$ and that OA is perpendicular to OC.

Find the vector $\overrightarrow{OB}$ given that $OABC$ is a square. The mid-point of OB is M and the mid-point of CM is L. Show that the position vector of L with respect to the origin is $-(5/4)(i-3j)$. (L)

12 (i) In a triangle ABC the altitudes through A and B meet in a point O. Let **a**, **b**, **c** be the position vectors of A, B, C relative to O as origin. Show that $\mathbf{a.b} = \mathbf{a.c}$ and $\mathbf{b.a} = \mathbf{b.c}$. Deduce that the altitudes of a triangle are concurrent.

(ii) Find the point of intersection of the line through the points $(2, 0, 1)$ and $(-1, 3, 4)$ and the line through the points $(-1, 3, 0)$ and $(4, -2, 5)$. Calculate the acute angle between the two lines. (L)

13 The vectors **a** and **b** are $(2\mathbf{i}-\mathbf{j}+3\mathbf{k})$ and $(3\mathbf{i}+2\mathbf{j}-2\mathbf{k})$ respectively. The vector **a** is resolved into two components, one in the direction of **b** and the other perpendicular to **b**. Find these components. (L)

14 Given that the points A and B have position vectors $(2\mathbf{i}+4\mathbf{j}+7\mathbf{k})$ and $(-4\mathbf{i}+\mathbf{j}+\mathbf{k})$ respectively, find the position vector of the point P on AB which is such that $\overrightarrow{AP} = 2\overrightarrow{PB}$. (L)

15 Given that $\mathbf{a} = -\mathbf{i}+\mathbf{j}+2\mathbf{k}$ and $\mathbf{b} = \mathbf{j}+\mathbf{k}$, find $|\mathbf{a}|$, $|\mathbf{b}|$ and the acute angle between **a** and **b**. (JMB)

16 Given the vectors $\mathbf{u} = 3\mathbf{i}+2\mathbf{j}$ and $\mathbf{v} = 2\mathbf{i}+\lambda\mathbf{j}$, determine the values of λ so that

(a) **u** and **v** are at right angles,

(b) **u** and **v** are parallel,

(c) the acute angle between **u** and **v** is $\pi/4$. (L)

17 The angle between the vectors $(\mathbf{i}+\mathbf{j})$ and $(\mathbf{i}+\mathbf{j}+p\mathbf{k})$ is $\pi/4$. Find the possible values of p. (L)

18 Given that A and B are the points whose position vectors referred to the origin O are $(\mathbf{i}+2\mathbf{j}+\mathbf{k})$ and $(5\mathbf{i}-2\mathbf{j}+3\mathbf{k})$ respectively, determine $|\overrightarrow{AB}|$ and direction cosines for the line AB.

19 Find the resolved part of the vector $3\mathbf{i}-\mathbf{j}+3\mathbf{k}$ in the direction of the vector $6\mathbf{i}+3\mathbf{j}+2\mathbf{k}$.

20 The line l passes through the points $A(-1, -3, -3)$ and $B(5, 0, 6)$. Write down, in terms of a single parameter, the position vector of a general point P on l relative to the origin O.

Find the position of P for which OP is perpendicular to l. Hence find the minimum distance from the origin to the line l. (SMP)

21 Find the vector equation of the line through the origin and parallel to the line

of intersection of the planes $\mathbf{r} \cdot \begin{pmatrix} 2 \\ 1 \\ 3 \end{pmatrix} = 6$ and $\mathbf{r} \cdot \begin{pmatrix} 1 \\ -1 \\ 2 \end{pmatrix} = -2$.

22 Find the coordinates of the point of intersection of:

(i) the line $\mathbf{r} = \mathbf{i}-\mathbf{j}+2\mathbf{k}+t(3\mathbf{j}+4\mathbf{k})$ and the plane $\mathbf{r} \cdot (\mathbf{i}+\mathbf{j}-\mathbf{k}) = 6$,

(ii) the line $\mathbf{r} = \begin{pmatrix} 1 \\ 2 \\ 3 \end{pmatrix} + t \begin{pmatrix} 4 \\ 2 \\ -1 \end{pmatrix}$ and the plane $\mathbf{r} \cdot \begin{pmatrix} -2 \\ 0 \\ 1 \end{pmatrix} = 4$.

23 The point $P(14+2\lambda, 5+2\lambda, 2-\lambda)$ lies on a fixed straight line for all values of λ. Find Cartesian equations for this line and find the cosine of the acute angle between this line and the line $x = z = 0$.

Show that the line $2x = -y = -z$ is perpendicular to the locus of P.

Hence, or otherwise, find the equation of the plane containing the origin and all possible positions of *P*.　　　　　　　　　　　　　　　　　　(L)

24　Find a vector equation for the plane passing through the points *A, B, C* with position vectors $(\mathbf{i} - \mathbf{k})$, $(2\mathbf{i} + \mathbf{j} + 3\mathbf{k})$, $(3\mathbf{i} + 2\mathbf{j} + \mathbf{k})$ respectively. By finding the scalar product $\overrightarrow{AC}.\overrightarrow{BC}$, or otherwise, show that angle *ACB* is a right angle.　　　　　　　　　　　　　　　　　　　　　　　　　(L)

25　Find a unit vector which is perpendicular to the vector $(4\mathbf{i} + 4\mathbf{j} - 7\mathbf{k})$ and to the vector $(2\mathbf{i} + 2\mathbf{j} + \mathbf{k})$.　　　　　　　　　　　　　　　　(L)

26　Points *O, A, B* in space have coordinates $(0,0,0)$, $(-2,1,2)$ and $(-1,0,1)$ respectively. Show that the cosine of angle *AOB* is equal to $\frac{2}{3}\sqrt{2}$.

　　If *C* divides *AB* in the ratio $k:1-k$, find the coordinates of *C* in terms of *k*. Find *k* if *OC* is perpendicular to *AB*.　　　　　　　　　(SMP)

27　Prove that $\dfrac{1}{7}\begin{pmatrix} 2 \\ -3 \\ 6 \end{pmatrix}$ is a unit vector. Hence find the Cartesian equation of

one of the two planes perpendicular to this vector whose distance from the origin is 10 units.　　　　　　　　　　　　　　　　　　　(SMP)

28　The point $A(5, 1, 5)$ has position vector **a** relative to the origin *O* and the point $B(4, 2, 6)$ has position vector **b**. The line *l* is given by $\mathbf{r} = \mathbf{a} + s(5\mathbf{i} - 2\mathbf{j} + 5\mathbf{k})$; the line *m* is given by $\mathbf{r} = \mathbf{b} + t(4\mathbf{i} - \mathbf{j} + 6\mathbf{k})$. Show that the lines *l* and *m* intersect and state the coordinates of the common point. Prove that *AB* is perpendicular to *m* and, hence, write down the coordinates of the reflection of *A* in *m*.

29　A plane passes through the three points *A, B, C* whose position vectors, referred to an origin *O*, are $(\mathbf{i} + 3\mathbf{j} + 3\mathbf{k})$, $(3\mathbf{i} + \mathbf{j} + 4\mathbf{k})$, $(2\mathbf{i} + 4\mathbf{j} + \mathbf{k})$ respectively. Find, in the form $(l\mathbf{i} + m\mathbf{j} + n\mathbf{k})$, a unit vector normal to this plane.

　　Find also the Cartesian equation of the plane, and the perpendicular distance from the origin to this plane.　　　　　　　　　　　　　(L)

30　Of the following equations, which represent lines and which represent planes?

(i)　$\dfrac{x-2}{1} = \dfrac{y-1}{2} = \dfrac{z-3}{-1}$;

(ii)　$x + 2y - z = 1$;

(iii)　$\begin{pmatrix} x \\ y \\ z \end{pmatrix} = \begin{pmatrix} 2 \\ 1 \\ 3 \end{pmatrix} + t\begin{pmatrix} 1 \\ -1 \\ -1 \end{pmatrix}$.

Describe, or show in a clear diagram, how these lines and planes are related to each other.　　　　　　　　　　　　　　　　　　　(SMP)

31　The angles between the non-zero vectors **b** and **c**, **c** and **a**, **a** and **b** are α, β, γ respectively. The vectors **u** and **v** are defined as

$$\mathbf{u} = (\mathbf{a}.\mathbf{c})\mathbf{b} - (\mathbf{a}.\mathbf{b})\mathbf{c}, \quad \mathbf{v} = (\mathbf{a}.\mathbf{c})\mathbf{b} - (\mathbf{b}.\mathbf{c})\mathbf{a}.$$

Given that **u** and **v** are at right angles, show that either $\cos\beta = \cos\alpha \cos\gamma$, or **a** is perpendicular to **c**.　　　　　　　　　　　　　　　(L)

32　The lines *m* and *n* are given by

$$\mathbf{r} = \begin{pmatrix} 3 \\ 4 \\ 1 \end{pmatrix} + s\begin{pmatrix} 2 \\ -1 \\ 1 \end{pmatrix} \quad \text{and} \quad \mathbf{r} = \begin{pmatrix} 1 \\ 5 \\ 7 \end{pmatrix} + t\begin{pmatrix} 1 \\ 0 \\ 1 \end{pmatrix},$$

respectively. Show that the lines m and n are skew and find the acute angle between them.

33 The position vectors of the points A and B are given by

$$\mathbf{a} = 5\mathbf{i} + \mathbf{j} + 2\mathbf{k} \quad \text{and} \quad \mathbf{b} = -\mathbf{i} + 7\mathbf{j} + 8\mathbf{k}$$

respectively. Show that the two lines

$$\mathbf{r} = \mathbf{a} + \lambda\mathbf{l} \quad \text{and} \quad \mathbf{r} = \mathbf{b} + \mu\mathbf{m},$$

where $\mathbf{l} = -4\mathbf{i} + \mathbf{j} - \mathbf{k}$ and $\mathbf{m} = 2\mathbf{i} - 5\mathbf{j} - 7\mathbf{k}$, intersect, and find the position vector of the point of intersection C.

   If D has position vector $3\mathbf{i} + 7\mathbf{j} - 2\mathbf{k}$ show that the line CD is perpendicular to the line AB.   (*JMB*)

34 Find an equation, in both Cartesian and vector form, of the plane containing the point $(1, 1, 1)$ and the line defined by the equations

$$x - 2y + 3z = 1, \quad 2x + y + z = -3.$$

State direction cosines of a vector which is normal to this plane, and write down a unit normal vector to this plane.

   Find the lengths of the perpendiculars from (*a*) the origin, (*b*) the point $(2, 2, 2)$ to the plane.   (*L*)

35 The equations of two lines, l_1 and l_2, are

$$\frac{x-3}{2} = \frac{y}{-2} = \frac{z}{3} \quad \text{and} \quad x = \frac{y-6}{-4} = \frac{z}{-3}$$

respectively. Show that l_1 and l_2 intersect at a point, P, and find the coordinates of P. Find also the equation of the plane, Π, in which both l_1 and l_2 lie.

   Show that the line

$$x + 1 = \frac{y+4}{-2}, \, z = 1,$$

is parallel to the plane Π, and find its distance from Π.   (*JMB*)

36 A pyramid has a square base $OABC$ and vertex V. The position vectors of A, B, C, V referred to O as origin are given by $\overrightarrow{OA} = 2\mathbf{i}$, $\overrightarrow{OB} = 2\mathbf{i} + 2\mathbf{j}$, $\overrightarrow{OC} = 2\mathbf{j}$, $\overrightarrow{OV} = \mathbf{i} + \mathbf{j} + 3\mathbf{k}$.
   (i) Express $\overrightarrow{AV}$ in terms of $\mathbf{i}$, $\mathbf{j}$ and $\mathbf{k}$.
   (ii) Using scalar products, or otherwise, find a vector $\mathbf{x}$ which is perpendicular to both $\overrightarrow{OV}$ and $\overrightarrow{AV}$.
   (iii) Calculate the angle between the vector $\mathbf{x}$, found in (ii), and $\overrightarrow{VB}$, giving your answer to the nearest degree.
   (iv) Write down the acute angle between VB and the plane OVA.   (*C*)

37 In three dimensions, O is the origin of position vectors and points A and B are given by $\overrightarrow{OA} = \mathbf{i} + \mathbf{k}$, $\overrightarrow{OB} = \mathbf{j} + \mathbf{k}$ respectively. The position vector of a general point P in the plane OAB is given by $\overrightarrow{OP} = \lambda\overrightarrow{OA} + \mu\overrightarrow{OB}$, where λ and μ are variable scalars. The position vector of the fixed point Q (which is not in the plane OAB) is given by $\overrightarrow{OQ} = \mathbf{i} + \mathbf{j} + \mathbf{k}$. Determine λ and μ such that QP is perpendicular to both OA and OB (that is, such that QP is perpendicular to

the plane OAB). Hence, or otherwise, find the acute angle between OQ and the plane OAB to the nearest half degree. (C)

38   The points O, P, Q, R have coordinates $(0, 0, 0)$, $(2, 6, -2)$, $(2, 4, -1)$, $(4, 6, 0)$ respectively. Find a vector perpendicular to both PQ and QR and hence, or otherwise, determine an equation for the plane PQR.

The line
$$\frac{x-2}{1} = \frac{y}{1} = \frac{z-1}{3}$$

meets the plane PQR at the point T, and the point S on this line is such that T is the mid-point of OS. Find
(a) the cosine of the acute angle between the line and the plane PQR,
(b) the perpendicular distance from S to the plane PQR. (L)

39   The coordinates of a point A are $(3, -1, 0)$, and the equation of a plane Π is

$$x - y + 2z = -2.$$

(i) Find, in parametric form, the equation of the line through A perpendicular to Π.
(ii) Find the coordinates of the foot of the perpendicular from A to Π.
(iii) Find the coordinates of the reflection A' of A in Π.

The line through A parallel to the vector $\begin{pmatrix} 1 \\ -2 \\ 3 \end{pmatrix}$ is denoted by l.

(iv) Find the coordinates of the point where l meets Π.
(v) Using your answers to (iii) and (iv), show that the reflection l' of l in Π has direction $\begin{pmatrix} 2 \\ -1 \\ 3 \end{pmatrix}$, and find the equation of l' in parametric form. (SMP)

40   The points A, B, C, D have coordinates $(1, 0, -1)$, $(2, -1, 2)$, $(0, 1, 0)$, $(-1, 0, 1)$ respectively. Find the values of λ and μ if the vector $\begin{pmatrix} \lambda \\ \mu \\ 1 \end{pmatrix}$ is perpendicular to both AB and CD. Hence find in the form $\mathbf{r.n} = k$ the equation of the plane through CD parallel to AB.

Write down the vector parametric equation of the line through A normal to this plane, and hence find the perpendicular distance from A to the plane.

Explain why your answer gives the length of the common perpendicular to the lines AB and CD. (SMP)

41   Two points A and B have position vectors $\mathbf{a}$ and $\mathbf{b}$ respectively. Show that the point which divides AB internally in the ratio $m:n$ has position vector

$$\frac{n\mathbf{a} + m\mathbf{b}}{n + m}.$$

Three non-collinear points A, B and C have position vectors $\mathbf{a}$, $\mathbf{b}$ and $\mathbf{c}$ respectively. The point D divides AB internally in the ratio $2:1$. The point E divides BC internally in the ratio $2:1$. Show that DE produced meets AC

produced at the point with position vector

$$\frac{4}{3}\mathbf{c} - \frac{1}{3}\mathbf{a}. \tag{L}$$

42 The plane Π_1 is normal to the vector $\begin{pmatrix} 1 \\ -2 \\ 1 \end{pmatrix}$ and passes through the point

$A(3, 1, -1)$. The plane Π_2 has equation $x - y = 1$. Find the acute angle between the planes Π_1 and Π_2.

If Π_1 and Π_2 meet in the line l, verify that l passes through $(1, 0, -1)$ and is

parallel to the vector $\begin{pmatrix} 1 \\ 1 \\ 1 \end{pmatrix}$. Write down a parametric equation for l, and

hence find the point C on l such that AC is perpendicular to l.

If the normal through A to Π_2 meets Π_2 in B, show that the area of the triangle ACB is $\frac{1}{4}\sqrt{3}$ square units. *(SMP)*

43 If $\mathbf{a}$ is a fixed non-zero vector in 3-dimensional space, describe geometrically the set S of points whose position vectors $\mathbf{r}$ are given by $\mathbf{r} = t\mathbf{a}$, where t is a variable real number.

The position vectors $\mathbf{r}$ of the points of a plane Z satisfy the equation $\mathbf{r} . \mathbf{n} = k$, where $\mathbf{n}$ is a fixed non-zero vector and $k \neq 0$. State (i) how the direction of $\mathbf{n}$ is related to Z, (ii) the geometrical significance of the condition $k \neq 0$.

Find the value of t which gives a point of S which lies in Z. How are S and Z related if $\mathbf{a} . \mathbf{n} = 0$? *(SMP)*

44 A, B, C, D are points with position vectors $\mathbf{j} + 2\mathbf{k}$, $-\mathbf{i} - \mathbf{j}$, $4\mathbf{i} + \mathbf{k}$ and $3\mathbf{i} + \mathbf{j} + 2\mathbf{k}$ respectively. Prove that triangle ABC is right-angled and that triangle ABD is isosceles.

Prove that the vector $\mathbf{j} - \mathbf{k}$ is perpendicular to the plane of triangle ABC and that A, B, C and D are coplanar.

Show that BD passes through the mid-point, E, of AC and find the ratio $BE : ED$. *(C)*

45 The points A, B, C, D have position vectors $\mathbf{p} + \mathbf{q}$, $2\mathbf{p} + 3\mathbf{q}$, $4\mathbf{p} + 7\mathbf{q}$, $5\mathbf{p} - 3\mathbf{q}$ respectively. Given that $|\mathbf{p}| = 2|\mathbf{q}|$, show that
(a) A, B, C are collinear, (b) AC is perpendicular to BD.
Given also that $\mathbf{p} = 8\mathbf{i} - 6\mathbf{j}$ and $\mathbf{q} = 3\mathbf{i} + 4\mathbf{j}$, find
(c) the cosine of the angle BAD, (d) the area of the triangle BAD. *(L)*

46 The lines L_1 and L_2 are given by the equations

$$L_1 : \mathbf{r} = \begin{pmatrix} 1 \\ 6 \\ 3 \end{pmatrix} + t\begin{pmatrix} 2 \\ -1 \\ 1 \end{pmatrix}, \qquad L_2 : \mathbf{r} = \begin{pmatrix} 3 \\ 3 \\ 8 \end{pmatrix} + s\begin{pmatrix} 1 \\ 0 \\ 1 \end{pmatrix}.$$

(i) Calculate the angle between the directions of L_1, L_2.
(ii) Show that the lines do not intersect.

(iii) Verify that the vector $\mathbf{a} = \begin{pmatrix} 1 \\ 1 \\ -1 \end{pmatrix}$ is perpendicular to each of the lines.

The point P on L_1 is given by $t = p$; the point Q on L_2 is given by $s = q$. Write down the column vector representing $\overrightarrow{PQ}$. Hence calculate p and q so that the vectors $\overrightarrow{PQ}$ and $\mathbf{a}$ are parallel. *(JMB)*

47 Prove that the two lines with equations

$$\mathbf{r} = \begin{pmatrix} 0 \\ 2 \\ -3 \end{pmatrix} + s \begin{pmatrix} 1 \\ -1 \\ -1 \end{pmatrix} \quad \text{and} \quad \mathbf{r} = \begin{pmatrix} -1 \\ +6 \\ -1 \end{pmatrix} + t \begin{pmatrix} 2 \\ 1 \\ -1 \end{pmatrix}$$

have a point in common.

Find, in parametric form, an equation for the plane containing the two lines.   (*SMP*)

13 Inequalities

13.1 Ordering the real numbers

Consider the real line as the x-axis, with the number zero represented by the origin O, with any positive number x represented by a point to the right of O distant x from O, and with any negative number x represented by a point to the left of O distant $(-x)$ from O (see Fig. 13.1). For any real number x, just one of these three statements is true:

	(i) x is positive, that is, x is greater than 0,	written '$x > 0$';
or	(ii) x is negative, that is, x is less than 0,	written '$x < 0$';
or	(iii) x is equal to 0,	written '$x = 0$'.

The real line

negative numbers : positive numbers

Fig. 13.1

Notation

$<$ means 'is less than' $\leqslant$ means 'is less than or equal to'
$\not<$ means 'is not less than' $\not\leqslant$ means 'is not less than or equal to'
$>$ means 'is greater than' $\geqslant$ means 'is greater than or equal to'
$\not>$ means 'is not greater than' $\not\geqslant$ means 'is not greater than or equal to'

The notations $<$ and $>$ are called strict inequalities, since equality is excluded. For example: $2 < 5$, $-3 \leqslant 2$, $-6 \not\geqslant -3$, $4 \leqslant 4$, $3 > -5$, $3 \not< 3$.
   We now define an order relation on the real numbers in terms of positive numbers.

Definition   Given two real numbers x and y:

x is less than $y \Leftrightarrow (y - x)$ is positive $\Leftrightarrow y$ is greater than x

that is, $\qquad x < y \Leftrightarrow (y - x) > 0 \Leftrightarrow y > x$.

   It then follows that if x is positive, $0 < x = 0 - (-x)$ so $-x$ is negative. Similarly, if x is negative then $-x$ is positive.

Thus $x < y$ means that x is to the left of y on the real axis,
and $x > y$ means that x is to the right of y on the real axis.

Similar results to the above will hold for $<$ and $>$ replaced by $\leqslant$ and $\geqslant$, with the addition that for any two real numbers x, y either $x \leqslant y$ or $y \leqslant x$, and if $x \leqslant y$ and $y \leqslant x$ then $x = y$.

Transitivity

The inequality relation is transitive. Namely, for all x, y, z

$$x < y \text{ and } y < z \Rightarrow x < z.$$

Proof If $x < y$ and $y < z$ then $y - x > 0$ and $z - y > 0$, so $z - x = (z - y) + (y - x) > 0$ and hence $x < z$.

Some of the processes which are used in manipulation of equations can also be used for inequalities, but not all. We list these results, and then give examples and proofs. Let a, b, c, d be real numbers.

Equations	Inequalities
(i) $a = b \Rightarrow a + c = b + c$	(I) $a < b \Rightarrow a + c < b + c$
(ii) $a = b \Rightarrow a - c = b - c$	(II) $a < b \Rightarrow a - c < b - c$
(iii) $a = b \Rightarrow ac = bc$	(IIIA) $a < b$ and $c > 0 \Rightarrow ac < bc$
	(IIIB) $a < b$ and $c < 0 \Rightarrow bc < ac$

EXAMPLES: (I) $3 < 7$ and $3 + 4 < 7 + 4$, i.e. $7 < 11$;
            (II) $3 < 7$ and $3 - 9 < 7 - 9$, i.e. $-6 < -2$;
          (IIIA) $3 < 7$ and $3 \times 4 < 7 \times 4$, i.e. $12 < 28$;
          (IIIB) $3 < 7$ and $3 \times (-2) > 7 \times (-2)$, i.e. $-6 > -14$.

Proofs:
   (I) $a < b \Rightarrow 0 < b - a \Rightarrow 0 < (b + c) - (a + c) \Rightarrow a + c < b + c,$
  (II) $a < b \Rightarrow 0 < b - a \Rightarrow 0 < (b - c) - (a - c) \Rightarrow a - c < b - c,$
(IIIA) $a < b$ and $c > 0 \Rightarrow 0 < b - a$ and $0 < c \Rightarrow 0 < (b - a)c = bc - ac$
$$\Rightarrow ac < bc,$$
(IIIB) $a < b$ and $c < 0 \Rightarrow 0 < b - a$ and $0 < -c \Rightarrow 0 < (b - a)(-c)$
$$\Rightarrow 0 < ac - bc \Rightarrow bc < ac.$$

If $d \neq 0$, then in (III) c can be replaced by $1/d$, which is of the same sign as d. Then we see that an inequality can also be divided by a positive number without reversing the inequality, while division by a negative number reverses the inequality, just as occurs with multiplication.

Intervals

If x satisfies both inequalities $2 < x$ and $x < 5$, then these may be written as one expression $2 < x < 5$. The set S_1 of all x which satisfy both these inequalities is a finite interval on the real line. This is shown by a thick line

in Fig. 13.2(a). In set notation,

$$S_1 = \{x : 2 < x\} \cap \{x : x < 5\} = \{x : 2 < x < 5\}.$$

The set of all x satisfying the inequality $5 < x$ is S_2, where $S_2 = \{x : 5 < x\}$. This is an infinite interval on the real line, shown in Fig. 13.2(b).

(a) The real interval: $S_1 = \{x : 2 < x < 5\}$

(b) The infinite interval: $S_2 = \{x : 5 < x\}$

(c) The two intervals: $S_3 = \{x : 5 < x\} \cup \{x : x < 2\}$

Fig. 13.2

If the set S_3 consists of all x satisfying either $5 < x$ or $x < 2$, then S_3 is the union of two infinite intervals, Fig. 13.2(c), so that

$$S_3 = \{x : 5 < x \text{ or } x < 2\} = \{x : 5 < x\} \cup \{x : x < 2\}.$$

Note that, in this case it is wrong to write $5 < x < 2$, since the two inequalities are not both true at once. If they were, then the transitivity of the order relation would imply that $5 < 2$, which is nonsense.

Note   In these examples, the strict inequalities have been used, so that the end points 2 and 5 are excluded from the intervals. If any of the inequalities are replaced by non-strict inequalities, then the corresponding end points of the intervals would be included.

EXAMPLE 1   *Solve the inequality $3x - 4 < 5x + 6$.*

Add $(-3x - 6)$ to both sides of the inequality, to give $-10 < 2x$. Multiply by $\frac{1}{2}$, which is positive and so preserves the inequality, $-5 < x$, and the solution set is $\{x : x > -5\}$.

EXAMPLE 2   *Solve $2 \leqslant 5 - 3x \leqslant 8$.*

Subtract 5 from each side of the inequalities, $-3 \leqslant -3x \leqslant 3$. Divide by (-3), which is negative and so reverses the inequalities, $1 \geqslant x \geqslant -1$, giving the solution set $\{x: -1 \leqslant x \leqslant 1\}$.

EXERCISE 13.1

1 Write down, using the inequality symbols:
(i) a is less than b, (ii) c is greater than b, (iii) x is not greater than y,
(iv) y is less than or equal to z, (v) x is greater than -1 and less than 5.

2 Write down, using the inequality symbols, for points on the real line:
(i) x is to the left of 2, (ii) y is to the right of 4, (iii) z lies between -4 and 2,
(iv) w does not lie between 5 and 9, inclusive.
In each case, give one value of the variable which satisfies the conditions.

3 Describe in words the subsets of the real numbers:
(i) $\{x: x < 4\}$, (ii) $\{x: x - 3 < 4\}$, (iii) $\{x: 3x + 5 \leqslant -4\}$,
(iv) $\{x: -2 \leqslant x < 3\}$, (v) $\{x: x \leqslant -2\} \cup \{x: 2 < x\}$.

4 Solve the inequality:
(i) $2x - 3 < 5x + 3$, (ii) $3x + 4 \leqslant 6x - 5$, (iii) $6x - 5 < 2x + 1$,
(iv) $2x + \dfrac{x-2}{3} < 4x - \tfrac{3}{4}$, (v) $(2x + 1)^2 \leqslant 9$.

5 Solve the following so that x lies alone between the inequality signs:
(i) $2 < x - 3 < 4$, (ii) $-2 \leqslant 3x + 4 \leqslant 1$, (iii) $4 < 2x - 5 \leqslant 7$,
(iv) $3 < 5 - 2x < 7$.

6 Given that $x > 0$ prove that $x + \dfrac{1}{x} \geqslant 2$. (Hint: $\left(a - \dfrac{1}{a}\right)^2$ is positive.)

7 If a and b are both positive, prove that $a < b \Leftrightarrow a^2 < b^2$. (Remember that the implication has to be proved in each direction.)

13.2 Use of the modulus sign

The *absolute value*, or the *modulus*, of a real number a is $|a|$, given by
$$|a| = \sqrt{(a^2)}.$$

Thus $|a| = a$ if $a \geqslant 0$ and $|a| = -a$ if $a < 0$.

For example: $|7| = 7$, $|-2| = 2$, $|\sqrt{2}| = \sqrt{2}$, $|-\pi| = \pi$.
For all a, $0 \leqslant |a|$, and $0 = |a| \Leftrightarrow a = 0$.

On the real line, $|x|$ is the distance of the number x from O, and similarly $|a - b| = |b - a|$ is the distance from the point a to the point b (see Fig. 13.3). This means that a single inequality involving a modulus is

Fig. 13.3 Moduli of real numbers.

equivalent to two inequalities. Thus $|x| < 3$ means that the distance of x from O is less than 3 units, so that both $x < 3$ and $-x < 3$, that is, $x > -3$ or $-3 < x$. Hence $|x| < 3 \Leftrightarrow -3 < x < 3$.

On the other hand, $5 < |x|$ means that 5 is nearer to the origin than is x, and so either $x < -5$ or $x > 5$.

EXAMPLE 1   *Solve the inequality* $|2x - 3| < 7$.

This means that $2x - 3$ is nearer to the origin than is 7 and so the inequality is equivalent to the two inequalities $-7 < 2x - 3 < 7$. Add 3 to each term to give $-4 < 2x < 10$, and on dividing by 2, which is positive, $-2 < x < 5$.

EXAMPLE 2   *The subset S of the real numbers is the interval on the real line which is centred at the point a and is of length 2b, b > 0. Describe S in terms of the modulus sign.*

S is the set of real numbers whose distance from a is less than or equal to b and so $S = \{x : a - b \leqslant x \leqslant a + b\}$. The distance of x from a is $|x - a|$ and so $a - b \leqslant x \leqslant a + b$ provided $|x - a| \leqslant b$. Therefore, $S = \{x : |x - a| \leqslant b\}$.

EXERCISE 13.2

1   Rewrite, without using the modulus sign:
   (i) $|x| < 3$,   (ii) $|x - 3| < 4$,   (iii) $|3x - 1| \leqslant 7$,   (iv) $|x| \geqslant 5$,
   (v) $|2x + 4| > 6$.
2   Describe the set in terms of a single inequality involving the modulus sign:
   (i) $\{x : -2 < x < 2\}$,   (ii) $\{x : x \geqslant 7 \text{ or } x \leqslant -7\}$,   (iii) $\{x : -1 < x < 3\}$,
   (iv) $\{x : x \geqslant 2 \text{ or } x \leqslant -4\}$,
   (v) $\{x : x \text{ is a real number less than 5 units distant from the origin}\}$,
   (vi) the set of all real numbers more than 2 units away from 6.
3   Prove that, for any real number a, $-|a| \leqslant a \leqslant |a|$ and $-|a| \leqslant -a \leqslant |a|$.
4   Prove that, for real numbers a and b,
   (i) $|a||b| = |ab|$,   (ii) $|a| - |b| \leqslant |a + b| \leqslant |a| + |b|$.
5   On the same diagram, draw the graph of
   (i) $y = x$,   (ii) $y = |x|$,   (iii) $y = x + |x|$,   (iv) $y = x - |x|$,   (v) $y = 3|x|$,
   (vi) $y = |x - 2|$,   (vii) $y = |3(x - 2)|$,   (viii) $y = |3x + 4|$.

13.3 Solution of inequalities involving linear quotients

So far, we have dealt with linear inequalities and the solution has been obtained by means of addition and multiplication by a constant. When the inequality involves the quotient of one linear term by another we can use both graphical and algebraic methods of solution.

EXAMPLE 1   *Solve the inequality* $(3x + 4)/x > 3$.

The left-hand side may be simplified by separation into two terms, thus

$3 + 4/x > 3$, which is the same as $4/x > 0$, so the solution is $x > 0$, since the quotient is positive when numerator and denominator are the same sign.

EXAMPLE 2   *Solve the inequality* $\dfrac{(2x - 3)}{x} \leqslant 5$.

Method 1   Simplify the left-hand side, as in Example 1. Then $2 - \dfrac{3}{x} \leqslant 5$. Adding $(3/x - 5)$ to both sides:

$$2 - 5 \leqslant 5 + \left(\frac{3}{x} - 5\right) \quad \text{or} \quad -3 \leqslant \frac{3}{x}.$$

Dividing by 3, $-1 \leqslant 1/x$.

Consider the graph $y = 1/x$ in Fig. 13.4(a) and observe that $1/x \geqslant -1$ for two parts of the graph, namely for $x > 0$ and for $x \leqslant -1$. The solution is, therefore, $\{x \colon x \leqslant -1\} \cup \{x \colon x > 0\}$.

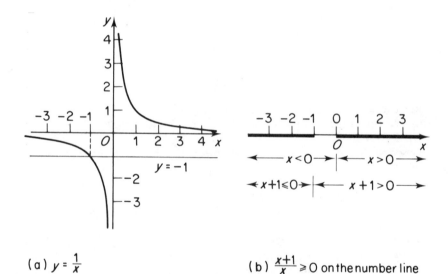

(a) $y = \dfrac{1}{x}$

(b) $\dfrac{x+1}{x} \geqslant 0$ on the number line

Fig. 13.4

Method 2   Subtract $(2x - 3)/x$ from both sides of the inequality to bring all the terms to one side,

$$0 \leqslant 5 - \frac{2x - 3}{x} = \frac{5x - (2x - 3)}{x} = \frac{3x + 3}{x} = 3\frac{x + 1}{x}.$$

Now $(x + 1)/x$ is positive when both numerator and denominator are the same sign. This occurs when $(x + 1)$ and x are both positive or when they are both negative. By considering the signs of $(x + 1)$ and of x on the number line in Fig. 13.4(b), we find the solution set is $\{x \colon x \leqslant -1\} \cup \{x \colon x > 0\}$, indicated on the number line by heavy shading.

EXAMPLE 3   *Solve the inequality* $\dfrac{3x+1}{x+1} < 1$.

Method 1 $\dfrac{3x+1}{x+1} = \dfrac{3(x+1)-2}{x+1} = 3 - \dfrac{2}{x+1}$, so the inequality becomes

$3 - \dfrac{2}{x+1} < 1$ or $3 - 1 < \dfrac{2}{x+1}$, i.e. $1 < \dfrac{1}{x+1}$. Now the graph of $y = 1/(x+1)$ is the graph of $y = 1/x$ translated a distance -1 in the direction Ox, and this graph is shown in Fig. 13.5(a). From the graph, we see that $1/(x+1) > 1$ for $-1 < x < 0$, so the solution set is $\{x: -1 < x < 0\}$.

Method 2   We bring all the terms to one side,

$$0 < 1 - \frac{3x+1}{x+1} = \frac{-2x}{x+1}, \text{ i.e. } \frac{x}{x+1} < 0.$$

This requires x and $(x+1)$ to be of opposite sign and, by reference to the number line in Fig. 13.5(b), we find the solution $\{x: -1 < x < 0\}$.

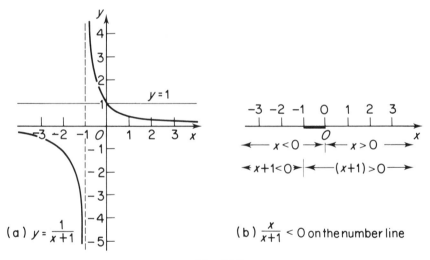

(a) $y = \dfrac{1}{x+1}$

(b) $\dfrac{x}{x+1} < 0$ on the number line

Fig. 13.5

EXERCISE 13.3

1   Solve the inequalities:

(i) $\dfrac{1}{x} < 5$,   (ii) $2 \leqslant \dfrac{x}{3}$,   (iii) $\dfrac{-2}{x} > 4$,   (iv) $2 + \dfrac{5}{x} \leqslant 7$,   (v) $\dfrac{2x-3}{x} > 5$,

(vi) $\dfrac{2-x}{x} \geqslant 3$,   (vii) $\dfrac{2x+1}{x} < 4$.

2   For what values of x are the inequalities satisfied:

(i) $\dfrac{5x}{x+3} < 2$,   (ii) $7 \leqslant \dfrac{2}{x-1}$,   (iii) $\dfrac{1-x}{x+2} < -2$,   (iv) $\dfrac{3x+4}{2x-1} \geqslant 7$.

3 Obtain the set of values of x for which $\dfrac{1}{x+3} < \dfrac{1}{x-3}$.

4 Find the set of values of x for which $\dfrac{1}{x-2} < \dfrac{1}{x+2}$. *(L)*

5 Find the set of values of x for which $\dfrac{4x}{(x+2)} > 1$. *(L)*

13.4 Quadratic inequalities

Inequalities which involve quadratic functions arise because the square of any real number is positive or zero, giving an inequality of the form $a^2 \geqslant 0$. There are three methods of dealing with a quadratic inequality:

I roughly sketching the graph of the function to determine its sign;
II factorisation and looking at the signs of the factors;
III completing the square and using the fact that the square is non-negative.

These methods are illustrated through examples.

EXAMPLE 1 *Solve the inequalities:* (i) $2x^2 + 5x - 12 < 0$,
(ii) $2x^2 + 5x - 12 > 0$, (iii) $5x \geqslant 6 + x^2$, (iv) $x^2 - 2x + 3 \geqslant 0$, (v) $x^2 - 2x + 3 \leqslant 0$.

I Use of the graph
(i) The expression is factorised by inspection,
$f(x) = 2x^2 + 5x - 12 = (2x - 3)(x + 4)$. The graph of f is clearly a parabola with its vertex downwards, and the graph crosses the x-axis at $(-4, 0)$ and $(\frac{3}{2}, 0)$ (see Fig. 13.6(a)). From this graph, $f(x) < 0$ for $-4 < x < \frac{3}{2}$.
(ii) Using the same graph as in (i), $f(x) > 0$, for $x < -4$ and for $x > 1\frac{1}{2}$, giving a solution set $\{x: x < -4\} \cup \{x: x > 1\frac{1}{2}\}$.
(iii) $5x \geqslant 6 + x^2$ can be rearranged, $-x^2 + 5x - 6 = g(x) \geqslant 0$, and, $g(x) = -(x - 2)(x - 3)$. The graph of g is a parabola, with vertex upwards, (Fig. 13.6(b)), crossing the x-axis at $(2, 0)$ and $(3, 0)$. Then $g(x) \geqslant 0$ for $2 \leqslant x \leqslant 3$.
(iv) The graph of h, where $h(x) = x^2 - 2x + 3$ is a parabola, with vertex downwards at the point $(1, 2)$, and this graph does not cross the x-axis (Fig. 13.6(c)). Thus, for all x, $h(x) \geqslant 0$ and the solution set is $\mathbb{R}$.
(v) Using the result of (iv), the solution set for $h(x) \leqslant 0$ is ϕ.

II Using factors
(i) and (ii) The signs of the factors are studied for various subsets of the domain and these are used to obtain the signs of $f(x)$. In §13.3, this was done by marking intervals on the real line. Here, we shall use a table.

	$2x - 3$	$x + 4$	$f(x) = (2x - 3)(x + 4)$
$x < -4$	$-$ ve	$-$ ve	$+$ ve
$-4 < x < 1\frac{1}{2}$	$-$ ve	$+$ ve	$-$ ve
$1\frac{1}{2} < x$	$+$ ve	$+$ ve	$+$ ve

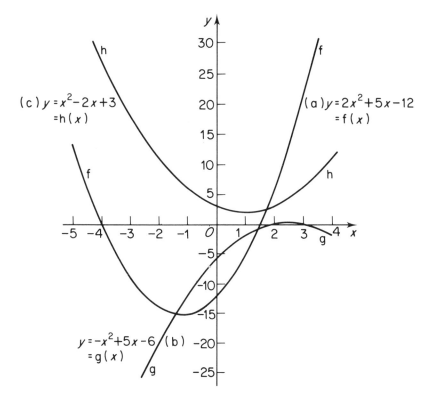

Fig. 13.6

Then the solution for (i), f(x) < 0, is the set $\{x: -4 < x < 1\frac{1}{2}\}$;
the solution set for   (ii), f(x) > 0, is the set $\{x: x < -4\} \cup \{x: x > 1\frac{1}{2}\}$.
(iii) Similarly, $g(x) = -x^2 + 5x - 6 = -(x-2)(x-3)$ and we tabulate the signs
of the factors of g(x).

	-1	$x-2$	$x-3$	$g(x) = -(x-2)(x-3)$
$x < 2$	$-$ve	$-$ve	$-$ve	$-$ve
$2 < x < 3$	$-$ve	$+$ve	$-$ve	$+$ve
$3 < x$	$-$ve	$+$ve	$+$ve	$-$ve

The solution set for $g(x) \geqslant 0$ is then $\{x: 2 \leqslant x \leqslant 3\}$.
(iv) and (v) Since h(x) does not factorise, the method cannot be used.

III Completing the square
(i) and (ii) $f(x) = 2(x+5/4)^2 - 121/8$, so $f(x) < 0$ when $(x+5/4)^2 < 121/16$,
which occurs for $-11/4 < x + 5/4 < 11/4$, which gives the solution for (i).
    Similarly, $f(x) > 0$ for $(x+5/4)^2 > 121/16$, that is, for either $x + 5/4 < -11/4$
or $11/4 < x + 5/4$, giving the solution for (ii), $\{x: x < -4\} \cup \{x: x > 1\frac{1}{2}\}$.

(iii) $g(x) = -(x - 5/2)^2 + \frac{1}{4} \geq 0$　for　$(x - 5/2)^2 \leq \frac{1}{4}$,　i.e.　$-\frac{1}{2} \leq x - 5/2 \leq \frac{1}{2}$ or $2 \leq x \leq 3$. (iv) and (v) $h(x) = (x - 1)^2 + 2 \geq 2$ for all x, so the solution set for (iv) is $\mathbb{R}$ and the solution set for (v) is ϕ.

The value of the technique of bringing all the terms to one side of the inequality is demonstrated in the next examples.

EXAMPLE 2　*Find the values of x which satisfy* $\dfrac{(x + 2)(x + 1)}{x} > \dfrac{x + 5}{3}$.

Subtract $(x + 5)/3$ from each side in order to bring all the terms to one side. The inequality becomes

$$\frac{(x + 2)(x + 1)}{x} - \frac{x + 5}{3} = \frac{3(x^2 + 3x + 2) - x(x + 5)}{3x} = \frac{2x^2 + 4x + 6}{3x} > 0.$$

Now $2x^2 + 4x + 6 = 2(x^2 + 2x + 1 + 2) = 2(x + 1)^2 + 4 > 0$ for all values of x because $(x + 1)^2 \geq 0$. Therefore, the quotient is positive when the denominator is positive, that is, when $x > 0$. Thus the solution set is $\mathbb{R}^+$.

EXAMPLE 3　*Solve the inequality* $\dfrac{x(x + 9)}{x - 1} > 18$.

Subtract 18 from each side and then we require $f(x)$ to be positive, where

$$f(x) = \frac{x(x + 9)}{x - 1} - 18 = \frac{x^2 + 9x - 18x + 18}{x - 1} = \frac{x^2 - 9x + 18}{x - 1} = \frac{(x - 3)(x - 6)}{x - 1}.$$

Of the three terms in this expression, either three or one must be positive in order for $f(x)$ to be positive. We look at the signs of the terms for various values of x;

	$x < 1$	$1 < x < 3$	$3 < x < 6$	$x > 6$
$x - 1$	− ve	+ ve	+ ve	+ ve
$x - 3$	− ve	− ve	+ ve	+ ve
$x - 6$	− ve	− ve	− ve	+ ve
$f(x)$	− ve	+ ve	− ve	+ ve

and pick out the solution set $\{x: 1 < x < 3\} \cup \{x: x > 6\}$.

EXERCISE 13.4

1　Solve the inequality:

(i) $(x - 1)(x + 2)(x - 3) > 0$,　　(ii) $\dfrac{(x + 2)(x - 3)}{x - 1} < 0$,　　(iii) $x^2 + x \leq 12$,

(iv) $x^2 + x + 1 > 0$.

2　Find the set of real values of x for which $\dfrac{x(x - 5)}{(x - 3)} > 6$.　　　　　　(L)

3　Given that $px^2 + 2px - 3 < 0$ for all real values of x, determine the set of possible values of p.　　　　　　(L)

4 Find the set of values of x for which $2x^2 + 3x + 2 < 4$.   (*L*)

5 Find the set of values of x for which $\dfrac{(2x-1)(x+4)}{(x-5)} > 0$.   (*L*)

6 Solve the inequality $(x+1)(x-2)(x+3)(x-4) > 0$.   (*L*)

13.5 Inequalities involving the modulus sign

We illustrate an algebraic method and a graphical method of solving an inequality which includes the modulus symbol.

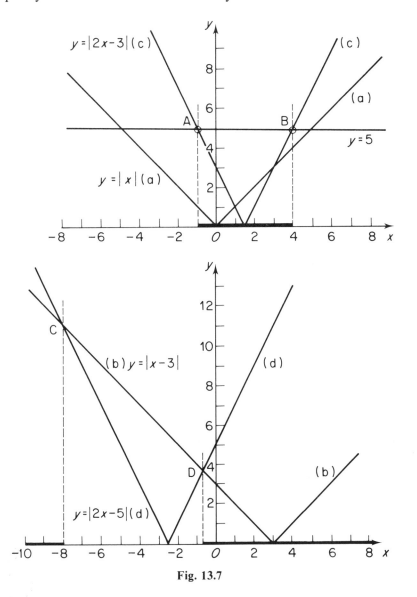

Fig. 13.7

EXAMPLE   *Solve the inequality:* (i) $|2x - 3| < 5$,   (ii) $|x - 3| < |2x + 5|$.

I Algebraic method

(i) $|2x - 3| < 5 \Leftrightarrow (2x - 3)^2 < 25 \Leftrightarrow 4x^2 - 12x + 9 - 25 < 0 \Leftrightarrow x^2 - 3x - 4 < 0$

$$\Leftrightarrow (x + 1)(x - 4) < 0 \Leftrightarrow -1 < x < 4,$$

since the quadratic function $(x + 1)(x - 4)$ has a graph which is a parabola with its vertex downwards, crossing the x-axis at $(-1, 0)$ and $(4, 0)$.

(ii) $|x - 3| < |2x + 5| \Leftrightarrow (x - 3)^2 < (2x + 5)^2 \Leftrightarrow x^2 - 6x + 9 < 4x^2 + 20x + 25$

$$\Leftrightarrow 3x^2 + 26x + 16 > 0 \Leftrightarrow (3x + 2)(x + 8) > 0$$

$$\Leftrightarrow \text{either } x > -\tfrac{2}{3} \text{ or } x < -8$$

since the graph of $3x^2 + 26x + 16$ is a parabola, with its vertex downwards, crossing the x-axis at $(-8, 0)$ and $(-\tfrac{2}{3}, 0)$.

II Graphical method

This requires graphs of the modulus function, which are shown in Fig. 13.7.

(a) The graph of $|x|$ is V-shaped and consists of two straight lines; for $x > 0$, $|x| = x$, a line with gradient 1, and for $x < 0$, $|x| = -x$, a line with gradient -1.

(b) The graph of $|x - 3|$ is V-shaped, with a line of gradient $+1$ for $x > 3$ and a line of gradient -1 for $x < 3$, the two lines meeting at $(3, 0)$.

(c) The graph of $|2x - 3|$, that is, $|2(x - \tfrac{3}{2})|$, is V-shaped and consists of two lines through $(\tfrac{3}{2}, 0)$, with gradient 2 for $x > \tfrac{3}{2}$ and gradient -2 for $x < \tfrac{3}{2}$.

(d) The graph of $|2x + 5|$ consists of two similar lines of gradients 2 and -2 through $(-\tfrac{5}{2}, 0)$.

(i) The graph (c) of $|2x - 3|$ meets the line $y = 5$ at $A(-1, 5)$ and at $B(4, 5)$. Between these two points $|2x - 3| < 5$, so the solution set is $\{x: -1 < x < 4\}$, shown as a heavy line segment on the x-axis.

(ii) The graph (b) of $|x - 3|$ meets the graph (d) of $|2x - 5|$ at $C(-8, 11)$ and at D $(-\tfrac{2}{3}, \tfrac{11}{3})$ and graph (b) lies below graph (d) outside the interval $-8 \leqslant x \leqslant -\tfrac{2}{3}$. Hence the solution set is $\{x: x < -8\} \cup \{x: x > -\tfrac{2}{3}\}$.

MISCELLANEOUS EXERCISE 13

1   Solve the inequality:

(i) $5x - 4 < 7$,   (ii) $\dfrac{5x - 4}{x} \leqslant 5$,   (iii) $5 - 2x > x - 7$,   (iv) $\dfrac{2x + 3}{x} \geqslant 2$,

(v) $\dfrac{4 - 2x}{3x} > 1$,   (vi) $\dfrac{8}{x + 3} < 1$,   (vii) $\dfrac{3x - 4}{x + 2} < 1$,   (viii) $\dfrac{2x - 3}{3x - 4} \leqslant 1$,

(ix) $\dfrac{5 - 2x}{4 - 3x} < 3$.

2   Find the set of values of x such that:
(i) $|x - 2| > 3$,   (ii) $|x + 2| \leqslant 3$,   (iii) $|x - 2| > |x + 2|$.

3   Find the set of values of x for which $x^2 - 4x + 3 > 0$.   (L)

4   Find graphically, or otherwise, the set of values of x for which $\sqrt{(16 - x^2)} > |x|$.   (L)

5   Find the set of values of x for which $\dfrac{x}{x - 2} > \dfrac{1}{x + 1}$.   (L)

6   Find the set of values of x for which $\dfrac{(x+2)}{(x+1)(x-2)} > 0.$ (L)

7   Find the set of values of x for which $|x-2| > 5|x-3|.$ (L)

8   Find the set of values of x for which $|x-1| > 2|x-2|.$ (L)

9   Show that, if x is real, $2x^2 + 6x + 9$ is always positive. Hence, or otherwise, solve the inequality

$$\frac{(x+1)(x+3)}{x} > \frac{(x+6)}{3}.$$ (JMB)

10 Find a quadratic inequality for which the solution set is:
    (i) $\{x: -1 < x < 1\}$, (ii) $\{x: a < x < b\}$, (iii) $\{x: x < 0\} \cup \{x: 4 < x\}$.

11 The curve $y = \dfrac{2x+3}{x-1}$ has asymptotes parallel to the coordinate axes. State
    the equations of these asymptotes. Draw a sketch of this curve, showing the asymptotes and giving the coordinates of the points where the curve meets the axes.
    Solve the inequalities

    (a) $2x + 3 \leqslant 3(x-1)$, (b) $\dfrac{2x+3}{x-1} \leqslant 3.$ (L)

12 Given that $3 - t \leqslant 4 + t \leqslant 13 - 2t$, find the least and greatest values of t.   (L)

13 Given that $y = ax^2 + bx + c$, that $y = 8$ when $x = 1$ and that $y = 2$ when $x = -1$, show that $b = 3$ and find a in terms of c.
    Find the range of values of c for which $y > 0$ for all real values of x.   (JMB)

14 Prove that, for all real values of a and b:
    (i) $a^2 + 2ab + b^2 \geqslant 0$, (ii) $a^2 - ab + b^2 \geqslant 0$.
    Deduce that $a^4 + a^3 b + ab^3 + b^4 \geqslant 0$.

15 Given that $x \in \mathbb{R}$, find the solution set of $x^2 - 1 < 2(x+1)$.   (L)

16 Find the set of values of θ, lying in the interval $-\pi \leqslant \theta \leqslant \pi$, for which

$$2\cos^2 \theta + 3\sin \theta < 0.$$ (JMB)

17 Solve the inequality $x^2 - |x| - 12 < 0.$ (JMB)

18 Find the sets of values of x for which

    (a) $0 < \dfrac{(x-1)(x+3)}{(3x-1)} < 1$, (b) $|x^2 + 1| < |x^2 - 4|.$ (L)

19 Find the set of values of θ, where $|\theta| < \pi/2$, for which

$$\frac{1}{1 + \cos 2\theta} < 1.$$ (L)

20 Solve the inequalities $(x+3)^2 < (x-2)^2 < 9.$

21 Find the equation of the tangent to the curve $y = x(x-3)$ at the point $P(2, -2)$. Using the same axes sketch the curve and the tangent at P.
    Using sketches, or otherwise, find the values of x for which

    (a) $x(x-3) \leqslant x - 4$, (b) $x - 3 < \dfrac{x-4}{x}$, (c) $\dfrac{1}{x-3} < \dfrac{x}{x-4}.$ (L)

14 Numerical Methods for Solving Equations

14.1 Graphical methods

Consider the problem of solving the equation $x^3 + x - 4 = 0$. As a first step, some idea of the behaviour of the function f, where $f(x) = x^3 + x - 4$, can be obtained from a sketch graph by plotting a few points and joining them by a smooth curve (Fig. 14.1).

$$x: \quad -2 \quad -1 \quad 0 \quad 1 \quad 2 \quad 3$$
$$f(x): \quad -14 \quad -6 \quad -4 \quad -2 \quad 6 \quad 26$$

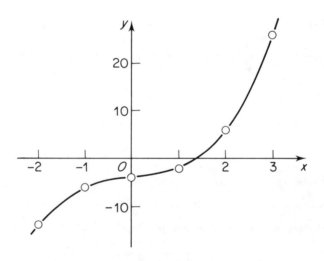

Fig. 14.1 Graph of $x^3 + x - 4 = 0$.

The sketch suggests that the graph of f crosses the x-axis between $x = 1$ and $x = 2$, in fact, somewhere near $x = 1 \cdot 4$. This assumes that the graph of the cubic function f is continuous, so that, because $f(1) < 0$ and $f(2) > 0$, there must be a root of the equation $f(x) = 0$ between $x = 1$ and $x = 2$. The graph must cross the x-axis somewhere between these two points. The gradient of $f(x)$, given by $f'(x)$, is always positive so $f(x)$ can only intercept the x-axis in one point.

It is important to remember that the function must be continuous for this method to give an approximate root. For example, if $g(x) = \dfrac{1}{x}$, then $g(1) = 1$ and $g(-1) = -1$, but there is no solution to $g(x) = 0$.

EXERCISE 14.1

1 On the same axes draw the graphs of $y = x^3$ and $y = -x + 4$ and find the value of x where these two graphs meet. Explain how this answer can be used to find the zero of $f(x)$ where

$$f(x) = x^3 + x - 4.$$

In the rest of this chapter, we demonstrate some methods for obtaining better approximations to the root than can be obtained from the graph. The reader should repeat the working on a calculator. Indeed, much of the chapter involves repeated calculation and, if available, a microcomputer could well be used to demonstrate the methods.

14.2 Decimal search

The first method involves sandwiching the root between decimal numbers, with an increasing number of decimal places. For the function f of §14.1, the root lies between 1 and 2. One could plot more points, draw the graph between $x = 1$ and $x = 2$ with a larger scale and so obtain a more accurate approximation to the root. The same result can be obtained numerically by using a decimal approximation method. First calculate $f(x)$ at the nine points between 1 and 2, with interval 0·1, to obtain two decimals between which the root lies. Then repeat the procedure for the nine points at an interval of 0·01 between the two points just found. The calculations are shown in tabular form:

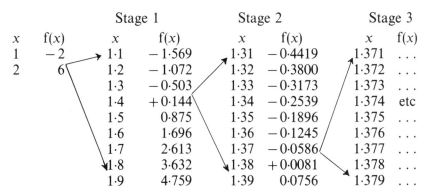

	Stage 1			Stage 2			Stage 3	
x	$f(x)$	x	$f(x)$	x	$f(x)$	x	$f(x)$
1	-2	1·1	$-1·569$	1·31	$-0·4419$	1·371	...
2	6	1·2	$-1·072$	1·32	$-0·3800$	1·372	...
		1·3	$-0·503$	1·33	$-0·3173$	1·373	...
		1·4	$+0·144$	1·34	$-0·2539$	1·374	etc
		1·5	0·875	1·35	$-0·1896$	1·375	...
		1·6	1·696	1·36	$-0·1245$	1·376	...
		1·7	2·613	1·37	$-0·0586$	1·377	...
		1·8	3·632	1·38	$+0·0081$	1·378	...
		1·9	4·759	1·39	0·0756	1·379	...

The change in sign of $f(x)$ between $x = 1·3$ and $1·4$ indicates that these bracket the root. It takes nine calculations to reduce the interval from $2-1 = 1$ to $1\cdot4 - 1\cdot3 = 0\cdot1$. Repeating the calculations for stage 2 reduces the interval to $0\cdot01$ and the table shows that the root lies between $1\cdot37$ and $1\cdot38$. If we need more accuracy, we then move to stage 3 and reduce the interval to $0\cdot001$. If we do not wish to go to stage 3, we can note that $f(1\cdot37)$ is roughly 7 times $f(1\cdot38)$ and so it is likely that the root lies nearer to $1\cdot38$ than to $1\cdot37$. Thus, after 18 calculations, we have achieved an accuracy of two decimal places. This is not particularly impressive although it might be a satisfactory way to solve the problem by machine.

Comments on the method

(i) Quite a large number of the calculations could have been omitted. For instance, in stage 1, it would have been sensible to have started with $f(1\cdot5)$ and, since this turns out to be positive, there would be little point in calculating $f(1\cdot6)$, $f(1\cdot7)$, $f(1\cdot8)$ and $f(1\cdot9)$, since the root lies between 1 and $1\cdot5$. This idea of halving the interval, from 1 to $0\cdot5$, and so on, is used in §14.3. Another way of reducing the number of calculations would be to stop during each stage as soon as $f(x)$ changes sign and there are two numbers bracketing the root.

(ii) It was found above that an accuracy of two decimal places is obtained after 18 calculations. However, if the values at the change of sign of $f(x)$ had been more evenly spaced, say if $f(1\cdot37) = -0\cdot06$ and $f(1\cdot38) = 0\cdot06$, a further calculation would have been needed, namely to calculate the sign of $f(1\cdot375)$ in order to be sure whether the root is $1\cdot37$ or $1\cdot38$ to two decimal places of accuracy. So 19 calculations are needed for the stated level of accuracy.

EXERCISE 14.2

1   Continue the approximation process of §14.2 to find a three-decimal approximation to the root of the equation $x^3 + x - 4 = 0$.

2   Sketch a graph to find an approximate root of the equation $x^3 + 3x - 1 = 0$. Use a decimal-search method to improve your answer to an accuracy of two decimal places.

3   Show that the equation $x^2 + 2x - 7 = 0$ has a root between 1 and 2.
(a) Find the root, accurate to three decimal places, by using a decimal search.
(b) Use the formula for solution of a quadratic equation to find, in surd form, the exact value of this root.
    State the error in your decimal search approximation.

4   Solve the equation $x + 2/x - 5 = 0$, giving your answers to a suitable level of accuracy, using the decimal-search method. (Note that there are two solutions.)

5   (For those with access to a computer.) Write a computer program to solve an equation $f(x) = 0$ by the decimal-search method. Remember to allow for the user to enter the first two values and the number of stages to be calculated. The flow chart in Fig. 14.2 may help you.

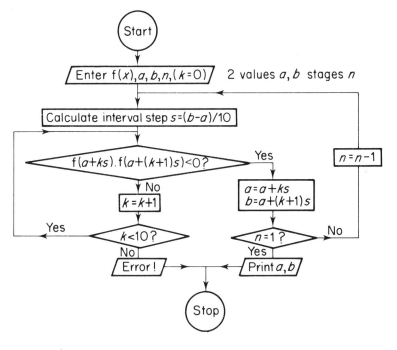

Fig. 14.2

14.3 The midpoint method (interval bisection)

An alternative to the decimal search is to use the suggested idea of halving the interval. For example, given $f(1).f(2) < 0$, calculate $f(1.5)$, the sign of which will show on which side of 1.5 the root lies. The interval halving is then repeated until the desired accuracy is obtained. The same equation, $f(x) = x^3 + x - 4 = 0$, is used to demonstrate the method.

Step 1: $f(1) = -2$ and $f(2) = 6$, so calculate $f(1.5) = 0.875$ which is greater than 0 so the root lies between 1 and 1.5. Now repeat the process for step 2. The work may be laid out as follows:

$f(1) = -2$

$f(1.25) = -0.8$

$f(1.375) = -0.03$

$f(1.4375) = 0.41 \ldots$

$f(1.5) = 0.9$

$f(2) = 6$

step 1   step 2   step 3   step 4

This shows the first four steps. Each step required one calculation. The initial interval 1 has been successively halved, so that, after 4 steps, the interval is $1 \times \frac{1}{2} \times \frac{1}{2} \times \frac{1}{2} \times \frac{1}{2} = \frac{1}{16} = 0.0625$, and its end points are 1·375 and 1·4375. After four calculations the approximation to one decimal place is 1·4 and this needed nine calculations by the decimal search. So the interval halving method gives a considerable saving in calculations, compared with the decimal search.

Comments on the method   (i) The method is the same as decimal search, with the base 10 being replaced by base 2. Only one calculation is needed at each step but the values of x required are less easily recognisable, and their decimal form becomes quite long. Hand calculation becomes very tedious but a calculator can easily handle the long decimals.
(ii) The desired level of accuracy is easily tested in terms of the powers of $\frac{1}{2}$, but it is not so clear when a desired level of accuracy has been reached, when working in decimals.
(iii) Each step is called an *iteration* since the same calculation is made with a new starting point found from the previous calculation.

EXERCISE 14.3

1   Continue the calculations of the above example for nine steps and compare your answer with the answer given by question **1** of Exercise 14.2 after nine steps.
2   Find the positive root of the equation $x^4 + 3x^2 - x - 8 = 0$ by the midpoint method, using eight steps. Give your answer to the best level of accuracy that these calculations allow.
3   Find the complete solution of the equation $x^2 - 7 = 0$ by the midpoint method, giving your answer accurate to three decimal places. Use a calculator or tables to find $\sqrt{7}$ and explain why the answer is similar to one of your answers.
4   The solution of $4x - x^3 - 6 = 0$ is -2.525, accurate to three decimal places. Find how many iterations are needed to produce this answer by interval halving, if the first two values taken are -3 and -2.
5   Find $\sqrt{(99)}$ accurate to one decimal place, using the midpoint method.
6   Use both a decimal search and the midpoint method to solve the equation $2x^3 + 4x^2 - x + 8 = 0$, accurate to two decimal places. Write down how many calculations were needed in each method.
7   Fig. 14.3 indicates another technique for improving an approximation to the root of an equation, this time, for the equation $x^3 - 3 = 0$. Given two points on the graph on opposite sides of the x-axis, $(1, -2)$ and $(2, 5)$, join them by a chord and find the point of intersection of the chord with the x-axis; in this case $x = 9/7$. Then calculate the value of $x^3 - 3$ at this value of x and repeat the process. Use the process a total of three times to find more accurate solutions. Compare the speed of improving the accuracy with the two previous methods by going through three steps of each method.

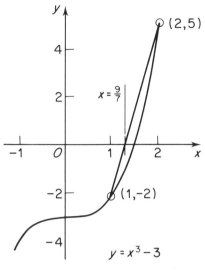

Fig. 14.3

14.4 Linear interpolation, the chord method

The technique described in question **7** of Exercise 14.3 uses the idea of approximating to the shape of a curve by a straight line joining two of its points, that is by a chord. This is a *linear approximation* to the curve. If the chord is then used to calculate an approximate root, the process is called *linear interpolation*.

Suppose that two points, A $(a, f(a))$ and B $(b, f(b))$, are taken on the graph of f, which are near to a point where the graph of f crosses the x-axis. This is shown in Fig. 14.4. In (a) the points A and B are on opposite sides of the x-axis but in (b) and (c) they are on the same side.

The chord AB crosses the x-axis at $(c, 0)$ and in case (a) it is clear that $x = c$ will be a better approximation to the root than $x = a$ and $x = b$. In (b) it is still true that c is a better approximation, but this may no longer be true in case (c). Much will depend upon the shape of the graph and, in particular, its gradient.

Let M, N, P be the points $(a, 0)$, $(b, 0)$ $(c, 0)$ respectively. Then triangles AMP and BNP are similar and $\dfrac{AM}{MP} = \dfrac{BN}{NP}$, so $AM \cdot NP = BN \cdot MP$.

Case (a), $-f(a)(b - c) = f(b)(c - a)$ or $c(f(a) - f(b)) = bf(a) - af(b)$.
Case (b), $f(a)(b - c) = f(b)(a - c)$; case (c), $-f(a)(c - b) = -f(b)(c - a)$; and again $c(f(a) - f(b)) = bf(a) - af(b)$.

So, in all three cases, provided that $f(a) \neq f(b)$, we find that

$$c = \frac{bf(a) - af(b)}{f(a) - f(b)}.$$

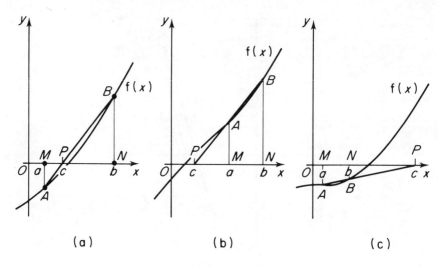

Fig. 14.4

Clearly we can expect that this will not give a good approximation when $f(a)$ and $f(b)$ are nearly equal. This is the case when the chord AB is nearly parallel to the x-axis.

EXAMPLE   *Use three steps of linear interpolation to obtain an approximate solution to the equation $x^3 - 3 = 0$.*

In Fig. 14.3, we see that two starting values are $x = 1$ and $x = 2$. So we use in the first step $a = 1, f(a) = -2, b = 2, f(b) = 5$. Then

$$c = \frac{2(-2)-5}{-2-5} = \frac{9}{7} = 1 \cdot 2857.$$

Now $f(1 \cdot 2857) = -0 \cdot 8747$, so, for step **2** we use $a = 1 \cdot 2857$ and $b = 2$. Then

$$c = \frac{2(-0 \cdot 8747) - 1 \cdot 2857(5)}{-0 \cdot 8747 - 5} = 1 \cdot 3920.$$

Then $f(c) = -0 \cdot 3028$, so, for step **3** we use $a = 1 \cdot 2857$ and $b = 1 \cdot 3920$. Then

$$c = \frac{1 \cdot 3920(-0 \cdot 8747) - 1 \cdot 2857(-0 \cdot 3028)}{-0 \cdot 8747 + 0 \cdot 3028} = \mathbf{1 \cdot 448},$$

which may be compared with $\sqrt[3]{3}$ to three decimal places, which is $1 \cdot 442$.

EXERCISE 14.4

1   Use the chord method again on the above example to find the next approximation to $\sqrt[3]{3}$. How many more steps are needed to ensure an accuracy to three decimal places?

2 Use the chord method to find an improved approximation to the root of the equation in the given interval:
(i) $2x^3 - 3x + 6 = 0$, $(-2, -1)$,   (ii) $3x^2 - 6x + 1 = 0$, $(0, 1)$,
(iii) $x - \dfrac{4}{x} + 2 = 0$, $(1, 2)$.

3 (i) Draw a large accurate graph of the function $x^3 + x - 4$ between $x = 1$ and $x = 2$;
(ii) apply the chord method once to find c, if $a = 1$ and $b = 2$;
(iii) apply the chord method again with $a = 1$ and $b = c$;
(iv) apply the chord method again with $a = c$ and $b = 2$;
(v) discuss which of (iii) and (iv) gives the better second approximation to the correct solution $1 \cdot 3788$, and suggest guidelines to decide which interval to use in the chord method.

4 The points $A(a, f(a))$ and $B(b, f(b))$ lie on the graph of the function f. Find the Cartesian equation of the line AB. Find the value of c such that the line AB meets the x-axis at $(c, 0)$ and prove that the expression obtained for c is the same as that obtained in §14.4.

5 On plotting values on a graph, a student thought that the equation $x^3 - 4x^2 + x + 7 = 0$ probably had a root between 2 and 3. Apply the chord method to this interval and explain by a diagram what happens. Solve the equation by the chord method giving your answer accurate to three decimal places. State whether the student was right or wrong.

14.5 The use of tangents

The three iterative methods considered in the last three sections have each required 2 values of x, bracketing the desired root, in order to produce a better approximation. There is another method which only requires one starting value and which converges faster for many functions. The method uses the tangent to the function at a point as a linear approximation and is demonstrated in Fig. 14.5.

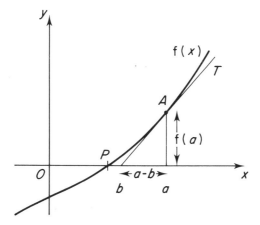

Fig. 14.5

Let the function f have a zero, given by the point P where its graph crosses the x-axis. Let a be a first approximation to the root of $f(x) = 0$, with a corresponding point $A(a, f(a))$ on the graph. The gradient of the tangent AT to the graph at A is $f'(a)$, the derivative of f evaluated at $x = a$. Taking the tangent as a linear approximation to the graph, a new approximation to the root is given by $x = b$, where the tangent AT crosses the x-axis. Then

$$\frac{f(a)}{a-b} = f'(a) \text{ and, by rearranging, } b = a - \frac{f(a)}{f'(a)}.$$

When the function is decreasing, with $f'(a)$ negative, instead of increasing as in Fig. 14.5, it can be shown that the same formula holds. This formula is called the *Newton-Raphson* formula,

$$b = a - \frac{f(a)}{f'(a)}.$$

Starting with a single initial value $a = p_1$, we may apply the formula repeatedly to produce a sequence of approximations to the root, namely

$$p_1, p_2, p_3, \ldots \text{ with } p_{n+1} = p_n - \frac{f(p_n)}{f'(p_n)}.$$

For many functions, the process, called the *Newton-Raphson process*, converges to the required root of the equation $f(x) = 0$.

Note   The process requires the function to be differentiated and so we restrict its use to the set of differentiable functions. Since, in the formula, we divide by $f'(a)$, the process will fail if the graph is parallel to the x-axis at $x = a$, and it will not give a good approximation if $f'(a)$ is small numerically.

EXAMPLE   *Use the Newton-Raphson process to improve the approximation $x = 4$ to the solution of the equation $x^3 - 50 = 0$.*

Since $f(x) = x^3 - 50$, $f'(x) = 3x^2$, so

$$p_{n+1} = p_n - \frac{p_n^3 - 50}{3p_n^2}, \quad \text{and so} \quad p_{n+1} = \frac{2p_n^3 + 50}{3p_n^2}.$$

Taking $p_1 = 4$, $p_2 = (2 \times 4^3 + 50)/3 \times 4^2 = (128 + 50)/48 = 3.7083$ and $p_3 = (2(3.7083)^3 + 50)/3(3.7083)^2 = \mathbf{3.68419}$. This result of only two iterations gives a result which is correct to three decimal places since, to six decimal places, $\sqrt[3]{50} = 3.6840315$.

Comments on method   As in most of the methods, the better the first approximation the quicker a good result is obtained. Also, if the graph of f is fairly steep near the root, then f' is numerically large and this speeds up the convergence. Also, it can normally be assumed that the error in the final approximation is less than the correction $-\dfrac{f(x)}{f'(x)}$ evaluated at the previous approximation.

EXERCISE 14.5

1 Use the Newton-Raphson method, twice in each case, to find improved approximations to the root of the equation, using the given starting value:
   (i) $x^3 + x - 4 = 0$, $x = 2$; (ii) $x^3 + 3x - 1 = 0$, $x = 1$;
   (iii) $x^2 + 2x - 7 = 0$, $x = -4$; (iv) $x^4 + 3x^2 - x - 8 = 0$, $x = -2$;
   (v) $x^3 - 25 = 0$, $x = 3$.

2 Show that $x - \dfrac{f(x)}{f'(x)} = \dfrac{3x^3 - 1}{3x^2 - 3}$, when $f(x) = x^3 - 3x + 1$.

   Use the Newton-Raphson method to find the roots of the equation $x^3 - 3x + 1 = 0$, accurate to three decimal places. (Hint: there are three answers).

3 Show that the Newton-Raphson method gives this iteration:

$$p_{n+1} = \frac{6p_n^3 - 1}{9p_n^2 - 1}, \text{ when } f(x) = 3x^3 - x - 1$$

   and find the solution of the equation $f(x) = 0$.

4 Use the function $f(x) = x^4 - 17$ to find $\sqrt[4]{(17)}$ accurate to five decimal places.

5 Find the negative roots of the equation $x^4 - 7x^2 + 1 = 0$ and check your answers by solving for x^2 directly.

6 Draw a flow chart to solve the equation $f(x) = 0$, using the Newton-Raphson method. Arrange to input the first value p_1, and to halt when the consecutive iterations differ by less than 10^{-5}, to obtain an answer correct to four decimal places.

7 Draw an alternative to Fig. 14.5 in which the function f is shown to be decreasing, instead of increasing. Prove that, in this case, the Newton-Raphson formula still holds.

MISCELLANEOUS EXERCISE 14

1 Show that the equation $x^3 - 4x^2 + 2 = 0$ has a root α between -1 and 0, a root β between 0 and 1, and that its third root γ is between 1 and 4.

   Use the Newton-Raphson method to find a second approximation to α with a first approximation of -1, and also a second approximation to β taking 1 as first approximation. Determine and explain what happens if 0 is used as the first approximation to either root.

   State, with reasons, a suitable first approximation to γ, and use this to find a second approximation to γ. (C)

2 The equation $f(x) = 0$ is known to have precisely one root in the interval $a \leqslant x \leqslant b$. Construct a flow diagram giving an algorithm to estimate this root, using the method of interval bisection. The following are given: the numbers a and b (with $a < b$), the function f, and the positive number δ which is the maximum permissible magnitude of the error in the root.

Demonstrate the working of your flow diagram by applying it to the equation $\cos x - x = 0$ with $a = 0$, $b = 1$ and $\delta = 0.1$, giving your answer correct to one decimal place.   (C)

3   By applying Newton's method to the function f defined by

$$f(x) = 1 - \frac{5}{x^2}$$

develop an iterative formula for calculating $\sqrt{5}$, and show that if x_n is in error by a small quantity d_n then the next approximation x_{n+1} is in error by about $0.7 d_n^2$.   (JMB)

4   Show that there is precisely one real root of the equation

$$x^3 + 2x - 1 = 0$$

and that it lies in the interval $0 < x < 1$. Use Newton's method to find the root to three decimal places.   (JMB)

5   Prove that the equation $e^{-x} - x + 2 = 0$ has a root between 0 and 3, and that the equation $e^x + x - 2 = 0$ has a root between 0 and 0.5.

By using the iterations $x_{n+1} = 2 + e^{-x_n}$ and $x_{n+1} = 2 - e^{x_n}$ respectively and taking, in each case, $x_1 = 0$ find, for each equation, values for x_2, x_3 and x_4 to three significant figures.

Show, by means of clear sketches with these values entered in, the manner in which the iteration for the first equation is converging and that for the second is diverging.

Find the root of $e^{-x} - x + 2 = 0$ correct to two decimal places, making it clear from your working why your answer is correct to that degree of accuracy.   (C)

6   Show that the equation $x^3 - 12x - 7.2 = 0$ has one positive and two negative roots. Obtain the positive root to three significant figures by the Newton-Raphson method.   (L)

7   Find, correct to one decimal place, the real root of the equation $x^3 + 2x - 1 = 0$.   (L)

8   Use the Newton-Raphson method to find the real root of the equation $x^3 + 2x^2 + 4x - 6 = 0$ taking $x = 0.9$ as the first approximation and carrying out one iteration.

Draw a flow diagram designed to evaluate this root using this method to within an accuracy of 0.001%, starting with $x = 0.9$.   (L)

9   Hero's method for finding the square root of the number k, starting with the value a, is given by the iterative formula:

$$p_1 = a, \quad p_{n+1} = \frac{1}{2}\left(p_n + \frac{k}{p_n}\right).$$

(i) Take $k = 5$, $a = 2$, and show how to find $\sqrt{5}$ to three decimal places;
(ii) take $k = 5$ and $a = 3$, and show how this process converges;
(iii) explain why the method works. (Hint: use Newton-Raphson method on the function $f(x) = x^2 - k$.)

10   Using the idea of question 9, generate an iterative process for finding the cube root of any given number.

11   Repeat question 9 to find the nth root of any positive number.

12   Show by means of a sketch how the Newton-Raphson iterative formula

$$x_{n+1} = x_n - \frac{f(x_n)}{f'(x_n)}$$

will, under suitable conditions, give a sequence $\{x_n\}$ converging to a root of the equation $f(x) = 0$.

The equation $\tan x = 2x$ has one positive root α in the interval $(0, \frac{1}{2}\pi)$. Taking 1 as a first approximation x_1, apply the Newton-Raphson formula once to obtain a second approximation x_2, giving three significant figures in your result.

By considering the graph of $y = \tan x - 2x$ for $0 < x < \frac{1}{2}\pi$, or otherwise, show that any initial approximation x_1 such that $\alpha < x_1 < \frac{1}{2}\pi$ will produce a sequence converging to α, whereas not all initial approximations less than α will do so. *(C)*

13   Sketch the graph of $y = \cos x$ for $0 \leqslant x \leqslant 4\pi$. (An accurately plotted curve on graph paper is *not* necessary.) Use your sketch to find the *number* of positive roots of the equation $\cos x = \frac{1}{10}x$.

Prove that the equation of the tangent to the curve $y = \cos x$ at $(\frac{1}{2}\pi, 0)$ is $y = \frac{1}{2}\pi - x$.

By using $\frac{1}{2}\pi - x$ as an approximation for $\cos x$ (valid for x near $\frac{1}{2}\pi$), calculate an estimate of the smallest positive root of the equation $\cos x = \frac{1}{10}x$, giving your answer to two decimal places.

Show on a new sketch the part of the curve $y = \cos x$ near $x = \frac{1}{2}\pi$ and the tangent at $x = \frac{1}{2}\pi$. Hence determine whether the estimate of the root calculated above is larger or smaller than the correct value. *(C)*

14   Show that the equation $x^3 - x - 2 = 0$ has a root between 1 and 2. Using Newton's approximation with starting point 1·5 (and showing all relevant working) determine, by means of two iterations, an approximation to this root, giving your answer to two decimal places. *(JMB)*

15 Complex Numbers

15.1 Extensions of number systems

As was demonstrated in Chapters 2 and 7, one technique for solving algebraic equations is to spot factors of quadratic and other polynomial functions. The factor theorem states that

$$f(\alpha) = 0 \Leftrightarrow (x - \alpha) \text{ is a factor of } f(x)$$

and this is used to find the roots of a polynomial equation, since

$$f(\alpha) = 0 \Leftrightarrow \alpha \text{ is a root of the equation } f(x) = 0.$$

For quadratic equations, the method of completing the square leads to a formula for the solution. The solution of the equation $ax^2 + bx + c = 0$ is given by

$$x = \frac{-b \pm \sqrt{(b^2 - 4ac)}}{2a}.$$

The existence of one root or of two distinct roots of the equation depends upon the sign of the discriminant $\Delta = b^2 - 4ac$.

If $\Delta > 0$, then $\sqrt{\Delta}$ is a real number and the equation has two roots

$$x = \frac{-b + \sqrt{\Delta}}{2a} = \frac{-b + \sqrt{(b^2 - 4ac)}}{2a} \quad \text{and} \quad x = \frac{-b - \sqrt{\Delta}}{2a}.$$

If $\Delta = 0$, then we have the situation of a repeated root, $x = \dfrac{-b}{2a}$, and the graph of the quadratic touches the x-axis at the point $\left(\dfrac{-b}{2a}, 0\right)$.

If $\Delta < 0$, then the equation has no real solution, since no real number can be the square root of a negative number. This corresponds to the graph of the quadratic lying either totally above, or totally below, the x-axis and never meeting it.

In many situations, although there is no real solution to the quadratic equation when $\Delta < 0$, it is very convenient to deal with the roots of the equation as if they were numbers, even if not real numbers. This means that we have to enlarge our definition of number. We have done this before in extending the natural numbers to the integers, then to the rationals and then to the real numbers.

Consider the natural numbers $\mathbb{N}$. In this system of numbers, we can add and multiply numbers but we cannot always subtract and divide and still obtain a natural number. We cannot solve the equation $x + 5 = 2$ in the set of natural numbers. We have to extend $\mathbb{N}$ to the set $\mathbb{Z}$, the set of integers, by introducing negative numbers. Then $x + 5 = 2$ has a solution, $x = -3$, in $\mathbb{Z}$.

In the set $\mathbb{Z}$, we can add, subtract and multiply and still obtain an integer. We say that $\mathbb{Z}$ is closed under the three operations $+, -, \times$. However, we cannot always divide and obtain another integer. For instance, the equation $5x = 2$ has no solution in the set of integers. It is necessary to extend the set of integers to the set of rational numbers, that is, the set $\mathbb{Q}$, in order to be able to solve this equation. The solution in $\mathbb{Q}$ of the equation is $x = \frac{2}{5}$. In the set $\mathbb{Q}$, we can add, subtract, multiply and divide by a non-zero, so we say that $\mathbb{Q}$ is closed under the four operations $+, -, \times, \div$.

However, in the set $\mathbb{Q}$, we are still unable to solve the equation $5x^2 = 2$, because the real number $\sqrt{\frac{2}{5}}$ is irrational. In order to have a number system in which we can take roots of all positive numbers, and also to include all numbers which are represented by infinite decimals, we need to extend $\mathbb{Q}$ to the set of all real numbers, that is, $\mathbb{R}$. We can represent every number in $\mathbb{R}$ by a length along a line and so all real numbers are represented by all the points along an axis, Ox, which we refer to as the real line.

We, therefore, have a chain of number systems, each contained in the next, and each with the property that, in it, more equations can be solved than in its predecessor; $\mathbb{N} \subset \mathbb{Z} \subset \mathbb{Q} \subset \mathbb{R}$. It is possible to insert other number systems in between two members of this chain. For example,

$$\text{let } \mathbb{Q}\,(\sqrt{2}) = \{a + b\sqrt{2} : a, b \in \mathbb{Q}\}.$$

Then $\mathbb{Q}(\sqrt{2})$ is formed by adding $\sqrt{2}$ to the rationals and forming all possible real numbers by using the four processes of arithmetic. Under these four operations, $\mathbb{Q}(\sqrt{2})$ is closed, for, suppose that a, b, c, d are all rational numbers,

then
$$(a + b\sqrt{2}) + (c + d\sqrt{2}) = (a + c) + (b + d)\sqrt{2},$$
$$(a + b\sqrt{2}) - (c + d\sqrt{2}) = (a - c) + (b - d)\sqrt{2},$$
$$(a + b\sqrt{2})\,(c + d\sqrt{2}) = (ac + 2bd) + (ad + bc)\sqrt{2},$$

and
$$(a + b\sqrt{2}) \div (c + d\sqrt{2}) = \frac{(a + b\sqrt{2})(c - d\sqrt{2})}{(c + d\sqrt{2})(c - d\sqrt{2})}$$
$$= \frac{ac - 2bd}{c^2 - 2d^2} + \frac{bc - ad}{c^2 - 2d^2}\sqrt{2}, \quad c + d\sqrt{2} \neq 0.$$

In each of the above four equations, the right hand side is of the form $x + y\sqrt{2}$, where x and y are rational numbers, so all these numbers lie in $\mathbb{Q}\,(\sqrt{2})$. Thus $\mathbb{Q}\,(\sqrt{2})$ is closed under the four arithmetical operations.

The above process of forming the set of numbers $\mathbb{Q}(\sqrt{2})$ can be described as extending the set $\mathbb{Q}$ in order to include the numbers which are solutions of the equation $x^2 = 2$. We now do the same thing for the equation $x^2 + 1 = 0$, or $x^2 = -1$, and extend the real numbers, $\mathbb{R}$, by adding a new number $\sqrt{(-1)}$, which is a solution of the equation $x^2 = -1$. We define this new number by the notation

$$i = \sqrt{(-1)}, \text{ so that } i^2 = -1.$$

Then the equation $x^2 + 1 = 0$ will have two solutions, $x = i$ and $x = -i$. Also, we can factorise the quadratic function $x^2 + 1$, since $x^2 + 1 = (x - i)(x + i)$.

Note The notation $i = \sqrt{(-1)}$ is not universal. Many engineers use $j = \sqrt{(-1)}$ instead, because they reserve the symbol i for the rate of flow of current in electrical theory. However, the notation i is more common in mathematical texts.

The new number, i, is not a real number so it does not appear as a point on the real line Ox. It is called an *imaginary* number because it is not real. This is unfortunate since i is no more imaginary than $\sqrt{2}$, if we use the everyday meaning of the word imaginary. We must regard the words *real* and *imaginary* as mathematical words having a clearly defined mathematical meaning, quite distinct from their everyday use. We now have the real numbers and the new number i, and we then form a set of numbers, which is an extension of $\mathbb{R}$, by using all the processes of algebra. The new set of numbers is called the set of complex numbers and is denoted by $\mathbb{C}$. Thus $\mathbb{C} = \{a + ib: a, b \in \mathbb{R}\}$. In $\mathbb{C}$ we replace i^2 by -1, wherever it occurs.

The four arithmetical operations are defined on the complex numbers in a natural way, by extending the corresponding operations on the real numbers. Thus, for all real numbers a, b, c, d,

$$(a + ib) + (c + id) = (a + c) + i(b + d),$$
$$(a + ib) - (c + id) = (a - c) + i(b - d),$$
$$(a + ib) \times (c + id) = (ac + ibid) + (aid + ibc)$$
$$= (ac - bd) + i(ad + bc),$$
$$(a + ib) \div (c + id) = \frac{(a + ib)(c - id)}{(c + id)(c - id)} = \frac{ac - ibid + ibc - aid}{cc - idid + idc - cid}$$
$$= \frac{ac + bd}{c^2 + d^2} + i\frac{bc - ad}{c^2 + d^2}, \text{ if } c^2 + d^2 \neq 0.$$

The right-hand sides of the above equations are all complex numbers so that $\mathbb{C}$ is closed under the four operations of arithmetic. Also, all the properties of arithmetical and algebraic manipulation are still valid in $\mathbb{C}$. For example, addition and multiplication are both commutative (i.e. the order does not matter), and we identify

$$a + ib = a + bi = ib + a = bi + a.$$

Compare the above rules with those we had for $\mathbb{Q}(\sqrt{2})$.

Equality

Consider two equal complex numbers, $a + ib = c + id$, then

$$a - c = id - ib = i(d - b)$$

and, on squaring both sides,

$$(a - c)^2 = -(d - b)^2.$$

Since each square is positive, the left side of the equation is positive and the right side is negative. Since the only number which is positive and negative is zero, we conclude that $a - c = 0 = d - b$, and so $a = c$ and $b = d$. In the complex number $a + ib$, with a and b real, a is called the *real* part and b is called the *imaginary* part. Thus, when we equate two complex numbers, we put their real parts equal and also their imaginary parts equal, giving two real equations for one complex one.

This process is called *equating of real and imaginary parts* of two complex numbers which are equal. It is a very useful process since, when we have one equation in $\mathbb{C}$, we can then obtain two equations in $\mathbb{R}$.

Notation   If $z = x + iy$, with $x, y \in \mathbb{R}$, then $\text{Re}(z) = x$ and $\text{Im}(z) = y$.

A real number a is a complex number, since $a = a + i0$, and it has zero imaginary part. A complex number ib, which is of the form, $0 + ib$ and which has zero real part is called a pure imaginary number. Thus, the equation $x^2 = -2 = -1 \times 2$ has two pure imaginary roots, namely $x = i\sqrt{2}$ and $x = -i\sqrt{2}$. Similarly, the equation $x^2 = -9$ has two pure imaginary roots $3i$ and $-3i$.

EXAMPLE   *Express* $\dfrac{2-i}{3+4i}$ *in the form $a + ib$, where a and b are real.*

$$\frac{2-i}{3+4i} = \frac{(2-i)(3-4i)}{(3+4i)(3-4i)} = \frac{6-8i-3i+4i^2}{3^2-4^2i^2} = \frac{6-4-(8+3)i}{9+16}$$

$$= \frac{2}{25} - \frac{11}{25}i.$$

EXERCISE 15.1

1 Express in the form $a + ib$, $a, b \in \mathbb{R}$:
   (i) $(2 + 3i) + (5 + 7i)$,   (ii) $(3 - 4i) + (4 - 3i)$,   (iii) $(5 - 6i) + (2 - 9i)$,
   (iv) $(4 - i) - (3 + 2i)$,   (v) $(14 - 3i) - (3 - 7i)$,   (vi) $(1 - i) - (1 + i)$.
2 Simplify:
   (i) $3(4 + 2i) - 2(5 + i)$,   (ii) $6(3 + i) + 2(5 + 3i)$,   (iii) $2(7 - i) - 7(3 - 2i)$.
3 Write as a single complex number:
   (i) $(2 + 3i)(4 + i)$,   (ii) $(3 - 4i)(4 - 3i)$,   (iii) $(5 + 2i)(4 - 3i)$,
   (iv) $(1 + i)(1 - i)$,   (v) $(2 + 3i)^2$,   (vi) $3i(2 + 5i)$,   (vii) $(3 - i)(2 + i)(3 + 2i)$,
   (viii) $(4 - 2i)^2 - (3 + i)^2$,   (ix) $(2 - i)(3i)(4 + i)$,   (x) $\left(-\dfrac{1}{2} + \dfrac{\sqrt{3}}{2}i\right)^3$.

4 Express the quotient in the form $a + ib$, with a and b real:

(i) $\dfrac{(2+i)}{(3+2i)}$,   (ii) $\dfrac{5-3i}{3-4i}$,   (iii) $\dfrac{4i}{2-5i}$,   (iv) $\dfrac{1}{1-i}$,   (v) $\dfrac{5+4i}{5-4i}$,   (vi) $\dfrac{(2+3i)}{(5+i)^2}$,

(vii) $\dfrac{(3+i)^2}{(4-i)^2}$.

5 Consider the alternative way of writing a complex number, if $a, b \in \mathbb{R}$, $a + ib \equiv (a, b)$, as an *ordered pair*, or pair of coordinates.

(a) Write the following using this new notation:

(i) $(3+2i)+(5+i)=(8+3i)$,   (ii) $(4-2i)+(6i)=(4+4i)$,

(iii) $(3+4i)-(8-2i)=(-5+6i)$,   (iv) $(-4-2i)-(7)=(-11-2i)$,

(v) $3(2-5i)=(6-15i)$,   (vi) $2(3i)-3(1+i)=-3+3i$,

(vii) $(5+2i)(3-4i)=(23-14i)$,   (viii) $(1-2i) \div (2-i)=(\frac{4}{5}-\frac{3}{5}i)$.

(b) Using the ordered pair notation for complex numbers, complete the equation:

(i) $(2,4)+(-2,3)=(\ ,\ )$,   (ii) $-(4,-6)+(-3,5)=(\ ,\ )$,

(iii) $(4,7)-(\ ,\ )=(7,2)$,   (iv) $(5,6)\times(1,3)=(\ ,\ )$,   (v) $(1,2)\times(0,1)=(\ ,\ )$,

(vi) $(2,3)\times(\ ,\ )=(-5,-1)$,   (vii) $(\ ,\ )\times(4,1)=(3,22)$,

(viii) $(5,6)\div(1,3)=(\ ,\ )$,   (ix) $(\ ,\ )\div(2,4)=(14,8)$,

(x) $(a,b)+(c,d)=(\ ,\ )$,   (xi) $(a,b)\times(c,d)=(\ ,\ )$,

(xii) $(a,b)\div(c,d)=(\ ,\ )$.

6 Given that $z = -1 + 3i$, express $z + 2/z$ in the form $a + ib$, where a and b are real.   (*L*)

7 Given that $\dfrac{1}{x+iy} + \dfrac{1}{1+2i} = 1$, where x, y are real, find x and y.   (*L*)

8 Find the real numbers x and y given that $\dfrac{1}{x+iy} = 2 - 3i$.   (*L*)

9 Write in as simple a form as possible the complex number $\dfrac{2+5i}{5-2i}$.

15.2 Solution of polynomial equations

In the set of complex numbers, a quadratic equation, with real coefficients, will have two roots. These may be two different real roots, or two equal real roots (that is, a double root), or two complex roots. The three cases correspond to the parabola with the quadratic equation meeting the x-axis in two points, or touching it at one (double) point, or not meeting it at all. The graph of a cubic polynomial will always cross the x-axis at at least one point, corresponding to the fact that a cubic equation always has one real root. If the cubic function is factorised into the product of a linear factor corresponding to this real root, the other factor will be quadratic. Thus the cubic equation with real coefficients will always have three roots, of which one will be real and the other two may be real or complex. Two or three of the real roots may be equal.

There is a fundamental theorem of algebra, which cannot be proved here, stating that a polynomial equation of degree n, with real coefficients, has *n* roots in the set of complex numbers, provided that repeated roots are counted as many times as they are repeated. In fact, the same is true of a polynomial equation with complex coefficients, and so no further extension of the system of numbers, beyond the complex numbers, is needed to ensure that every polynomial can be factorised into linear factors. In this sense, the set $\mathbb{C}$, of complex numbers, is as large a number set as we need, whereas the set $\mathbb{R}$, of real numbers, is not large enough.

These ideas are applied now to the solution of polynomial equations. One difficulty should be mentioned. For a polynomial equation of degree higher than two, there is no formula for its solution, in the same way that there is for the solution of a quadratic equation. The only tool at our disposal is the factor theorem, as far as finding exact roots is concerned. Otherwise, if we can locate a real root approximately, we can use numerical methods to improve the approximation.

EXAMPLE 1 *Find the solution, in the set of complex numbers, of the quadratic equation $x^2 + x + 1 = 0$.*

Use the formula for the roots of a quadratic equation and replace $\sqrt{(-1)}$ by i wherever it occurs. The solution of the equation is

$$x = \frac{-1 \pm \sqrt{(1-4)}}{2} = \frac{-1 \pm \sqrt{(-3)}}{2} = \frac{-1 \pm i\sqrt{3}}{2}$$

so the two roots are $\frac{1}{2}(-1+i\sqrt{3})$ and $\frac{1}{2}(-1-i\sqrt{3})$.

EXAMPLE 2 *Find the real and complex roots of the cubic equation*

$$x^3 - 11x - 20 = 0.$$

Let $f(x) = x^3 - 11x - 20$, then we use the factor theorem to investigate as possible roots the factors of -20, that is, $\pm 1, \pm 2, \pm 4, \pm 5, \pm 10, \pm 20$.
$f(1) = -30, f(2) = -34, f(4) = 0, f(5) = 50, f(10) = 870, f(20) = 7760,$
$f(-1) = -10, f(-2) = -6, f(-4) = -40, f(-5) = -90, f(-10) = -910,$
$f(-20) = -7800$
Therefore, there is a real root $x = 4$ with a corresponding factor $(x - 4)$. Now

$$f(x) = (x-4)(x^2 + 4x + 5),$$

so we investigate the roots of $x^2 + 4x + 5 = 0$. The discriminant
$\Delta = 4^2 - 4 \times 1 \times 5 = -4$, so there are no further real factors of $f(x)$. The formula for the roots of a quadratic equation gives the solutions

$$x = \frac{-4 \pm \sqrt{(16 - 20)}}{2} = \frac{-4 \pm 2i}{2}, \quad \text{that is,} \quad x = -2 + i \text{ and } -2 - i,$$

with the corresponding linear factors $x - (-2 + i)$ and $x - (-2 - i)$. Finally, the cubic function $f(x)$ factorises into one real and two complex factors,

$$f(x) = (x-4)(x+2-i)(x+2+i)$$

and the equation $f(x) = 0$ has the solution set $\{4, -2+i, -2-i\}$.

EXERCISE 15.2

1   Find the roots of the equation, in the set of real numbers:
   (i) $x^2 + 4x + 3 = 0$ (ii) $2x^2 - 7x + 5 = 0$ (iii) $x^2 - 6x + 6 = 0$
   (iv) $x^2 + 6x + 9 = 0$ (v) $3x^2 + 5x - 1 = 0$ (vi) $4x^2 - 7x + 2 = 0$.

2   Find the roots of the equation, in the set of complex numbers:
   (i) $x^2 - 4x + 5 = 0$ (ii) $x^2 - 6x + 10 = 0$ (iii) $x^2 - 8x + 17 = 0$
   (iv) $x^2 + 12x + 40 = 0$ (v) $3x^2 + x + 1 = 0$ (vi) $x^2 - x + 1 = 0$.

3   Verify that the given linear polynomial is a factor of $f(x)$ and factorise $f(x)$ into
   a product of real polynomials, as far as possible:
   (i) $f(x) = 3x^2 - 4x + 1$, $x - 1$ (ii) $f(x) = 2x^2 + 5x + 2$, $x + 2$
   (iii) $f(x) = x^3 + 3x^2 + 2x$, $x + 1$ (iv) $f(x) = x^3 - 4x$, $x - 2$.

4   Factorise $f(x)$ into a product of real polynomials, as far as possible:
   (i) $f(x) = 2x^2 + 3x + 2$ (ii) $f(x) = x^2 + 8x + 17$
   (iii) $f(x) = x^2 - 9x + 20$ (iv) $f(x) = 3x^2 - x + 6$
   (v) $f(x) = x^3 - x^2 + x - 1$ (vi) $f(x) = x^4 + 7x^2 + 10$
   (vii) $f(x) = x^4 - x^3 - 6x^2$ (viii) $f(x) = x^3 + 2x^2 - 4x - 8$.

5   Draw a sketch of a polynomial function with the properties:
   (i) a quadratic with two real roots, with positive coefficient of x^2;
   (ii) a quadratic with one repeated root, with negative coefficient of x^2;
   (iii) a quadratic with two complex roots, with positive constant coefficient;
   (iv) a cubic with three distinct real roots, with positive coefficient of x^3;
   (v) a cubic with one repeated real root and one distinct real root, with
   coefficient of x^3 negative;
   (vi) a cubic with one real root and two complex roots, with positive
   coefficient of x^3;
   (vii) a quartic with two real and two complex roots, with negative coefficient
   of x^4;
   (viii) a quartic with one repeated real root and two complex roots, with
   positive coefficient of x^4.

6   Express in the form $a + ib$, where a and b are real, the complex number:
   (i) i^3, (ii) i^4, (iii) i^5, (iv) $\dfrac{1}{i}$, (v) $\dfrac{1}{i^2}$, (vi) $\dfrac{1}{i^3}$.

7   Write down the square of:
   (i) $2i$; (ii) $i\sqrt{5}$; (iii) $-7i$; (iv) $-i\sqrt{2}$.

8   Write down the two square roots of:
   (i) -5, (ii) -25, (iii) -8, (iv) -27.

9   Express the pair of zeros of the quadratic in the form $a + ib$ and $a - ib$:
   (i) $x^2 - 5x + 8$, (ii) $2x^2 + 3x + 4$, (iii) $3x^2 - x + 5$.
   (a) Write down the sum of the two complex zeros in each case.
   (b) Write down the product of the two complex zeros in each case.
   (c) Explain why the answers to (a) and (b) are all real.

15.3 Representation of complex numbers

You may have noticed a strong similarity between the addition and
subtraction of complex numbers and the addition and subtraction of two

dimensional column vectors. For example compare

$$(3+4i)+(-2+i)=(1+5i) \quad \text{with} \quad \binom{3}{4}+\binom{-2}{1}=\binom{1}{5}.$$

A similar correspondence occurs when we consider the multiplication by a real number, for example compare

$$4(-2+3i)=(-8+12i) \quad \text{with} \quad 4\binom{-2}{3}=\binom{-8}{12}.$$

The structure of $\mathbb{C}$ under the operations of addition and of multiplication by a real number is precisely the same as the structure of all two-dimensional column vectors under the same operations. Also, the equality of two complex numbers corresponds to the equality of the corresponding vectors.* This means that we can use the geometrical properties of vectors, which we met in Chapter 5, to gain insight into the behaviour of complex numbers under addition and multiplication by real numbers. Such a use of an exact correspondence of structure of two apparently different areas of mathematics is an extremely valuable tool.

The representation of complex numbers as vectors in two dimensions is known as the *Argand diagram*, or sometimes as the *complex plane*. A complex number $3+4i$ is represented by the vector $\binom{3}{4}=\overrightarrow{OP}$, where P is the point with coordinates $(3,4)$ (see Fig. 15.1). In the vector, the top number corresponds to the *real* part of the complex number, and so this real part corresponds to the component of the vector parallel to Ox. A real number is represented by a vector parallel to Ox. Therefore, the axis Ox is the *real axis*, that is, *the real number line*. In the Argand diagram, the real numbers are represented by points on the real axis, Ox. A complex number, which is not real, such as $a+ib$, with $b \neq 0$, is represented by the point with coordinates (a,b) off the real axis. A purely imaginary number, such as bi, will be represented by a vector $\binom{0}{b}$, parallel to the axis Oy, so this axis is called the *imaginary axis*, or the i *axis*. There is, therefore, a correspondence between complex numbers, vectors and coordinates:

the complex number $a+ib$ corresponds to the vector $\binom{a}{b}$ which corresponds to the point (a,b).

In this way, the complex numbers, $\mathbb{C}$, are seen as an extension of the real numbers, $\mathbb{R}$, into a second dimension. The basis $\left\{\binom{1}{0},\binom{0}{1}\right\}$ of the two dimensional vector space $O(x,y)$ corresponds to a basis $\{1,i\}$ of $\mathbb{C}$.

---

* This complete correspondence one to one of the elements and the same correspondence of the structure under the given operations is called an *isomorphism* of the two systems.

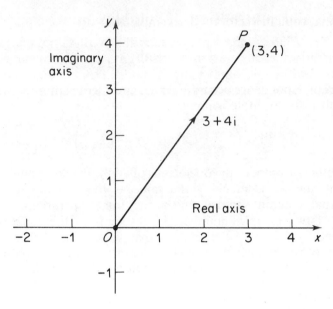

Fig. 15.1

EXERCISE 15.3A

1 Draw an Argand diagram and plot the points, draw in and label the vectors, which represent the following complex numbers:
(i) 1,   (ii) i,   (iii) -1,   (iv) $-i$,   (v) $1+i$,   (vi) $1-i$,   (vii) $-1+i$,
(viii) $-1-i$,   (ix) $3+4i$,   (x) $-4+3i$,   (xi) $-3-4i$,   (xii) $4-3i$.

2 Using the diagram you have drawn in question **1**, describe a geometrical transformation of the plane which transforms the first vector into the second vector, where the vector pair represent the given pair of complex numbers:
(i) 1, -1;   (ii) $3+4i$, $-3-4i$;   (iii) $1-i$, $-1+i$;   (iv) i, $-i$;
(v) $-1-i$, $-1+i$;   (vi) $1+i$, $1-i$;   (vii) 1, i;   (viii) $3+4i$, $-4+3i$;
(ix) $-4+3i$, $-3-4i$;   (x) 1, $-i$;   (xi) $3+4i$, $4-3i$;   (xii) -1, i.

3 Use the results of question **2** in order to pair off each of the following plane transformations with one of the operations on complex numbers:
(A) reflection in the axis Ox;   (a) multiply by -1;
(B) rotate (anticlockwise) 90°;   (b) multiply by i;
(C) rotate through 180°;   (c) multiply by $-i$;
(D) rotate through 270°;   (d) change the sign of i.

4 (a) Draw an Argand diagram to represent each of the complex numbers:
(i) $4+3i$,   (ii) $2-2i$,   (iii) $5+12i$,   (iv) $-6+8i$,   (v) $-3-i$.
(b) For each of the above, calculate the length of the vector and find the angle (in radians) between the vector and the positive real axis, measured positively anticlockwise.

5 Find the two square roots of $3-4i$ in the form $a+ib$, where a and b are real. Show, in an Argand diagram, the points P and Q representing these square roots.

Addition and subtraction of complex numbers

Suppose that a point $P(x, y)$ represents the complex number z in the Argand diagram, where $z = x + iy \in \mathbb{C}$. Then z is also represented by the vector $\overrightarrow{OP}$, and by any other vector equal to $\overrightarrow{OP}$. Consider two points $P_1(3, 4)$ and $P_2(-2, 1)$, representing z_1 and z_2, where $z_1 = 3 + 4i$ and $z_2 = -2 + i$ (see Fig. 15.2(a)).

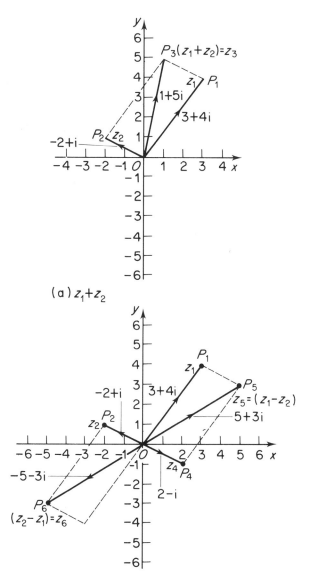

(a) $z_1 + z_2$

(b) $z_1 - z_2$ and $z_2 - z_1$

Fig. 15.2

Then $z_1 + z_2 = 1 + 5i = z_3$, the complex number represented by P_3, where $OP_1 P_3 P_2$ is a parallelogram. There is a correspondence between vector equations and complex number equations, thus

$$\overrightarrow{OP_3} = \overrightarrow{OP_1} + \overrightarrow{P_1 P_3} = \overrightarrow{OP_1} + \overrightarrow{OP_2} \quad \text{corresponds to } z_3 = z_1 + z_2, \text{ and}$$
$$\overrightarrow{OP_3} = \overrightarrow{OP_2} + \overrightarrow{P_2 P_3} = \overrightarrow{OP_2} + \overrightarrow{OP_1} \quad \text{corresponds to } z_3 = z_2 + z_1.$$

Similarly, the point P_4 $(2, -1)$ represents the number $z_4 = -z_2$, and P_5 $(5, 3)$ represents $z_5 = z_1 - z_2$, where $OP_4 P_5 P_1$ is a parallelogram, and P_6 $(-5, -3)$ represents

$$z_6 = z_2 - z_1 = -z_5 = -(z_1 - z_2) \text{ (Fig. 15.2(b)).}$$

EXERCISE 15.3B

1 Represent the complex number equation by means of vector triangles or polygons in the Argand diagram:
   (i) $(2 + 3i) + (5 + i) = (7 + 4i)$,   (ii) $(3 - 2i) - (4 + 3i) = (-1 - 5i)$,
   (iii) $2(4 - 3i) = (8 - 6i)$,   (iv) $-(3 - 2i) = (-3 + 2i)$,
   (v) $(2 + 3i) + (2 - 3i) = 4$,   (vi) $(2 + 3i) - (2 - 3i) = 6i$,
   (vii) $(1 + i) + (2 + 4i) + (-2 - 3i) = (1 + 2i)$,
   (viii) $(3 - 2i) + (4 + 3i) + (-7 - i) = 0$,
   (ix) $2(1) + 4(i) = (2 + 4i)$,   (x) $3(1 + i) + 6(1 - i) = (9 - 3i)$.

2 Given that $z_1 = (4 + 2i)$, $z_2 = (3 - 3i)$, on an Argand diagram, show the complex numbers z_1, z_2, $z_1 + z_2$, $z_1 - z_2$, $z_2 - z_1$.

3 Given that $z_1 = (3 + 4i)$, $z_2 = i$, on an Argand diagram show the numbers z_1, z_2, $z_1 z_2$, $z_1 z_2 z_2$, $z_1 z_2 z_2 z_2$, $z_1 z_2 z_2 z_2 z_2$. Explain, in geometrical terms, the effect that multiplication by i has on the vector representing z_1.

4 Given that $z_1 = (2 + i)$, $z_2 = 2i$, $z_3 = 3i$, $z_4 = 4i$, show, on an Argand diagram, the numbers z_1, $z_1 z_2$, $z_1 z_3$, $z_1 z_4$, $z_1 z_2 z_3$.
   Complete the following statement: "Multiplication of a complex number by ai (where a is real) is equivalent to the transformation, of the representative vector in the Argand diagram, given by a rotation of .... radians followed by an enlargement with scale factor ....."

5 Given that $z_1 = (3 - 2i)$, $z_2 = i$, calculate $\dfrac{z_1}{z_2}, \dfrac{z_1}{z_2^2}, \dfrac{z_1}{z_2^3}$, and draw the three vectors which represent these numbers on the Argand diagram. Explain the geometrical significance of division by i.

6 Given that $z_1 = 4 + 3i$, $z_2 = 1 + i$, calculate $z_1 z_2$ and draw vectors representing $z_1, z_2, z_1 z_2$, on an Argand diagram. Measure the lengths of the vectors and the angle between each vector and the real axis. Propose a geometrical transformation equivalent to multiplication by the complex number z_2.

15.4 Polar coordinates

The position of a point P in a plane is known when its position vector $\overrightarrow{OP}$ is known, where O is some chosen origin in the plane. In order to fix the vector $\overrightarrow{OP}$, we need to know its length and its direction. Suppose that

$OP = r$, then the length of $\overrightarrow{OP}$ is its modulus $|\overrightarrow{OP}| = r$. The direction of $\overrightarrow{OP}$ may be fixed by means of the angle that $\overrightarrow{OP}$ makes with some fixed line. If this line, called the initial line, is the axis Ox, then the direction of $\overrightarrow{OP}$ is fixed by the angle θ between $\overrightarrow{OP}$ and Ox. The angle θ is measured in radians and the angle is measured positively in an anticlockwise direction from Ox to $\overrightarrow{OP}$ (see Fig. 15.3). We note that the addition of an amount 2π to θ does not change the position of P.

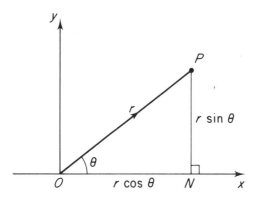

Polar coordinates (r, θ)

Fig. 15.3

Let PN be the perpendicular from P on to Ox, and let the coordinates of P, referred to Cartesian axes $O(x, y)$, be (x, y). The pair of numbers (r, θ) are called the *polar coordinates* of P and these are related to the Cartesian coordinates (x, y) by the equations

$$x = r\cos\theta, \quad r = \sqrt{(x^2 + y^2)},$$

$$y = r\sin\theta, \quad \theta \text{ is given by } \cos\theta = \frac{x}{\sqrt{(x^2 + y^2)}}, \quad \sin\theta = \frac{y}{\sqrt{(x^2 + y^2)}}.$$

Note that $r > 0$ and that the addition of an integer multiple of 2π to θ does not affect the position of the point with polar coordinates (r, θ). The curves $r = c$, where c is a constant, are concentric circles with their centre at the origin. The curves $\theta = \alpha$, where α is a constant, are radial lines extending outwards from the origin O.

Modulus and argument of a complex number

The use of polar coordinates in the complex plane leads to another way of expressing a complex number, called its *polar representation*. The modulus of the complex number z, where $z = x + iy$, is defined to be the length, or modulus, of its representative vector $\begin{pmatrix} x \\ y \end{pmatrix}$ in the Argand diagram, and the argument of z is defined to be the angle θ which $\begin{pmatrix} x \\ y \end{pmatrix}$ makes with the real axis Ox, measured positively in the anticlockwise sense, as usual. Using the letter r for the modulus, (r, θ) are then the polar coordinates of the point P in the Argand diagram representing the complex number z.

Definition   Let $z = x + iy$ be a complex number, with x, $y \in \mathbb{R}$, then
the *modulus* of z is $|z| = r = \sqrt{(x^2 + y^2)}$;
the *argument* of z is θ, where $x = r \cos \theta$ and $y = r \sin \theta$;
θ is denoted by arg z, and its principal value is when $-\pi < \theta \leqslant \pi$.

The choice of a principal value for the argument of a complex number is a matter of convenience. Generally, we think of the argument of z, not as a single angle α, but as the set of angles $\{\theta : \theta = \alpha + 2n\pi, n \in \mathbb{Z}\}$.

In terms of the modulus r and argument θ of a complex number z, the real part of z is $r \cos \theta$ and the imaginary part is $r \sin \theta$ so that

$$z = r \cos \theta + r \sin \theta\, i = r(\cos \theta + i \sin \theta).$$

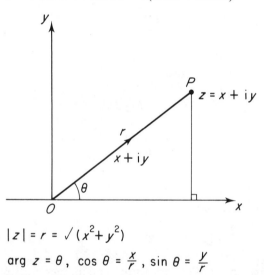

$$|z| = r = \sqrt{(x^2 + y^2)}$$

$$\text{arg } z = \theta, \quad \cos \theta = \frac{x}{r}, \quad \sin \theta = \frac{y}{r}$$

Fig. 15.4

Referring to Fig. 15.4, we can describe a complex number z in various ways:

Cartesian form	$z = x + iy$, real part x and imaginary part y;
polar form	$z = (r, \theta)$, modulus r and argument θ;
trigonometric form	$z = r(\cos \theta + i \sin \theta)$;
vector form	$\mathbf{z} = \begin{pmatrix} x \\ y \end{pmatrix}$;

with the relations

$$x = r \cos \theta, \quad y = r \sin \theta, \quad r = \sqrt{(x^2 + y^2)}.$$

EXAMPLE 1 *Express the complex numbers $z = -2 + 2i$ and $w = 1 - i\sqrt{3}$ in polar form. Show these two polar forms on one Argand diagram.*

$$|z| = \sqrt{((-2)^2 + 2^2)} = \sqrt{8} = 2\sqrt{2},$$

$$\arg z = \theta, \sin \theta = \frac{2}{2\sqrt{2}}, \cos \theta = \frac{-2}{2\sqrt{2}}, \theta = \frac{3}{4}\pi,$$

$$|w| = \sqrt{(1+3)} = 2,$$

$$\arg w = \phi, \sin \phi = -\frac{1}{2}\sqrt{3}, \cos \phi = \frac{1}{2}, \phi = -\frac{\pi}{3}.$$

These results are shown on the Argand diagram in Fig. 15.5.

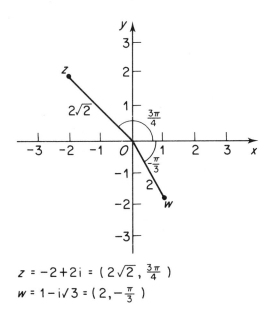

$z = -2 + 2i = (2\sqrt{2}, \frac{3\pi}{4})$

$w = 1 - i\sqrt{3} = (2, -\frac{\pi}{3})$

Fig. 15.5

EXAMPLE 2 *The complex numbers w and z are given in polar form $w = (2, \frac{\pi}{6})$ and $z = (3, \frac{\pi}{2})$. Calculate wz and express this complex number in polar form.*

$$w = (2, \tfrac{\pi}{6}) = 2\cos\tfrac{\pi}{6} + 2\sin\tfrac{\pi}{6}i = \sqrt{3} + i, \quad z = (3, \tfrac{\pi}{2}) = 0 + 3i = 3i.$$

$$wz = (\sqrt{3} + i)3i = 3\sqrt{3}i + 3i^2 = -3 + 3\sqrt{3}i,$$

so $|wz| = \sqrt{((-3)^2 + (3\sqrt{3})^2)}$, that is, $|wz| = \sqrt{(9 + 27)} = 6.$

Arg $(wz) = \theta$ where $\cos \theta = -\frac{3}{6} = -\frac{1}{2}$ and $\sin \theta = \frac{3\sqrt{3}}{6} = \frac{1}{2}\sqrt{3}$, so θ is in the

second quadrant and $\theta = \frac{2\pi}{3}$. Therefore, $wz = \left(6, \frac{2\pi}{3}\right) = \left(2, \frac{\pi}{6}\right) \times \left(3, \frac{\pi}{2}\right).$

Multiplication and division of complex numbers

In example 2, notice that $|wz| = |w|\,|z|$ and $\arg(wz) = \arg(w) + \arg(z)$. This result is true in general. It means that, although it is easier to add and subtract complex numbers when they are expressed in Cartesian form, it is much easier to multiply and divide complex numbers in polar form. The results are stated as a theorem.

Theorem 15.4 Suppose that $z_1 = (r_1, \theta_1)$ and $z_2 = (r_2, \theta_2)$, then
$$z_1 z_2 = (r_1 r_2, \theta_1 + \theta_2)$$
and, if $z_2 \neq 0$, $\qquad z_1/z_2 = (r_1/r_2, \theta_1 - \theta_2).$

Note that the arguments may be changed by an integer multiple of 2π. Put into words, we obtain the rules:

to multiply two complex numbers, multiply their moduli and add their arguments;

to divide two complex numbers, divide their moduli and subtract their arguments.

Proof $\begin{aligned}
z_1 z_2 &= (r_1 \cos\theta_1 + ir_1 \sin\theta_1)(r_2 \cos\theta_2 + ir_2 \sin\theta_2) \\
&= r_1 \cos\theta_1 \, r_2 \cos\theta_2 - r_1 \sin\theta_1 \, r_2 \sin\theta_2 \\
&\quad + ir_1 \sin\theta_1 \, r_2 \cos\theta_2 + ir_1 \cos\theta_1 \, r_2 \sin\theta_2 \\
&= r_1 r_2 (\cos\theta_1 \cos\theta_2 - \sin\theta_1 \sin\theta_2) \\
&\quad + ir_1 r_2 (\sin\theta_1 \cos\theta_2 + \cos\theta_1 \sin\theta_2) \\
&= r_1 r_2 \cos(\theta_1 + \theta_2) + ir_1 r_2 \sin(\theta_1 + \theta_2) \\
&= (r_1 r_2, \theta_1 + \theta_2) \text{ in polar form.}
\end{aligned}$

The proof for division is similar and is left as an exercise (Exercise 15.4, question 7).

EXERCISE 15.4

1 Draw the vectors, representing these complex numbers, on an Argand diagram and find the polar form of the numbers:
   (i) $1 + i$, (ii) $4 + 3i$, (iii) $5 - 12i$, (iv) $-12 + 5i$, (v) $4 - 4i$, (vi) $-6 - 8i$, (vii) $\sqrt{3} + i$, (viii) $-1 + i\sqrt{3}$, (ix) $2\sqrt{3} - 2i$, (x) $7 + 24i$, (xi) $3 - 4i$.

2 Rewrite, in Cartesian form, the complex numbers which are given in polar form:

   (i) $\left(2, \dfrac{1}{4}\pi\right)$, (ii) $\left(4, \dfrac{\pi}{6}\right)$, (iii) $\left(1, -\dfrac{1}{2}\pi\right)$, (iv) $\left(8, -\dfrac{\pi}{3}\right)$,

   (v) $\left(3, -\dfrac{5\pi}{6}\right)$, (vi) $\left(12, \dfrac{1}{2}\pi\right)$, (vii) $\left(1, \dfrac{3}{4}\pi\right)$,

   (viii) $\left(\sqrt{2}, -\dfrac{1}{4}\pi\right)$, (ix) $\left(2, \dfrac{\pi}{12}\right)$.

3 Find the product of the pair of complex numbers, (a) by direct multiplication, (b) by converting to polar form, multiplying by use of the rule, and then converting back:
(i) $(1+2i)(3+4i)$, (ii) $(5+12i)(2+2i)$, (iii) $(8-6i)(-1+i)$,
(iv) $(3+i)2i$, (v) $(4-5i)(7-8i)$, (vi) $(2+i)(3-5i)$.

4 (a) Write down the product $z_1 z_2$ and the quotient z_1/z_2, of the two numbers z_1 and z_2, given in polar form:

(i) $\left(2, \frac{1}{4}\pi\right), \left(3, \frac{1}{4}\pi\right)$; (ii) $\left(5, \frac{\pi}{3}\right), \left(2, \frac{\pi}{6}\right)$; (iii) $\left(1, \frac{\pi}{2}\right), \left(5, \frac{\pi}{12}\right)$;

(iv) $\left(1, \frac{3\pi}{4}\right), \left(7, -\frac{\pi}{3}\right)$; (v) $\left(2, -\frac{5\pi}{6}\right), \left(3, -\frac{3\pi}{4}\right)$;

(vi) $\left(2, \frac{\pi}{7}\right), \left(1, \frac{6\pi}{7}\right)$.

(b) For each of the six cases in part (a), draw the four vectors representing z_1, z_2, $z_1 z_2$, z_1/z_2.

5 Find the modulus and the argument of the complex number:
(i) $(1+i)^2$, (ii) $(1+i\sqrt{3})(\sqrt{3}+i)$, (iii) $(\frac{1}{2}+\frac{1}{2}\sqrt{3}i)^2$,

(iv) $\left(\frac{1}{\sqrt{2}}+\frac{i}{\sqrt{2}}\right)/(1-i)$, (v) $\left(\cos\frac{\pi}{6}+i\sin\frac{\pi}{6}\right)\left(\cos\frac{\pi}{4}+i\sin\frac{\pi}{4}\right)$,

(vi) $\left(\cos\frac{5\pi}{6}+i\sin\frac{5\pi}{6}\right)^3$, (vii) $\frac{(-1+i)}{(1-\sqrt{3}i)}$, (viii) $\frac{1+\sqrt{3}i}{-\sqrt{3}+i}$.

6 Given the complex numbers $z_1 = 2+i$ and $z_2 = 1+3i$. Find the vectors representing z_1+z_2, z_1-z_2, z_2-z_1, $z_1 z_2$, z_1/z_2, z_2/z_1. Draw these six vectors, together with z_1 and z_2, on an Argand diagram. List the eight vectors in increasing magnitude of their moduli.

7 The complex numbers z_1 and z_2 have polar form $z_1 = (r_1, \theta_1)$ and $z_2 = (r_2, \theta_2)$. By multiplying both the numerator and the denominator of

$$\frac{z_1}{z_2} = \frac{(r_1 \cos\theta_1 + r_1 \sin\theta_1 i)}{(r_2 \cos\theta_2 + r_2 \sin\theta_2 i)}$$

by $(r_2 \cos\theta_2 - r_2 \sin\theta_2 i)$, simplify this expression for $\frac{z_1}{z_2}$ and prove that

$$\frac{z_1}{z_2} = \left(\frac{r_1}{r_2}, \theta_1 - \theta_2\right).$$

8 Express $\dfrac{1}{1+i\sqrt{3}}$ in the form $r(\cos\theta + i\sin\theta)$ where $r > 0$ and $-\pi < \theta \leqslant \pi$.

(*JMB*)

9 (i) Find the modulus and argument of the complex number $\frac{1}{2}+i\frac{\sqrt{3}}{2}$.

(ii) Given that z_1 and z_2 are two complex numbers whose arguments are positive acute angles, express $|z_1 z_2|$ and $\arg(z_1 z_2)$ in terms of the moduli and arguments respectively of z_1 and z_2.

(iii) In an Argand diagram, O is the origin, and P represents $3 + i$. The point Q represents $a + bi$ (where a and b are both positive), and triangle OPQ is equilateral. Find a and b by calculation.   (C)

10   Find the modulus of each of the complex numbers

$$z_1 = 1 + 7i \text{ and } z_2 = -4 - 3i.$$

Hence, or otherwise, show that the modulus of z_1/z_2 is $\sqrt{2}$. Find also the argument of z_1/z_2.   (JMB)

11   Given that $\frac{1}{2}\pi < \theta < \pi$, find, in terms of θ, the modulus of $\cos^2 \theta + i \sin \theta \cos \theta$.   (L)

12   Given that $z = 4\left(\cos\dfrac{\pi}{3} + i \sin\dfrac{\pi}{3}\right)$ and $w = 2\left(\cos\dfrac{\pi}{6} - i \sin\dfrac{\pi}{6}\right)$, write down the modulus and the argument of each of the following:

(i) z,   (ii) w,   (iii) z^3,   (iv) $\dfrac{z^3}{w}$.

13   The complex numbers z_1, z_2, z_3, z_4 satisfy $\dfrac{z_1}{z_2} = \dfrac{z_3}{z_4}$. If $z_1 = 1 - 2i, z_2 = 4 + 3i$ and $z_3 = 10i$, find z_4, expressing your answer in the form $a + bi$.

Evaluate $|z_2 - z_1|^2$ and $|z_4 - z_3|^2$ and verify that $\dfrac{|z_4 - z_3|}{|z_2 - z_1|} = \dfrac{|z_3|}{|z_1|}$.   (C)

15.5 The triangle inequalities

In Fig. 15.6, the points P_1 and P_2 represent the complex numbers z_1 and z_2 in the Argand diagram. O is the midpoint of $P_2 P_4$ and $OP_1 P_3 P_2$ and $OP_1 P_5 P_4$ are parallelograms. Then P_3 and P_5 will represent the complex numbers $z_1 + z_2$ and $z_1 - z_2$, respectively.

Now $|z_1|$ is the length of $\overrightarrow{OP_1}$, $|z_2|$ is the length of $\overrightarrow{P_1 P_3}$ and $\overrightarrow{P_1 P_5}$,

$|z_1 + z_2|$ is the length of $\overrightarrow{OP_3}$, $|z_1 - z_2|$ is the length of $\overrightarrow{OP_5}$.

The length of one side of a triangle is always less than the sum of the lengths of the other two sides, because the shortest distance between two points is the straight line joining them. Therefore,

in the triangle $OP_1 P_3$, $|z_1 + z_2| \leqslant |z_1| + |z_2|$,

in the triangle $OP_1 P_5$, $|z_1| \leqslant |z_1 - z_2| + |z_2|$,

and $|z_2| \leqslant |z_1 - z_2| + |z_1|$.

The last two inequalities can be rearranged, to give

$$|z_1| - |z_2| \leqslant |z_1 - z_2| \text{ and } |z_2| - |z_1| \leqslant |z_1 - z_2|.$$

From the above results, we obtain the triangle inequalities, for any complex numbers z_1 and z_2,

$$|z_1 + z_2| \leqslant |z_1| + |z_2|,$$

and $$||z_1| - |z_2|| \leqslant |z_1 - z_2|.$$

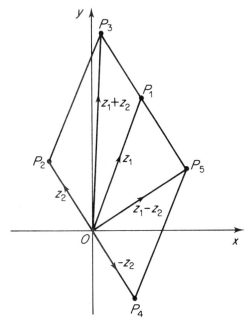

Fig. 15.6

EXERCISE 15.5

1 Let $\vec{OA}$ and $\vec{OC}$ be the vectors representing w and z, $w = 1 + 2i$ and $z = 4 + 3i$, respectively. Let B be the fourth vertex of the parallelogram $OABC$. Express $\vec{OB}$ in terms of w and z. Calculate $|w|$, $|z|$ and $|w + z|$, and show that $|w| + |z| > |w + z|$.

2 Find three complex numbers, z_1, z_2 and z_3, all distinct, such that

$$|z_1 + z_2| = |z_1| + |z_2|, \quad ||z_1| - |z_3|| = |z_1 - z_3|.$$

3 Given that $z_1 = 4 + i$ and $z_2 = 3 - 2i$, verify that:
(i) $|z_1| + |z_2| > |z_1 + z_2|$, (ii) $|z_1|^2 + |z_2|^2 < |z_1 + z_2|^2$.

4 Show, geometrically or otherwise, that for any two complex numbers z_1, z_2,

$$|z_1 + z_2| \geqslant |z_1| - |z_2|. \tag{L}$$

15.6 Complex conjugates

Let z be a complex number, with $z = x + iy$, x, y real. Then

the *conjugate* of z is defined as z^*, where $z^* = x - iy$.

This will mean that z is the conjugate of z^* so we call z and z^* a *pair of conjugates*. If $P(x, y)$ represents z in the complex plane, then $P^*(x, -y)$ represents z^*, so that P and P^* are reflections of one another in the real

axis Ox. Also
$$z + z^* = 2x \quad \text{and} \quad z - z^* = 2iy,$$
which means that the real part of z is $\frac{1}{2}(z + z^*)$ and the imaginary part of z is $\frac{1}{2i}(z - z^*)$.

The product of z with its conjugate z^* is the square of the modulus of z (or of the modulus of z^*, which is the same as that of z), for
$$zz^* = (x + iy)(x - iy) = x^2 - (iy)^2 = x^2 + y^2 = |z|^2.$$
So, if $|z| = r$, then $zz^* = r^2$ and the reciprocal of z is
$$z^{-1} = \frac{z^*}{r^2}.$$

We list some useful properties of conjugates, leaving the proofs as an exercise to the reader:

$$(z^*)^* = z;\ z + z^* \text{ and } zz^* \text{ are both real numbers;}$$
$$(z_1 + z_2)^* = z_1^* + z_2^*; \quad (z_1 - z_2)^* = z_1^* - z_2^*;$$
$$(z_1 z_2)^* = z_1^* z_2^*; \qquad (z_1/z_2)^* = z_1^*/z_2^*.$$

EXERCISE 15.6A

1   Write down the complex conjugate of:
   (i) $2 + 3i$, (ii) $3 - 4i$, (iii) 4, (iv) $3i$, (v) $\left(2, \dfrac{\pi}{4}\right)$, (vi) $\left(3, -\dfrac{3\pi}{4}\right)$.

2   Given that $z_1 = 3 + 4i$ and $z_2 = 4 - 3i$, verify that:
   (i) $(z_1^*)^* = z_1$, (ii) $(z_1 + z_2)^* = z_1^* + z_2^*$, (iii) $(z_1 - z_2)^* = z_1^* - z_2^*$,
   (iv) $(z_1 z_2)^* = z_1^* z_2^*$, (v) $(z_1/z_2)^* = z_1^*/z_2^*$, (vi) $z_1^{-1} = \dfrac{z_1^*}{|z_1|^2}$.

3   Writing z_1 and z_2 in Cartesian form, $z_1 = x_1 + iy_1$, $z_2 = x_2 + iy_2$, prove that:
   (i) $(z_1 + z_2)^* = z_1^* + z_2^*$, (ii) $(z_1 - z_2)^* = z_1^* - z_2^*$.

4   Writing z_1 and z_2 in polar form, $z_1 = (r_1, \theta_1)$, $z_2 = (r_2, \theta_2)$, prove that $(z_1 z_2)^* = z_1^* z_2^*$ and that $(z_1/z_2)^* = z_1^*/z_2^*$.

5   Prove that, for a complex number z:
   (i) $|z| = |z^*|$, (ii) $\arg(z) + \arg(z^*) = 0$, (iii) $\arg(zz^*) = 0$,
   (iv) $\arg(z/z^*) = 2 \arg(z)$.

6   Given that $z = -5 + 12i$, draw an Argand diagram on which you represent the complex numbers:
   (i) z, (ii) z^*, (iii) zz^*, (iv) $z + z^*$, (v) $z - z^*$, (vi) z/z^*, (vii) z^2,
   (viii) $(z^*)^2$, (ix) $(z^2)^*$, (x) $(z + z^*)^*$.

Roots of real polynomial equations

Consider a quadratic equation, with real coefficients and complex roots, that is, $ax^2 + bx + c = 0$ with a, b, c real numbers and with $\Delta = b^2 - 4ac < 0$. Let $\Delta = -k^2$, so that $\sqrt{\Delta} = ik$, then the roots of the quadratic equation are

$$z_1 = \frac{-b}{2a} + \frac{k}{2a}i \quad \text{and} \quad z_2 = \frac{-b}{2a} - \frac{k}{2a}i = z_1^*.$$

So the roots of a real quadratic equation are complex conjugates, if they are not real.

Let $f(x) = ax^2 + bx + c$ be a real quadratic function, so that $a, b, c \in \mathbb{R}$. Then, if z is a complex number $f(z) = az^2 + bz + c$ and so

$$f(z^*) = a(z^*)^2 + bz^* + c = a(z^2)^* + bz^* + c = (az^2 + bz + c)^* = (f(z))^*.$$

Therefore, if z is a root of the quadratic equation $f(x) = 0$, we find that $f(z) = 0$ and so $f(z^*) = f(z)^* = 0^* = 0$ and so z^* is also a root of the equation $f(x) = 0$. If z is a real number then $z = z^*$ and we have no extra information. However, if z is complex (and not real) we have a *second* root of the equation, namely $x = z^*$.

The proof of the factor theorem (§7.5) involved the manipulation of polynomials by means of the four operations of arithmetic, finding quotients and remainders, and all of this applies equally well to complex numbers as to real numbers. Therefore the factor theorem is repeated for complex numbers.

Factor theorem Let $f(x)$ be a polynomial in x, with complex or real coefficients, and let α be a complex number, then

$$(x - \alpha) \text{ is a factor of } f(x) \Leftrightarrow f(\alpha) = 0.$$

We apply this theorem to the quadratic function $f(x)$ with real coefficients, which has a complex (non-real) root z. Then $f(z) = 0$ and so $f(z^*) = f(z)^* = 0$, so that the roots are z and z^*. Then

$$f(x) = ax^2 + bx + c = a(x - z)(x - z^*).$$

Comparing coefficients of the powers of x,

$$\text{the sum of the roots} = z + z^* = -\frac{b}{a},$$

$$\text{the product of the roots} = zz^* = \frac{c}{a}.$$

These are the same results as were true for real roots. The results can be found by direct calculation from the form of the roots in terms of $k = -i\sqrt{\Delta}$, that is

$$z = \frac{-b + ki}{2a}, \quad \text{and} \quad z^* = \frac{-b - ki}{2a}.$$

More generally, suppose that $f(x)$ is a polynomial function, with real coefficients,

$$f(x) = a_n x^n + a_{n-1} x^{n-1} + \ldots + a_1 x + a_0, \ a_i \in \mathbb{R}, \ 0 \leqslant i \leqslant n.$$

Then, using the properties of conjugates, it will be seen that, for $z \in \mathbb{C}$,

$$f(z^*) = a_n z^{*n} + a_{n-1} z^{*n-1} + \ldots + a_1 z^* + a_0 = (f(z))^*.$$

If $x = z$ is a non-real solution of $f(x) = 0$, then $f(z) = 0$, so $f(z^*) = f(z)^* = 0$ and $x = z^*$ is also a solution of $f(x) = 0$. Therefore, $f(x)$ has as factors $(x - z)$ and $(x - z^*)$. This means that $f(x)$ has a quadratic factor

$$(x - z)(x - z^*) = x^2 - (z + z^*)x + zz^*,$$

which is a quadratic with real coefficients, since $z + z^*$ and zz^* are both real.

Thus a polynomial equation with *real* coefficients will have roots, which may be real or may be complex. But the *non-real roots* will occur in *conjugate pairs* and they will give rise to *quadratic factors* with *real* coefficients.

EXAMPLE   *Given that the polynomial equation* $x^4 + x^3 - 2x^2 + 2x + 4 = 0$ *has a root* $1 - i$, *find all the roots of this equation.*

Since the coefficients of the quartic are all real and the equation has the root $1 - i$, it must also have a root $(1 - i)^* = 1 + i$. Thus the quadratic factor is

$$(x - 1 + i)(x - 1 - i) = x^2 - 2x + 2.$$

We now divide this quadratic into the quartic to give the other quadratic factor

$$x^4 + x^3 - 2x^2 + 2x + 4 = (x^2 - 2x + 2)(x^2 + 3x + 2).$$

This second quadratic factor can be factorised by inspection as $(x + 2)(x + 1)$. By use of the factor theorem, the roots of the quartic equation are $\mathbf{1 - i, 1 + i, -2, -1}$.

EXERCISE 15.6B

1   The equation $x^3 - 7x^2 + 16x - 10 = 0$ has a root $3 + i$. Find the other two roots of this equation.

2   Given that $1 + 2i$ is one root of the equation
$$x^4 - 4x^3 - 15x^2 + 38x - 120 = 0$$
solve the equation.

3   Given that $2 + i$ is a root of the equation
$$z^3 - 11z + 20 = 0,$$
find the remaining roots.   (L)

4   Given that $z = 2 + 3i$ is a root of the equation
$$z^3 - 6z^2 + 21z - 26 = 0,$$
find the other two roots.   (L)

5   (i) Given that $3 + 4i = (x + iy)^2$, find x and y. Find also the square roots of i in the form $a + ib$, where a and b are real.
    (ii) Show that $1 + i$ is a root of the equation
$$z^3 - 4z^2 + 6z - 4 = 0$$
and find the other roots of this equation.   (L)

6 Obtain a quadratic function $f(z) = z^2 + az + b$, where a and b are real constants, such that $f(-1-2i) = 0$. (L)

7 (i) The equation $x^4 - 4x^3 + 3x^2 + 2x - 6 = 0$ has a root at $1 - i$. Find the three other roots.

(ii) Given that $1, \omega_1, \omega_2$ are the roots of the equation $z^3 = 1$ express ω_1 and ω_2 in the form $x + iy$ and hence, or otherwise, show that

(a) $1 + \omega_1 + \omega_2 = 0$, (b) $\dfrac{1}{\omega_1} = \omega_2$. (L)

15.7 Loci in the complex plane

The modulus and argument of a complex number give rise to algebraic descriptions of lines and circles in the complex plane. This is demonstrated by means of examples.

EXAMPLE 1 *Sketch the loci given by each of the two equations; $|z| = 2$ and $\arg(z) = \pi/3$. Find the complex number represented by the point of intersection of these loci.*

Since $|z|$ is the distance of the point z in the Argand diagram from the origin, the equation $|z| = 2$ gives the set of all points at a distance 2 units from O. The locus is the circle, centre O and radius 2. If the argument of z is $\pi/3$, then the vector representing z makes an angle $\pi/3$ with the x-axis. The locus is therefore a *half-line*, starting from the origin O, at an angle of $\pi/3$ with Ox. The two loci are shown in Fig. 15.7. They intersect at just one point, where $|z| = 2$ and $\arg(z) = \pi/3$. This is the point $z = (2, \pi/3) = 1 + i\sqrt{3}$.

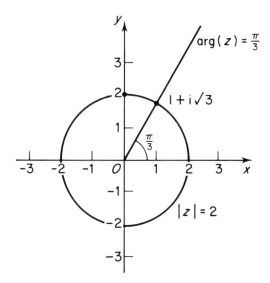

Fig. 15.7

EXAMPLE 2 *Describe the locus of z in the complex plane given by* arg $(z+3) = -\pi/4$.

Since $z+3 = z-(-3)$, if the complex numbers z and -3 are represented by P and A, then

$$\overrightarrow{AP} = \overrightarrow{OP} - \overrightarrow{OA} = z - (-3) = z + 3.$$

Therefore, the locus is the set of points, P, such that $\overrightarrow{AP}$ makes an angle $-\pi/4$ with the real axis, as shown in Fig. 15.8.

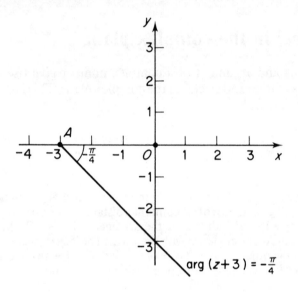

Fig. 15.8

EXAMPLE 3 *Draw a diagram showing the intersection of the two regions in the complex plane; given by:* (i) $|z-3| \geq |2i-z|$, (ii) $|z-(4-3i)| \leq 5$.

(i) As in Example 2, we let $A = 2i$, $B = 3$ and $P = z$, in the complex plane. Then $|z-3|$ is the distance BP and $|2i-z|$ is the distance AP. The equation $|z-3| = |2i-z|$ is the equation of the line of points equidistant from A and B, that is, the *mediator* (or *perpendicular bisector*) of AB (see Fig. 15.9). The region in which P must lie to satisfy the inequality $|z-3| \geq |2i-z|$ is that side of the line nearer to, and therefore containing, A.

(ii) $|z-(4-3i)|$ is the distance from the point z to the point $4-3i$. Let $4-3i$ be represented by C then the locus given by the equation $|z-(4-3i)| = 5$ is the circle, centre C, radius 5. Therefore, the region of the complex plane where the inequality $|z-(4-3i)| \leq 5$ is satisfied is the inside of the above circle.

The curves which are the boundaries of the regions (i) and (ii) are shown in Fig. 15.9. The required region, where the two inequalities, $|z-3| \geq |2i-z|$ and $|z-(4-3i)| \leq 5$, are satisfied, is shaded.

Note In the above example, the required inequalities include *equality*, so the required region of the plane includes the boundary of the region.

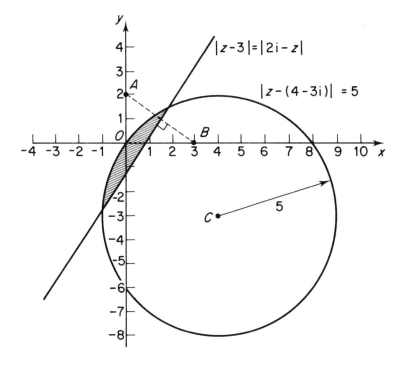

Shaded region: $|z-3| \geq |2i - z|$ and $|z-(4-3i)| \leq 5$

Fig. 15.9

Therefore, the boundary is shown as a solid curve. For a strict inequality, with equality excluded, the boundary could be dotted.

EXAMPLE 4 *The point P in an Argand diagram represents a complex number z. Given that z satisfies the equation* $2|z-2| = |z-6i|$, *show that P lies on a circle and find the radius and the centre of the circle.*

Let $z = x + iy$, then the equation can be manipulated as follows:

$$2|z-2| = |z-6i| \Leftrightarrow 2|(x-2)+iy| = |x+i(y-6)|$$
$$\Leftrightarrow 2\sqrt{\{(x-2)^2 + y^2\}} = \sqrt{\{x^2 + (y-6)^2\}}$$
$$\Leftrightarrow 4(x-2)^2 + 4y^2 = x^2 + (y-6)^2$$
$$\Leftrightarrow 4x^2 - 16x + 16 + 4y^2 = x^2 + y^2 - 12y + 36$$
$$\Leftrightarrow 3x^2 - 16x + 3y^2 + 12y = 20$$
$$\Leftrightarrow 3(x-8/3)^2 + 3(y+2)^2 = 20 + 64/3 + 12$$
$$\Leftrightarrow (x-8/3)^2 + (y+2)^2 = 160/9 = \left(\frac{4\sqrt{(10)}}{3}\right)^2.$$

The final equation is of a circle with **centre** $\frac{8}{3} - 2i$ and **radius** $(\frac{4}{3})\sqrt{(10)}$.

EXERCISE 15.7

1 Sketch the circle $|z-3| = 2$ on an Argand diagram. State the greatest value of $|z|$ when $|z-3| = 2$.   *(L)*

2 Sketch the circle $|z-2| = 2$ and the straight line $|z-i| = |z-1|$ on the same Argand diagram.   *(L)*

3 The points A, B and Z represent, in the Argand diagram, the complex numbers a, b and z respectively. If a and b are constant and z varies, describe in geometrical terms the locus of Z if
  (i) $|z-a| = |z-b|$,
  (ii) arg $(z-a) = \frac{1}{4}\pi$.
  If $a = 2+3i$, $b = -7i$ and $z = x+yi$, find, in simplified form, relations between x and y which determine each locus.   *(C)*

4 Express in the form $|z-a-ib| = R$ the equation of the circle in the Argand diagram which passes through the points given by $z = 4$, $z = 2i$ and $z = 4+2i$.   *(L)*

5 Indicate in an Argand diagram the region in which z lies, given that both
$$|z-1| \leqslant 1 \quad \text{and} \quad 0 \leqslant \arg z \leqslant \pi/4$$
are satisfied.

6 In the Argand diagram the fixed points A and B represent the complex numbers $z_1 = 2(\cos \pi/3 + i \sin \pi/3)$ and $z_2 = -2$ respectively, and the variable point P represents the complex number z. Show the positions of A and B on the Argand diagram and find
  (i) the modulus and argument of $(z_1 - z_2)$,
  (ii) the Cartesian equation of the locus of P if arg $(z - z_1) = 2\pi/3$, showing the locus on the Argand diagram.   *(JMB)*

MISCELLANEOUS EXERCISE 15

1 Given that $z_1 = 2+i$, $z_2 = 1 - 2i$ and $\dfrac{1}{z_3} = \dfrac{1}{z_1} - \dfrac{1}{z_2}$, find z_3 in the form $a + ib$, where a and b are real.   *(L)*

2 Given that $z_1 = 2+i$ and $z_2 = 1 + 2i$, express z_1/z_2 in the form $a + ib$, where a and b are real.   *(L)*

3 Find the complex numbers z and w satisfying the simultaneous equations
$$iz + (1+2i)w = 1,$$
$$(2+i)z + (2-i)w = -3.$$ *(JMB)*

4 Express $(6+5i)(7+2i)$ in the form $a+ib$. Write down $(6-5i)(7-2i)$ in a similar form. Hence find the prime factors of $32^2 + 47^2$.   *(JMB)*

5 Given that $(1-i)$ is a root of the equation
$$z^3 - 4z^2 + 6z - 4 = 0,$$
find the other roots.   *(L)*

6 If $z^2 = 3 - i4$, find the two values of z in the form $a + ib$, where a and b are real.   *(L)*

7 Find, in a simple form not involving i the quadratic equation whose roots are $r(\cos \theta \pm i \sin \theta)$, where $r > 0$.
  If this equation is $x^2 + 2px + q = 0$ deduce that $r = \sqrt{q}$, and express $\cos \theta$ in terms of p and q.   *(SMP)*

8 The roots of the quadratic equation $z^2 + pz + q = 0$ are $1 + i$ and $4 + 3i$. Find the complex numbers p and q.

It is given that $1 + i$ is also a root of the equation $z^2 + (a + 2i)z + 5 + ib = 0$, where a and b are real. Determine the values of a and b. *(JMB)*

9 Verify that both $-\frac{1}{2}$ and i are roots of the equation

$$2z^5 - 7z^4 + 8z^3 - 2z^2 + 6z + 5 = 0.$$

Find all the roots of this equation.

Show that the quartic equation satisfied by the non-real roots can be written in the form

$$(z - p)^4 + q = 0,$$

where p and q are integers, and so find the four fourth roots of -4, expressing each root in the form $a + ib$. *(JMB)*

10 (i) Given that α and β are the roots of the quadratic equation

$$2x^2 - 3x + 4 = 0,$$

form an equation with integer coefficients whose roots are $\alpha(\alpha + \beta)$ and $\beta(\alpha + \beta)$.

(ii) Find the set of real values of k, $k \neq -1$, for which the roots of the equation

$$x^2 + 4x - 1 + k(x^2 + 2x + 1) = 0$$

are

(a) real and distinct,

(b) real and equal,

(c) complex with positive real part. *(L)*

11 Given that the roots of the equation $x^2 - 2x + 3 = 0$ are α and β, find a quadratic equation whose roots are α^2 and β^2. *(L)*

12 In an Argand diagram, the origin and the point representing the complex number $(1 + i)$ form two vertices of an equilateral triangle. Find, in any form, the complex number represented by the third vertex, given that its real part is positive. *(L)*

13 (i) Express in modulus-argument form the complex numbers

(a) $-1 + i\sqrt{3}$, (b) $\dfrac{(1 + i)}{(1 - i)}$.

(ii) Find the pairs of values of the real constants a and b such that $7 + 24i = -(a + ib)^2$.

(iii) Three complex numbers α, β and γ are represented in the Argand diagram by the three points A, B and C respectively. Find the complex number represented by D when $ABCD$ forms a parallelogram having BD as a diagonal. *(L)*

14 (i) Given that $z_1 = 3 + 4i$ and $z_2 = -1 + 2i$, represent z_1, z_2, $(z_1 + z_2)$ and $(z_2 - z_1)$ by vectors in the Argand diagram. Express $(z_1 + z_2)/(z_2 - z_1)$ in the form $a + ib$, where a and b are real. Find the magnitude of the angle between the vectors representing $(z_1 + z_2)$ and $(z_2 - z_1)$.

(ii) One root of the equation $z^3 - 6z^2 + 13z + k = 0$, where k is real, is $z = 2 + i$. Find the other roots and the value of k. *(L)*

15 Given that $z_1 = -\dfrac{1}{2} + \dfrac{i\sqrt{3}}{2}$, obtain $|z_1|$ and $\arg z_1$. Represent z_1, $1/z_1$ and $(z_1 - 1/z_1)$ by vectors in an Argand diagram.

Find in algebraic form all the roots of the equation $z^3 - 1 = 0$. Represent these roots by points on an Argand diagram, indicating their polar coordinates.   (L)

16 Two non-zero complex numbers z_1 and z_2 are such that $|z_1 + z_2| = |z_1 - z_2|$. Represent $z_1, z_2, z_1 + z_2$ and $z_1 - z_2$ by vectors on an Argand diagram. Hence, or otherwise, find the possible values of $\arg\left(\dfrac{z_1}{z_2}\right)$.   (JMB)

17 In the complex plane the points P_1, P_2 correspond to the numbers $\alpha_1 + \beta_1 i$, $\alpha_2 + \beta_2 i$. What complex number represents the displacement $\overrightarrow{P_1 P_2}$, and what complex number can be used by multiplication to rotate $\overrightarrow{P_1 P_2}$ anticlockwise through an angle θ and enlarge $|\overrightarrow{P_1 P_2}|$ by a factor k?

The points A, B and C correspond respectively to the numbers $4\sqrt{3} + 2i$, $5\sqrt{3} + i$ and $6\sqrt{3} + 4i$. Write down the complex numbers z_1, z_2 representing the displacements $\overrightarrow{AB}$, $\overrightarrow{AC}$. Find z_3 such that $z_2 = z_3 z_1$. By writing z_3 in modulus-argument form, or otherwise, show that ABC is half an equilateral triangle ADC and give the complex number to which D corresponds.

The triangle ABC is now rotated through an angle of $\frac{1}{3}\pi$ anticlockwise about B. Find the new position of A.   (SMP)

18 Given that $z_1 = 1 + i\sqrt{3}$, $z_2 = 1 - i\sqrt{3}$, plot the points corresponding to z_1 and z_2 on an Argand diagram, and obtain the modulus and argument of each.

Show that $z_1^3 = z_2^3$, and indicate the points corresponding to $z_1 + z_2$, $z_1 z_2$ and z_1^3 on your diagram. Hence, or otherwise, obtain a quadratic equation with real coefficients which has z_1 as a root.

Find the values of the real constants a and b if the equation

$$z^3 + z^2 + az + b = 0$$

also has z_1 as a root.   (L)

19 If $a = \cos 3\theta + i \sin 3\theta$ and $b = \cos 7\theta + i \sin 7\theta$, find the modulus and argument of the complex number $c = a + b$. (You may assume that $0 < \theta < \frac{1}{10}\pi$.)   (SMP)

20 Sketch the locus in the Argand diagram of the point P representing z, where $|z - 1 + i| = 2$.   (L)

21 Find the modulus and argument of $z_1 = \sqrt{3} + i$. If $z_2 = \sqrt{3} - i$ express $q = z_1/z_2$ in the form $a + ib$ where a and b are real.

Plot z_1, z_2 and q on an Argand diagram and sketch the curve given by the equation

$$|z - z_2| = |q - z_1|.$$ (L)

22 Indicate on an Argand diagram the region in which z lies, given that both

$$|z - (3 + i)| \leqslant 3 \quad \text{and} \quad \frac{\pi}{4} \leqslant \arg[z - (1 + i)] \leqslant \frac{\pi}{2}$$

are satisfied.   (JMB)

23 (a) Express in the form $r(\cos\theta + i\sin\theta)$, where $r > 0$ and $180° < \theta \leqslant 180°$, each of the complex numbers $10i$, $-3 + 4i$, $\dfrac{10i}{-3 + 4i}$, giving each value of θ to the nearest $0.1°$.

(b) In each of the following two cases, show, by a clear drawing in an Argand diagram, the set of points representing z, given that

(i) $\arg(z-1) = \frac{1}{4}\pi$,

(ii) $\arg(z+i) - \arg(z-i) = \frac{1}{2}\pi$.

Using Cartesian co-ordinates, describe each of these sets.   (C)

24 Given that z is a variable complex number such that

$$|z - 2 - 2i| = 2,$$

show, on an Argand diagram, the locus of the point P which represents z. Hence, or otherwise, find

(i) the greatest value of $|z|$,

(ii) z in the form $x + iy$ when $\arg(z - 2 - 2i) = 2\pi/3$.   (JMB)

25 The real number 5 is represented on the Argand diagram by the point A and the complex numbers u, v and w are represented by the points U, V and W respectively. Interpret geometrically the conditions that

(i) $|u - 5| = 3$,   (ii) $\arg\left(\dfrac{u-5}{v-5}\right) = \pi/2$,   (iii) $w - u = u - 5$.

Given that these three conditions are all satisfied and also that

$$\left|\frac{u-5}{v-5}\right| = \left|\frac{v-5}{w-5}\right|$$

show that the triangles UAV and VAW are similar and find the length of AV.

(JMB)

26 (i) Find, without the use of tables, the two square roots of $5 - 12i$ in the form $x + iy$, where x and y are real.

(ii) Represent on an Argand diagram the loci $|z - 2| = 2$ and $|z - 4| = 2$. Calculate the complex numbers corresponding to the points of intersection of these loci.   (L)

27 The complex numbers $z_1 = \dfrac{a}{1+i}$, $z_2 = \dfrac{b}{1+2i}$, where a and b are real, are such that $z_1 + z_2 = 1$. Find a and b.

With these values of a and b, find the distance between the points which represent z_1 and z_2 in the Argand diagram.

28 Express the complex number $z_1 = \dfrac{11+2i}{3-4i}$ in the form $x + iy$ where x and y are real. Given that

$$z_2 = 2 - 5i,$$

find the distance between the points in the Argand diagram which represent z_1 and z_2.

Determine the real numbers α, β such that

$$\alpha z_1 + \beta z_2 = -4 + i.$$ (JMB)

29 Find the complex roots z_1, z_2 of the equation $z^2 - (\sqrt{3})z + 3 = 0$ and mark on an Argand diagram the points Z_1 and Z_2 representing them.

The points Z_1, Z_2, Z_3, Z_4 form a square $Z_1 Z_2 Z_3 Z_4$ which encloses the origin. Find the complex numbers z_3 and z_4 represented by the points Z_3 and Z_4.

Form a quadratic equation (with numerical coefficients) having roots z_3 and z_4.   (C)

30 Given that $z = 1 + i\sqrt{2}$, express in the form $a + ib$ each of the complex numbers

$$p = z + \frac{1}{z} \quad \text{and} \quad q = z - \frac{1}{z}.$$

In an Argand diagram, P and Q are the points which represent p and q respectively, O is the origin, M is the midpoint of PQ and G is the point on OM such that $OG = \frac{2}{3}OM$. Prove that the angle PGQ is a right angle.

(*JMB*)

31 If $z = \cos\theta + i\sin\theta$, prove that $\dfrac{1+z}{1-z} = i\cot\frac{1}{2}\theta$.

In an Argand diagram, the points O, A, Z, P, Q represent the complex numbers 0, 1, z, $1 + z$ and $1 - z$ respectively. Show these points on a diagram. Prove that $P\hat{O}Q = \frac{1}{2}\pi$ and find, in terms of θ, the ratio $\left|\dfrac{OP}{OQ}\right|$.

(*C*)

32 (i) Express the complex number $\dfrac{5 + 12i}{3 + 4i}$ in the form $a + ib$ and in the form $r(\cos\theta + i\sin\theta)$, giving the values of a, b, r, $\cos\theta$, $\sin\theta$.

(ii) The points in the Argand diagram representing the complex numbers z_1, z_2, w_1, w_2 are Z_1, Z_2, W_1, W_2, and O is the origin. If the triangles OZ_1Z_2 and OW_1W_2 are similar (and in the same sense) with the angles O, Z_1, Z_2 of the first triangle corresponding respectively to the angles O, W_1, W_2 of the second triangle, find the relation connecting z_1, z_2, w_1, w_2.

(*L*)

33 Two complex numbers z_1 and z_2 are given by $z_1 = 10 - 2i$ and $z_2 = 2 - 3i$.

Show that $\dfrac{z_1}{z_2}$ is of the form $k(1 + i)$ where k is real.

If $z = x + yi$ is any non-zero complex number such that $\dfrac{z_1}{z} = a(1 + i)$ where a is real, prove that $3x + 2y = 0$. Hence find the possible values of $\arg z$, giving your answers in degrees correct to the nearest degree. (Take $\arg z$ to be in the interval $-180° < \arg z \leqslant 180°$.)

(*C*)

34 (a) Express the complex number $z = \dfrac{1 + i}{3 - 2i}$ in the form $a + bi$ ($a, b \in \mathbb{R}$), and find the argument of z, giving your answer in radians correct to three significant figures. Write down the argument of z^2, and find the exact value of $|z^2|$.

(b) The conjugate of the non-zero complex number z is denoted by z^*. In an Argand diagram with origin O, the point P represents z and Q represents $1/z^*$. Prove that O, P and Q are collinear, and find the ratio $OP:OQ$ in terms of $|z|$.

(*C*)

35 In an Argand diagram, the point P represents the complex number z, where $z = x + iy$. Given that

$$z + 2 = \lambda i(z + 8),$$

where λ is a real parameter, find the Cartesian equation of the locus of P as λ varies.

If also

$$z = \mu(4 + 3i),$$

where μ is real, prove that there is only one possible position for P.

(*JMB*)

36 Sketch the circle C with Cartesian equation $x^2 + (y-1)^2 = 1$. The point P, representing the non-zero complex number z, lies on C. Express $|z|$ in terms of θ, the argument of z. Given that $z' = 1/z$, find the modulus and argument of z' in terms of θ.

Show that, whatever the position of P on the circle C, the point P' representing z' lies on a certain line, the equation of which is to be determined.
(JMB)

37 (i) Represent on the same Argand diagram the loci given by the equations $|z-3| = 3$ and $|z| = |z-2|$. Obtain the complex numbers corresponding to the points of intersection of these loci.

(ii) Find a complex number z whose argument is $\pi/4$ and which satisfies the equation
$$|z+2+i| = |z-4+i|.$$
(L)

38 (i) Given that $(1+5i)p - 2q = 3 + 7i$, find p and q when
(a) p and q are real, (b) p and q are conjugate complex numbers.

(ii) Shade on the Argand diagram the region for which $3\pi/4 < \arg z < \pi$ and $0 < |z| < 1$. Choose a point in the region and label it A. If A represents the complex number z, label clearly the points B, C, D and E which represent $-z$, iz, $z+1$ and z^2 respectively.
(L)

39 The complex number $z = x + iy$ is such that $\dfrac{z+3}{z-4i} = \lambda i$ where λ is real. Show that
$$x(x+3) + y(y-4) = 0.$$

If z is represented in an Argand diagram by the point P, deduce that, when λ varies, P moves on a circle. Find the radius of this circle and the complex number corresponding to its centre.
(JMB)

40 (i) Given that x and y are real, find the values of x and y which satisfy the equation
$$\frac{2y+4i}{2x+y} - \frac{y}{x-i} = 0.$$

(ii) Given that $z = x + iy$, where x and y are real,

(a) show that, when $\operatorname{Im}\left(\dfrac{z+i}{z+2}\right) = 0$, the point (x, y) lies on a straight line,

(b) show that, when $\operatorname{Re}\left(\dfrac{z+i}{z+2}\right) = 0$, the point (x, y) lies on a circle with centre $(-1, -\tfrac{1}{2})$ and radius $\tfrac{1}{2}\sqrt{5}$.
(L)

41 Given that $(a+ib)^2 = 1 + i2\sqrt{2}$, where a and b are real, find the possible pairs of values of a and b.
(JMB)

42 Given that α is the complex number $1 - \sqrt{3}i$, write $(z-\alpha)(z-\alpha^*)$ as a quadratic expression in z with real coefficients (where α^* denotes the complex conjugate of α).

Express α in modulus-argument form. Deduce the values of α^2 and α^3, and show that α is a root of
$$z^3 - z^2 + 2z + 4 = 0.$$
Find all three roots of this equation.

Plot these roots on the complex plane as triangle ABC (where vertex A corresponds to the root in the first quadrant, vertex B to the real root).

What complex number represents the displacement $\overrightarrow{BA}$? What complex number can be used by multiplication to rotate $\overrightarrow{BA}$ through 30° anticlockwise?

If, in a 30° anticlockwise rotation about B, $A \rightarrow A'$, find the complex number that corresponds to the point A'.   (SMP)

43 Using a scale of 1 cm to a unit, show on graph paper the point representing the complex number z such that $|z| = 3$ and $\arg z = \frac{1}{6}\pi$.

Show also on your diagram the points representing $2z$, iz and $w = (2+i)z$. (This should be done by construction, not calculation.)

Draw an arrow on your diagram to show a displacement corresponding to the complex number $w + 1$. Measure $|w + 1|$, giving your answer to one place of decimals. Measure $\arg (w + 1)$, and give its value in radians to one place of decimals.   (SMP)

44 A regular hexagon $ABCDEF$ in the Argand diagram has its centre at the origin O and its vertex A at the point $z = 2$.

(a) Indicate in a diagram the region in the hexagon in which both the inequalities $|z| \geq 1$ and $-\pi/3 \leq \arg z \leq \pi/3$ are satisfied.

(b) Find in the form $|z - c| = R$ the equation of the circle through the points O, B, F.

(c) Find the values of z corresponding to the points C and E.

(d) The hexagon is now rotated clockwise about the origin through an angle of 45°. Express in the form $r (\cos \theta + i \sin \theta)$ the values of z corresponding to the new positions of the points C and E.   (L)

45 (i) If $\operatorname{Im} \left(\dfrac{2z+1}{iz+1} \right) = -2$, show that the locus of the point representing z in the Argand diagram is a straight line.

(ii) If z_1 and z_2 represent points in the Argand diagram, show geometrically, or otherwise, that

$$|z_1| + |z_2| \geq |z_1 + z_2| \geq |z_1| - |z_2|.$$ (L)

Answers to Part A

Exercise 1.1A (p. 5)

1 (i) $\{a,b,c,d,e,f\}$ (ii) $\{a,c\}$ (iii) ϕ (iv) ϕ (v) $\{a,b,c,d\}$ (vi) $\{a,b,c,d,e\}$
(vii) $\{b,d\}$ (viii) $\{a,c\}$ (ix) $\{a,b,c,d\}$ (x) ϕ.
2 $\{a,b,c\}, \{a,b,d\}, \{a,b,e\}, \{a,c,d\}, \{a,\ c,e\}, \{a,d,e\}, \{b,c,d\}, \{b,c,e\}, \{b,d,e\}, \{c,d,e\}$.
3 (i) T   (ii) T   (iii) I   (iv) I   (v) F   (vi) T   (vii) T   (viii) F   (ix) T   (x) F.
4 (i) $\{-2,2\}$ (ii) ϕ (iii) $\{-1\}$ (iv) $\{0,1,2,3,4,5\}$ (v) $\{\pm4, \pm5, \pm6, \pm7\}$.
5 (i) ϕ, $\{1\}, \{2\}, \{1,2\}$ (ii) ϕ, $\{a\},\{b\},\{c\},\{d\}, \{a,b\}, \{a,c\}, \{a,d\}, \{b,c\},$
$\{b,d\}, \{c,d\}, \{a,b,c\}, \{a,b,d\}, \{a,c,d\}, \{b,c,d\}, \{a,b,c,d\}$.
6 (i) $\{0,2\}$ (ii) $\{2n+2:n\in\mathbb{N}\}$ (iii) $\{x:x \geqslant 3\}$ (iv) $\{x:2 \neq x$ and $x < 3\}$ (v) $\{2\}$
(vi) $\{0\}$ (vii) $\{0\}$ (viii) $\{x:x < 3$ or $x\in\mathbb{Z}\}$.
7 $x\in A \cap (B\cup C) \Leftrightarrow x\in A$ and $(x\in B$ or $x\in C) \Leftrightarrow (x\in A$ and $x\in B)$ or $(x\in A$ and $x\in C)$
$\Leftrightarrow x\in (A\cap B)\cup(A\cap C)$. Hence $A\cap(B\cup C) = (A\cap B)\cup(A\cap C)$.

Exercise 1.1B (p. 5)

1 (i) T   (ii) I   (iii) T   (iv) T   (v) I   (vi) T   (vii) F   (viii) F.
2 (i) T   (ii) F   (iii) T   (iv) F   (v) F   (vi) T   (vii) T   (viii) F   (ix) T.
3 (i) $\{x: x$ is a positive odd number less than $9\}$ (ii) $\{x: x = n^3, n\in\mathbb{N}, 1 \leqslant n \leqslant 4\}$
(iii) $\{x:x(x^2 - 4) = 0\}$.   **4** $\{-5, -4, -3, -2, -1, 0, 1, 2, 3, 4, 5\}$.
5 (i) T   (ii) T   (iii) F, any set containing just one integer   (iv) F, $\mathbb{Z}\setminus\{0\}$
(v) T   (vi) F,$\{0\}$ (vii) T   (viii) T   (ix) T   (x) F, $\{0,1\}$ (xi) F,$\{-1,2\}$
(xii) T   (xiii) F,$\{1\}$ (xiv) F,$\{2\}$ (xv) F,$\{x:x\in\mathbb{Z}, x \leqslant 1\}$.
6 A non-empty set A contains 2 subsets ϕ and A. The empty set is the only set with just
one subset.   **7** (i) $\{a\}, \{a,b\}, \{a,c\}, \{a,d\}, \{a,b,c\}, \{a,b,d\}, \{a,c,d\}, \{a,b,c,d\}$
(ii) $\{a,b\}, \{a,b,c\}, \{a,b,d\}, \{a,b,c,d\}$.   **8** (i) T   (ii) F   (iii) T   (iv) T   (v) T
(vi) T   (vii) T   (viii) F   (ix) F; $A = (0,4)$, $B = (2,5)$, $C = (1,3)$, $A\cap B = (2,4)$,
$B\cup C = (1,5)$, $(A\cap B)\cup C = (1,4) = A\cap(B\cup C)$.
9 (i) $P \not\Rightarrow R$, e.g. $A = \phi$, $R \not\Rightarrow P$ (ii) $Q \not\Rightarrow R$, $R \not\Rightarrow Q$
(iii) if $A\cap B \neq \phi$, then it contains an element of A which is in B, conversely a member of A
which is in B is in $A\cap B$, so $R\Leftrightarrow S$ (iv) $A\cup B \neq \phi \not\Rightarrow A\cap B \neq \phi$, $T \not\Rightarrow R$, $R \Rightarrow T$.

Exercise 1.2 (p. 10)

Throughout, $\mathbb{R}_0^+$ is used as defined in question **3**.
1 (i) $\{2,4,6,8\}$ (ii) $\{1,2,3,4\}$ (iii) $\{-3,0,5,12\}$ (iv) $\{1, \sqrt{2}, \sqrt{3}, 2\}$.
2 (i) $0\in\mathbb{Z}$, $f(0)\notin\mathbb{N}$ (ii) 4 elements in domain so not more than 4 in range
(iii) $2\in\mathbb{N}$, $f(x)^2 = x$ does not give unique $f(x)$, $\{\sqrt{2}, -\sqrt{2}\}$ (iv) $f(0)$ not defined.
3 Let $\mathbb{R}_0^+ = \mathbb{R}^+ \cup\{0\}$; (i) yes, $\mathbb{R}, \mathbb{R}$ (ii) yes, $\mathbb{R}$ (iii) yes, $\mathbb{R}, \mathbb{R}_0^+$ (iv) no
(v) yes, $\mathbb{R}, \mathbb{R}$ (vi) no   (vii) yes, $\{0\}, \{0\}$ (viii) yes, $\mathbb{R}_0^+, \mathbb{R}_0^+$.   **4** (i) $\mathbb{R}, \mathbb{R}$ (ii) $\mathbb{R}, \mathbb{R}_0^+$
(iii) $\mathbb{R}, \mathbb{R}$ (iv) $\mathbb{R}_0^+, \mathbb{R}_0^+$ (v) $\mathbb{R}, \{x:x \geqslant -1\}$ (vi) $\mathbb{R}\setminus\{2\}, \mathbb{R}\setminus\{0\}$ (vii) $\mathbb{R}^+, \mathbb{R}$ (viii) $\mathbb{R}, \mathbb{R}^+$
(ix) $\{x:x \leqslant -2\} \cup\{x:x \geqslant 2\}, \mathbb{R}_0^+$ (x) $\{x:-3 \leqslant x \leqslant 3\}, \{x:0 \leqslant x \leqslant 3\}$.
5 (i) $x^2, \mathbb{R}, \mathbb{R}_0^+$ (ii) $\sqrt{(-x)}, \{x:x \leqslant 0\}, \mathbb{R}_0^+$ (iii) $2x^2 + \sqrt{(-x)}, \{x:x \leqslant 0\}, \mathbb{R}_0^+$

(iv) $3x^2\sqrt{(-x)}, \{x:x\leqslant 0\}, \mathbb{R}_0^+$ (v) $x, \{x:x\leqslant 0\}, \{x:x\leqslant 0\}$
(vi) $x^2/\sqrt{(-x)}, \{x:x<0\}, \mathbb{R}^+$ (vii) $\sqrt{(-x)}/x^2, \{x:x<0\}, \mathbb{R}^+$.   **6** (i) 2
(ii) 4 (iii) 0.   **7**   (a), (c), (f).   **8** (i) $\mathbb{R}_0^+$ (ii) $\mathbb{Z}$ (iii) $\mathbb{R}_0^+$ (iv) $\{x:x\leqslant 0\}$ (v) $\mathbb{R}$
(vi) $\{1,-1\}$ (vii) $\{x:0\leqslant x<1\}$.

Exercise 1.3 (p. 12)

1 (i) $3x$ (ii) $-\frac{1}{2}x$ (iii) mx.   **2** (i) $x/3, 1/3$ (ii) $-3x/5, -3/5$ (iii) $2x/3, 2/3$
(iv) $3x/2, 3/2$ (v) $ax/b, a/b, (b\neq 0)$ (vi) $2(2-x)/3, -2/3$ (vii) $5x+3, 5$
(viii) $-5/3, 0$ (ix) $-(ax+c)/b, -a/b, b\neq 0$.   **3** $\{2\}$, graphs cross at $(2,4)$.

4 $f(x)=\dfrac{5-3x}{4}, g(y)=\dfrac{5-4y}{3}, g(x)=\dfrac{5-4x}{3}$.   **5** $-1, 3-x, x=3$.

6 $AB, 6-\dfrac{3x}{2}; BC, \dfrac{x-4}{8}; AC, \dfrac{2x+5}{3}; 90°, -1, -1$.   **7** $(-\frac{5}{2}, 3)$.

Exercise 2.1 (p. 15)

1 (i) $y-x$ (ii) $2x$ (iii) a (iv) $xy+2x-y$ (v) x^2+4 (vi) $5x^2+6x+1$
(vii) $3a^2-12b^2$ (viii) -6 (ix) $-4a+13b-3c$ (x) $r^2-s^2+2st-t^2$ (xi) $2ab-2b^2$
(xii) $x^3+3x^2y+3xy^2+y^3$ (xiii) $8x^3-36x^2+54x-27$ (xiv) a^3-b^3
(xv) $x^2+4y^2+9z^2-4xy+6xz-12yz$ (xvi) x^4-2x^2+1 (xvii) x^6+1

(xviii) $2abc+a^2b+bc^2-ac^2-a^2c-ab^2-b^2c$.   **2** (i) $\dfrac{x+y-1}{xy}$ (ii) $\dfrac{a^2-b^2}{ab}$

(iii) $\dfrac{15-2x}{12}$ (iv) $\dfrac{3}{x}$ (v) $\dfrac{5}{12x}$ (vi) $\dfrac{3y}{2x}$ (vii) $\dfrac{2x^2-3y^2}{xy}$ (viii) $\dfrac{3x-2y}{x^2y^2}$

(ix) $\dfrac{4x}{x^2-1}$ (x) $\dfrac{2x^2}{x-y}$ (xi) $\dfrac{x^3+xy^2+x^2-y^2}{(x^2-y^2)x}$ (xii) $\dfrac{2xy+y^2}{x^2-y^2}$.

3 (i) $2(a+b)$ (ii) $x(x+3)$ (iii) $x^2(x-1)$ (iv) $(a+c)b$ (v) $(a+b)(a-b)$
(vi) $(x+2y)(x-2y)$ (vii) $(6t+2)(6t-2)$ (viii) $b(a+c)(a-c)$ (ix) $(2x-1)(x+2)$
(x) $(2t-5)(t+6)$ (xi) $(x+y+z)(x+y-z)$ (xii) $(\sqrt{2}x+1)(\sqrt{2}x-1)(x+1)$
(xiii) $(a-b)(a^2+ab+b^2)$ (xiv) $(2x-3y)(4x^2+6xy+9y^2)$ (xv) $(r-st)(r^2+rst+s^2t^2)$
(xvi) $2(x+y)(x^2-xy+y^2)$ (xvii) $(a-b)(a+b)(a^2+b^2)$

(xviii) $(y+1)(y-1)(y^2+y+1)(y^2-y+1)$.   **4** (i) $\dfrac{-2b}{a^2-b^2}$ (ii) $\dfrac{2}{a^2+ab+b^2}$

(iii) $-\dfrac{x+2}{x+3}$ (iv) $\dfrac{y}{y^2-x^2}$ (v) q (vi) -2 (vii) $\dfrac{-1}{36}$ (viii) $\dfrac{5x-7}{x^3-4x^2+5x-2}$

(ix) $\dfrac{5a-8}{2a^2-8}$ (x) $\dfrac{a^2+b^2}{a^2-b^2}$ (xi) $\dfrac{4x}{1-x^4}$ (xii) $\dfrac{y}{x+y}$.
5 (i) $\sqrt{3}$ (ii) $4+\sqrt{3}$ (iii) $2+\sqrt{2}$ (iv) $\sqrt{6}$ (v) $9\sqrt{2}$ (vi) $\sqrt{6}-2\sqrt{3}$ (vii) $2\sqrt{2}$
(viii) $5\sqrt{2}+3\sqrt{5}-\sqrt{(10)}$ (ix) $6\sqrt{6}$ (x) 3 (xi) 12 (xii) $\frac{1}{2}$ (xiii) $3+2\sqrt{2}$
(xiv) $5-2\sqrt{6}$ (xv) $5\sqrt{6}$ (xvi) -1 (xvii) $a-b$ (xviii) $26+15\sqrt{3}$.

6 (i) $\dfrac{\sqrt{3}}{3}$ (ii) $\dfrac{2\sqrt{5}}{5}$ (iii) $\dfrac{\sqrt{6}}{2}$ (iv) $\dfrac{\sqrt{2}}{6}$ (v) $\sqrt{2}+1$ (vi) $\dfrac{\sqrt{5}-\sqrt{2}}{3}$

(vii) $\dfrac{\sqrt{6}-\sqrt{2}}{2}$ (viii) $\dfrac{10-2\sqrt{2}}{23}$ (ix) $3-2\sqrt{2}$ (x) $\dfrac{2\sqrt{3}-\sqrt{6}}{6}$ (xi) $7+5\sqrt{2}$

(xii) $\sqrt{(30)}+5-6\sqrt{2}-2\sqrt{(15)}$.   **7** (i) $3+2\sqrt{2}$ (ii) $2+2\sqrt{2}-\sqrt{3}-\sqrt{6}$

(iii) $2+2\sqrt{2}+\sqrt{3}+\sqrt{6}$ (iv) $3+\sqrt{2}+\sqrt{3}$ (v) $\dfrac{3\sqrt{2}+\sqrt{6}}{6}$ (vi) $1+\sqrt{2}+\sqrt{3}$

(vii) $4+2\sqrt{6}$ (viii) $\dfrac{2+\sqrt{2}-\sqrt{6}}{4}$ (ix) $4\sqrt{2}+2\sqrt{3}$.

Exercise 2.2 (p. 17)

1 (i) yes (ii) no (iii) no (iv) no (v) yes (vi) yes. **2** (i) $1, -2$ (ii) $-4, -5$
(iii) $\frac{1}{2}, -3$ (iv) $0, -\frac{2}{3}$ (v) 4 (vi) $\frac{5}{3}$ (vii) $\frac{3}{2}, -\frac{2}{3}$ (viii) a, b (ix) $-1, 3$ (x) $-2, 3$
(xi) $-\frac{1}{3}, \frac{11}{3}$ (xii) $\dfrac{b+c}{a}, \dfrac{b-c}{a}$. **3** (i) $(x-5)(x+3), 5, -3$ (ii) $(x-4)(x+3), 4, -3$
(iii) $(x-6)(x+9), 6, -9$ (iv) $(x+6)(x+7), -6, -7$ (v) $(x+24)(x-13), -24, 13$
(vi) $(3x-1)(x-1), \frac{1}{3}, 1$ (vii) $(2x+3)(x-4), -\frac{3}{2}, 4$ (viii) $(5x+2)(x-4), -\frac{2}{5}, 4$
(ix) $2(2x+5)(2x+1), -\frac{5}{2}, -\frac{1}{2}$ (x) $2(7x+3)(2x-1), -\frac{3}{7}, \frac{1}{2}$ (xi) $(3x-5)(3x-4), \frac{5}{3}, \frac{4}{3}$
(xii) $(x-17)(x-16), 17, 16$ (xiii) $2(x-5)(6x+1), 5, -\frac{1}{6}$ (xiv) $(3x-1)(2x+3), \frac{1}{3}, -\frac{3}{2}$
(xv) $(2x-7)(x+2), \frac{7}{2}, -2$ (xvi) $(x-2)^2, 2$ (xvii) $(x+2)(-2), -2$
(xviii) $(2x+1)(x-3), -\frac{1}{2}, 3$ (xix) as (xviii) (xx) $2(x-1), 1$.
4 (i) $x^2+4x+4 = (x+2)^2$ (ii) $x^2-10x+25 = (x-5)^2$ (iii) $s^2-3s+\frac{9}{4} = (s-\frac{3}{2})^2$
(iv) $x^2+2ax+a^2 = (x+a)^2$ (v) $x^2+x+\frac{1}{4} = (x+\frac{1}{2})^2$ (vi) $x^2+4xy+4y^2 = (x+2y)^2$.

5 (i) 36 (ii) 9 (iii) a^2 (iv) $\frac{9}{4}$ (v) 4 (vi) 1 (vii) $\frac{1}{2}$ (viii) $\frac{25}{12}$ (ix) $\dfrac{b^2}{4a}$.

6 (i) $(x-2)^2 = 3, 2+\sqrt{3}, 2-\sqrt{3}$ (ii) $(x-1)^2 = 5, 1+\sqrt{5}, 1-\sqrt{5}$
(iii) $(x-3)^2 = 2, 3+\sqrt{2}, 3-\sqrt{2}$ (iv) $(x-\frac{3}{2})^2 = \frac{5}{4}, \dfrac{3+\sqrt{5}}{2}, \dfrac{3-\sqrt{5}}{2}$

(v) $(2x-3)^2 = 2, \dfrac{3+\sqrt{2}}{2}, \dfrac{3-\sqrt{2}}{2}$ (vi) $(3x-1)^2 = 5, \dfrac{1+\sqrt{5}}{3}, \dfrac{1-\sqrt{5}}{3}$

(vii) $(x-a)^2 = a^2-b, a+\sqrt{(a^2-b)}, a-\sqrt{(a^2-b)}$ (viii) $(ax-1)^2 = 3, \dfrac{1+\sqrt{3}}{a}, \dfrac{1-\sqrt{3}}{a}$

(ix) $a\left(x+\dfrac{b}{2a}\right)^2 = \dfrac{b^2}{4a} - c, \dfrac{-b+\sqrt{(b^2-4ac)}}{2a}, \dfrac{-b-\sqrt{(b^2-4ac)}}{2a}$.

Exercise 2.3 (p. 21)

1 $(-1, 0), x = -1$ (ii) $(1, -4), x = 1$ (iii) $(-\frac{1}{2}, -\frac{9}{4}), x = -\frac{1}{2}$ (iv) $(\frac{3}{4}, \frac{121}{8}), x = \frac{3}{4}$
(v) $(\frac{1}{3}, \frac{1}{3}), x = \frac{1}{3}$ (vi) $(\frac{3}{4}, \frac{25}{8}), x = \frac{3}{4}$. **2** (i) $y-3 = (x-2)^2$, vertex downwards
(ii) $y-4 = -(x+3)^2$, vertex upwards.

Exercise 2.4 (p. 22)

1 As for question **3** of Exercise 2.2.

Exercise 2.5 (p. 24)

1 (i) $0, 1$ (ii) $-8, 0$ (iii) $0, 1$ (iv) $1, 2$. **2** (i) 2 (ii) 2 (iii) 0 (iv) 1
(v) 2 (vi) 1. **3** $x^2-8x+18 = (x-4)^2+2, \{x:x \geqslant 2\}$. **4** (i) $\{x:x \geqslant 8\}, 0$
(ii) $\{x:x \geqslant -\frac{25}{12}\}, 2$ (iii) $\{x:x \geqslant \frac{23}{16}\}, 0$ (iv) $\{x:x \leqslant 3\}, 2$ (v) $\{x:x \leqslant \frac{1}{4}\}, 2$
(vi) $\{x:x \leqslant -\frac{3}{4}\}, 0$. **5** (i) $1, 2, \{y:y \geqslant -\frac{13}{2}\}$ (ii) $1, 2, \{y:y \geqslant -\frac{125}{4}\}$
(iii) $1, 2, \{y:y \leqslant \frac{31}{3}\}$ (iv) $1, 1, \{y:y \leqslant 0\}$ (v) $1, 2, \{y:y \geqslant -1\}$ (vi) $1, 2, \{y:y \leqslant 1\}$.
6 (i) $f(x) = -\frac{1}{10}x^2 - \frac{1}{10}x + 2$ (ii) $f(x) = \frac{7}{6}x^2 - \frac{7}{6}x - 7$ (iii) $f(x) = x^2-4x+3$
(iv) $f(x) = -3x^2+6x+2$. **7** $x = 5, x = -3$. **8** $3(x-2)^2+2$, x-shift 2, y-stretch 3,
y-shift 2. **10** $f(0) = -8, x = \frac{4}{3}, x = -2, \{x:x < -2 \text{ or } x > \frac{4}{3}\}$.

Exercise 2.6 (p. 25)

1 Roots are real if $\Delta \geqslant 0$. We list Δ, sum, product of roots (i) $29, -3, -5$ (ii) $28, \frac{2}{3}, -\frac{2}{3}$
(iii) $52, -\frac{5}{2}, \frac{3}{4}$ (iv) $20d^2, -4d, -d^2$ (v) $12, 4, 1$ (vi) $41, \frac{3}{2}, -2$.
2 (i) $-9, 9, 29, 25, \frac{3}{5}, 13, -27, 45, -72$
(iii) $-15/2, 25/4, 13/4, 9/16, -10/3, 53/4, -125/8, -45/8, -10$
(v) $12, 16, 12, 1, 4, 33, 64, 12, 52$.

3 (i) $x^2 - 19x + 25, 5x^2 - 3x - 1, x^2 + 9x + 13, x^2 - 29, 5x^2 + 12x - 16, x^2 + 72x - 125$
(iii) $16x^2 - 76x + 9, 3x^2 + 10x + 4, 4x^2 + 30x + 53, 4x^2 - 13, 12x^2 + 70x + 49,$
$64x^2 + 640x + 27$ (v) $x^2 - 14x + 1, x^2 - 4x + 1, x^2 - 12x + 33, x^2 - 12, x^2 - 8x + 4,$
$x^2 - 52x + 1.$ **4** $p = -3, q = 19.$ **5** $\dfrac{a - b + c}{a}.$

Miscellaneous Exercise 2 (p. 26)

2 $q^2 x^2 - (p^2 - 2q)x + 1 = 0.$ **3** Hint: $x = 1$ is the common root.
5 (a) $p = \frac{1}{3}$ or -1, (b) $p > \frac{1}{3}$ or $p < -1; p = -2$ vertex $(-\frac{1}{2}, -\frac{7}{2})$ up; $p = 1$ vertex $(1, 4)$
down.   **6** $a = -1$ or $\frac{1}{4}.$ **7** $n > 3$ or $n < -3.$ **8** (b) $k \leqslant 0$ or $k \geqslant 3$ (c) $k \geqslant 3.$
10 $x^2 - 47x + 1 = 0.$ **11** $(-\frac{1}{4}, -\frac{121}{8}), (\frac{7}{4}, -\frac{185}{8}), (-\frac{9}{4}, -\frac{185}{8}).$
12 $k \leqslant 2$ or $k \geqslant 18$, $\{x : x \leqslant 2\} \cup \{x : x \geqslant 18\}.$
13 $9q - 2p^2.$ **14** $p = -\alpha - \beta, q = \alpha\beta, x^2 + 2px + 16q - 3p^2 = 0.$
15 $k = 7.$ **16** $3bc - b^3 - c - c^2.$ **17** $0, 0$ or $-1, 0$ or $1, 1$ or $-2, 1.$

Exercise 3.1 (p. 30)

2 (a) $A = 53\cdot1^\circ, C = 36\cdot9^\circ$ (b) $AB = 4\cdot6$, $BC = 3\cdot9, C = 50^\circ$ (c) $BC = 1\cdot8, AC = 5\cdot3.$
3 $196\cdot7^\circ, 599\,\text{km}.$ **4** (a) $17\cdot3\,\text{m}$ (b) $15\cdot3\,\text{m}.$ **5** $0\cdot0577\,\text{m}.$ **7** $(1 - 0\cdot8\cos\theta)\,\text{m}.$
10 $\tan\frac{1}{2}\theta$, if $\theta < 90^\circ.$ **11** (i) $\sqrt{(r^2 + h^2)}$ (ii) $h/\sqrt{(r^2 + h^2)}$ (iii) $r/\sqrt{(r^2 + h^2)}$
(iv) $\pi r \sqrt{(r^2 + h^2)}.$

Exercise 3.2A (p. 32)

1 $(+, +)(-, -)(+, -)(-, +)(+, +)(+, -)$

Exercise 3.2B (p. 35)

1 Angle	θ°	$-\theta^\circ$	$(180 + \theta)^\circ$	$(180 - \theta)^\circ$	$(90 + \theta)^\circ$	$(90 - \theta)^\circ$
Quadrant	1	4	3	2	2	1
	2	3	4	1	3	4
	3	2	1	4	4	3
	4	1	2	3	1	2

2 Let $\cos\theta = c, \sin\theta = s$: (i) c (ii) $-s$ (iii) $-s/c$ (iv) $-c$ (v) $-s$ (vi) s/c (vii) $-c$
(viii) s (ix) $-s/c$ (x) $-s$ (xi) c (xii) $-c/s$ (xiii) s (xiv) c (xv) $c/s.$
3 (i) F (ii) T (iii) F (iv) F (v) F (vi) T.   **4** (a) $\cos\theta = 3/5$ and $\tan\theta = 4/3$ or
$\cos\theta = -3/5$ and $\tan\theta = -4/3$ (b) $\cos\theta = 12/13$ and $\sin\theta = -5/13$ or
$\cos\theta = -12/13$ and $\sin\theta = 5/13.$

Exercise 3.2C (p. 36)

1 (a) $\mathbb{R} \backslash \{(2n + 1) \times 90 : n \in \mathbb{Z}\}, \{x : x \geqslant 1\} \cup \{x : x \leqslant -1\}, 360$
(b) $\mathbb{R} \backslash \{n \times 180 : n \in \mathbb{Z}\}, \{x : x \geqslant 1\} \cup \{x : x \leqslant -1\}, 360$ (c) $\mathbb{R} \backslash \{n \times 180 : n \in \mathbb{Z}\}, \mathbb{R}, 180.$
4 (i) $\cos\theta$ (ii) 1 (iii) 1 (iv) 2 (v) $\sec\theta$ (vi) $\tan\theta + \sec\theta$

Exercise 3.3 (p. 39)

1 (i) $\{210, 330\}$ (ii) $\{0, 45, 135, 180, 225, 315\}$ (iii) $\{60, 300\}$ (iv) $\{199\cdot5, 340\cdot5\}.$
2 (i) $\{90n : n \in \mathbb{Z}\}$ (ii) $\{36 + 72n, 360n : n \in \mathbb{Z}\}$ (iii) $\{30 + 120n, 90 + 360n : n \in \mathbb{Z}\}$
(iv) $\{135 + 180n : n \in \mathbb{Z}\}.$ **3** (i) $\{0\}$ (ii) $\{0, 90\}$ (iii) $\{90, 180\}$ (iv) $\{-90, -60, 60\}.$
4 (i) $\{135, 153\cdot43\}$ (ii) $\{30, 150\}$ (iii) $\{0, 90\}$ (iv) $\{30, 150\}.$
5 (a) $\{150, 210\}$ (b) $\{135, 315\}.$ **6** $\{90 + \alpha + 360n, 90 - \alpha + 360n : n \in \mathbb{Z}\}.$ **7** $\{\frac{1}{2}, \frac{1}{3}\}.$

Exercise 3.4A (p. 41)

1

x	$\cos x$	$\sin x$	$\tan x$	$\sec x$	$\operatorname{cosec} x$	$\cot x$
$\dfrac{2\pi}{3}$	$-\dfrac{1}{2}$	$\dfrac{\sqrt{3}}{2}$	$-\sqrt{3}$	-2	$\dfrac{2}{\sqrt{3}}$	$-\dfrac{1}{\sqrt{3}}$
$\dfrac{3\pi}{4}$	$-\dfrac{1}{\sqrt{2}}$	$\dfrac{1}{\sqrt{2}}$	-1	$-\sqrt{2}$	$\sqrt{2}$	-1
$\dfrac{5\pi}{6}$	$-\dfrac{\sqrt{3}}{2}$	$\dfrac{1}{2}$	$-\dfrac{1}{\sqrt{3}}$	$-\dfrac{2}{\sqrt{3}}$	2	$-\sqrt{3}$
π	-1	0	0	-1	—	—

Exercise 3.4B (p. 43)

1 $\{0, \frac{\pi}{3}, \pi\}$. **2** $\{\frac{\pi}{6}, \frac{5\pi}{6}, \frac{3\pi}{2}\}$. **3** $\{(n+\frac{1}{3})\pi, (2n+\frac{1}{6})\pi, (2n+\frac{5}{6})\pi: n \in \mathbb{Z}\}$.
4 $\{n\pi, (2n+\frac{2}{3})\pi, (2n+\frac{4}{3})\pi: n \in \mathbb{Z}\}$. **5** $\{\frac{\pi}{4}, \frac{\pi}{2}, \frac{3\pi}{4}\}$. **6** $\{\frac{\pi}{4}, \frac{\pi}{2}, \frac{3\pi}{4}\}$.
7 $\{\frac{\pi}{6}, \frac{5\pi}{6}\}$. **8** (a) $\{\frac{3\pi}{8}, \frac{7\pi}{8}, \frac{11\pi}{8}, \frac{15\pi}{8}\}$ (b) $\{0, \frac{2}{3}\pi, \frac{4}{3}\pi, 2\pi\}$.
9 $(x^2 - y^2)^2 = (x - 2y)^2 + (y - 2x)^2$.

Exercise 3.5 (p. 45)

1 (i) $12{\cdot}5$ m, $31{\cdot}25$ m^2 (ii) 6π cm, 24π cm^2 (iii) $\frac{5}{3}\pi$ m, $\frac{25}{12}\pi$ m^2
(iv) $0{\cdot}088\pi$ m, $0{\cdot}05808\pi$ m^2. **2** $28{\cdot}65°$. **3** $6{\cdot}64$ m^2, $10{\cdot}71$ m.
4 (i) $\dfrac{\pi}{6} - \dfrac{\sqrt{3}}{4} : \dfrac{5\pi}{6} + \dfrac{\sqrt{3}}{4}$ (ii) $\dfrac{4\pi}{3} - \sqrt{3} : \dfrac{2\pi}{3} + \sqrt{3}$ (iii) $1 : 6{\cdot}02$.
5 $\dfrac{a\pi}{a+b} - \dfrac{1}{2}\sin\left(\dfrac{2\pi a}{a+b}\right) : \dfrac{b\pi}{a+b} + \dfrac{1}{2}\sin\left(\dfrac{2\pi a}{a+b}\right)$. **6** $\left(\sqrt{3} - \dfrac{\pi}{6}\right)a^2$.

Exercise 3.6A (p. 47)

1 (a) (i) 2 (ii) $\sqrt{3}$ (iii) $\sqrt{2}$ (iv) 1 (v) 0 (vi) -1 (vii) $-\sqrt{2}$ (viii) $-\sqrt{3}$
(ix) -2 (b) (i) 0 (ii) $\frac{1}{4}$ (iii) $\dfrac{1}{2\sqrt{2}}$ (iv) $\dfrac{\sqrt{3}}{4}$ (v) $\frac{1}{2}$ (vi) $\dfrac{\sqrt{3}}{4}$ (vii) $\dfrac{1}{2\sqrt{2}}$ (viii) $\frac{1}{4}$
(ix) 0 (c) (i) 3 (ii) $\dfrac{3\sqrt{3}+4}{2}$ (iii) $\dfrac{7}{\sqrt{2}}$ (iv) $\dfrac{3+4\sqrt{3}}{2}$
(v) 4 (vi) $\dfrac{4\sqrt{3}-3}{2}$ (vii) $\dfrac{1}{\sqrt{2}}$ (viii) $\dfrac{4-3\sqrt{3}}{3}$ (ix) -3.
2 cosine shape with amplitude 5. **3** $\cos 2x$ (i) 1 (ii) $\frac{1}{2}$ (iii) 0 (iv) $-\frac{1}{2}$ (v) -1
(vi) $-\frac{1}{2}$ (vii) 0 (viii) $\frac{1}{2}$ (ix) 1, $\sin 2x$ (i) 0 (ii) $\dfrac{\sqrt{3}}{2}$ (iii) 1 (iv) $\dfrac{\sqrt{3}}{2}$
(v) 0 (vi) $-\dfrac{\sqrt{3}}{2}$ (vii) -1 (viii) $-\dfrac{\sqrt{3}}{2}$ (ix) 0, $\{\frac{\pi}{4} + \frac{1}{2}n\pi: n \in \mathbb{Z}\}$. **4** a, b, a, b.

Exercise 3.6B (p. 49)

1 (i) $1, -1, \pi, (0, 1), (\frac{\pi}{4}, 0), (-\frac{\pi}{4}, 0)$ (ii) $1, -1, 2\pi, (0, -\sin 1), (1 - \pi, 0), (1, 0)$
(iii) $1, 1, 2, (0, \cos 2), (\frac{\pi}{2} - 2, 0), (\frac{3\pi}{2} - 2, 0)$ (iv) $2, -2, 6\pi, (0, 0), (3\pi, 0), (-3\pi, 0)$
(v) $6, -6, \frac{4\pi}{5}, (0, 6\cos 2), (\frac{4-\pi}{5}, 0), (\frac{4-3\pi}{5}, 0)$ (vi) $5, -5, 8, (0, 0), (4, 0), (-4, 0)$.
2 $3\cos 8x$. **3** $a = 2, b = -2$ or $a = -2, b = 2$. **4** (i) 5 (ii) 1 (iii) $\frac{2}{3}\pi$.

Exercise 3.7 (p. 52)

3 Hint: $\tan(A+B) = \dfrac{\sin(A+B)}{\cos(A+B)}$.   **4** (i) $2\sin A\cos B$ (ii) $2\cos A\cos B$ (iii) $\cos 3A$

(iv) $\cos A$ (v) $\cos B$ (vi) $\tan B$ (vii) $\cot B$ (viii) $\cos A\sin 2B$ (ix) $\tan 2A$ (x) $\cos A - \sin A$
(xi) $\tan A$ (xii) $\cot A$ (xiii) $\cos A$ (xiv) $\cos A$. **5** (i) $-\frac{7}{25}, \frac{24}{25}, -\frac{24}{7}$ (ii) $-\frac{7}{25}, -\frac{24}{25}, \frac{24}{7}$
(iii) $-\frac{119}{169}, \frac{120}{169}, -\frac{120}{119}$ (iv) $-\frac{119}{169}, -\frac{120}{169}, \frac{120}{119}$ (v) $\frac{1519}{1681}, \frac{720}{1681}, \frac{720}{1519}$.
7 $\{\frac{3}{4}, 0, -1\}$, $\{131\cdot4°, 180°, 270°\}$, $\{\theta: 131\cdot4° < \theta < 180°\}$. **9** (i) $\{30°, 90°, 150°\}$

(ii) $\{120°\}$. **10** 1. **11** $\frac{1}{2}$. **12** $\tan\theta$. **13** $\dfrac{1+\tan\theta}{1-\tan\theta}$ (i) $2+\sqrt{3}$ (ii) $2\sec 2\theta$. **14** $\frac{16}{33}$.

Exercise 3.8 (p. 58)

1 (i) $C = 50°$, $a = 11\cdot35$, $b = 9\cdot62$ (ii) $A = 30°$, $a = 7\cdot57$, $b = 14\cdot04$
(iii) $B = 46°$, $b = 2\cdot52$, $c = 0\cdot79$ (iv) $B = 61°$, $a = 13\cdot33$, $c = 21\cdot52$. **2** (i) $B = 22\cdot8°$,
$C = 142\cdot2°$, $c = 4\cdot74$ or $B = 157\cdot2°$, $C = 7\cdot8°$, $c = 1\cdot05$
(ii) $A = 45\cdot6°$, $C = 52\cdot4°$, $a = 3\cdot61$ (iii) $A = 55\cdot2°$, $C = 86\cdot8°$, $c = 14\cdot6$ or $A = 124\cdot8°$,
$C = 17\cdot2°$, $c = 4\cdot32$ (iv) $A = 17\cdot5°$, $B = 12\cdot5°$, $b = 4\cdot33$ (v) $B = 70\cdot4°$, $C = 16\cdot6°$, $b = 6\cdot6$
(vi) $B = 28\cdot3°$, $C = 110\cdot7°$, $c = 25\cdot66$. **3** (i) $B = 44\cdot4°$, $C = 101\cdot6°$, $a = 4\cdot0$
(ii) $A = 80\cdot8°$, $B = 41\cdot2°$, $c = 10\cdot31$ (iii) $A = 53\cdot5°$, $C = 15\cdot5°$, $b = 10\cdot46$
(iv) $A = 41\cdot4°$, $B = 55\cdot8°$, $C = 82\cdot8°$ (v) $A = 90°$, $C = 67\cdot4°$, $B = 22\cdot6$
(vi) $A = 21\cdot8°$, $B = 120°$, $C = 38\cdot2°$. **4** 5 m. **5** $-\frac{1}{5}$. **6** $46°34'$.
7 (a) $10/\sqrt{3}$ cm (b) $50/\sqrt{3}$ cm². **8** (i) (a) $\{36\cdot9, 143\cdot1\}$ (b) $\{228\cdot6, 311\cdot4\}$.
9 (a) 5 km (b) 330° (c) 7·05 km.

Miscellaneous Exercise 3 (p. 59)

1 (i) (a) $\{105°, 165°, 285°, 345°\}$ (b) $\{90°, 180°, 270°\}$ (ii) $38\cdot36°$.
2 $120°, 60°$. **3** $61\cdot0°, 73\cdot7°, 134\cdot8°, 10\cdot8$ m. **4** $\{5, 6, 7\}$.
6 $0 < \theta < \frac{\pi}{3}$, $\cos\theta \equiv \dfrac{2p^2 - 1}{2p^2}$, $x = 0\cdot37$.

8 Either $A = (180n + 45)°$, $n \in \mathbb{Z}$ or $B = (180n - 45)°$, $n \in \mathbb{Z}$.
9 $\{\frac{3}{4}\pi, \frac{7}{4}\pi\}$. **10** $\{30°, 150°, 210°, 330°\}$. **11** $0\cdot6, 0\cdot8$.
12 (i) $\{\frac{\pi}{3}, \frac{5\pi}{3}, \pi - \cos^{-1}\frac{1}{3}, \pi + \cos^{-1}\frac{1}{3}\}$ (ii) (a) 13 (b) $67\cdot4$; $232\cdot6°, 352\cdot6°$.
14 (a) $p = 5$, $q = 2$ (c) $2\cdot35$ hours. **15** $A = 2n\pi$ or $B = 2n\pi$ or $(A + B) = 2n\pi$, $n \in \mathbb{Z}$.

Exercise 4.1 (p. 62)

2 $3/5, 8, -5/3$. **3** $1/3, (3,4)$. **4** (i) 3, (ii) 18, (iii) -9, (iv) -4.
5

x	1	1·3	1·6	1·8	1·9	2	2·1	2·2	2·4	2·7	3
$f(x)$	1	2·38	4·12	5·48	6·22	7	7·82	8·68	10·52	13·58	17
grad. PQ	6	6·6	7·2	7·6	7·8	—	8·2	8·4	8·8	9·4	10

gradient of tangent is 8.

Exercise 4.2 (p. 64)

1 (d) $56\,\text{ms}^{-1}$

Exercise 4.7 (p. 71)

1 (i) $5x^4$ (ii) $-4x^{-5}$ (iii) $14x^6$ (iv) $-3/x^2$ (v) $-4/x^3$ (vi) $2x+2$ (vii) $2x$
(viii) $3+4x$ (ix) $9x^2+2$ (x) $4x^3-12x^2+4x$ (xi) $-3-8x$ (xii) $5x^4-20x^3$
(xiii) $2\cos x+3\sin x$ (xiv) $-\sin x-\cos x$ (xv) $3\cos 3x$. **2** (i) $8x-6$ (ii) $2x-1$
(iii) $6x^2+6x$ (iv) $1-\dfrac{1}{x^2}$ (v) $4x^3$ (vi) $2x-\dfrac{2}{x^3}$. **3** (i) $3x^2-2$ (ii) $1\sin 3x$ (iii) $1-\dfrac{1}{x^2}$

(iv) $6x - 5$ (v) $4 - \dfrac{2}{x^3}$ (vi) $1 + 2\sin 2x$ (vii) $6x - 8x^3$ (viii) $24x^2 + 24x + 6$ (ix) $2 - \dfrac{2}{x^2}$

(x) $3x^2 - 3 - \dfrac{3}{x^2} + \dfrac{3}{x^4}$. 4 (i) $1 - 6t$ (ii) $4\pi r^2$ (iii) $u + at$ (iv) $-\dfrac{25}{V^2}$.

5 (i) $12, y = 12x - 46$ (ii) $0, y = -1$. 6 (i) $2, y = 2x - 3$ (ii) $6, y = 6x - 2$
(iii) $4/3, 3y = 4x + 20$. 7 $-10, -6, -2, 2, 6\,\mathrm{ms}^{-1}$; $\tfrac{5}{3}$s, 5s, $10\,\mathrm{ms}^{-1}$.
8 $-\tfrac{5\pi}{12}\sin\tfrac{\pi}{12}(x + 3)$, 13 m. 9 (a) 2 (b) $24\,\mathrm{ms}^{-1}$.

Exercise 5.2 (p. 77)

2 (i) $\overrightarrow{OD}$ (ii) $\overrightarrow{OJ}$ (iii) $\overrightarrow{OE}$ (iv) $\overrightarrow{OK}$ (v) $\overrightarrow{OM}$ (vi) $\overrightarrow{OQ}$ (vii) $\overrightarrow{ON}$ (viii) $\overrightarrow{OL}$ (ix) $\overrightarrow{OP}$.
3 (i) $2\mathbf{a}$ (ii) $3\mathbf{a}$ (iii) $2\mathbf{b}$ (iv) $2\mathbf{a} + \mathbf{b}$ (v) $\mathbf{a} + 2\mathbf{b}$ (vi) $2\mathbf{a} - \mathbf{b}$ (vii) $3\mathbf{b} - 2\mathbf{a}$ (viii) $-\mathbf{a} - 2\mathbf{b}$
(ix) $-4\mathbf{b}$ (x) $-4\mathbf{a} - \mathbf{b}$. 4 (i) $\overrightarrow{OC}, \overrightarrow{AE}, \overrightarrow{PF}$ (ii) $\overrightarrow{BP}, \overrightarrow{HG}, \overrightarrow{ID}$ (iii) $\overrightarrow{EO}, \overrightarrow{HB}, \overrightarrow{GP}$
(iv) $\overrightarrow{GO}, \overrightarrow{KD}, \overrightarrow{HA}$. 5 (i) $\mathbf{t} - \mathbf{s}$ (ii) $\mathbf{s} - \mathbf{t}$ (iii) $2\mathbf{t} - \mathbf{s}$ (iv) $2\mathbf{s} - 2\mathbf{t}$ (v) $\mathbf{t} - \mathbf{s}$.

Exercise 5.3 (p. 79)

1 (i) $\mathbf{r} = \mathbf{c} + \lambda(\mathbf{c} + \mathbf{d})$ (ii) $\mathbf{r} = 2\mathbf{d} + \lambda\mathbf{c}$ (iii) $\mathbf{r} = 3\mathbf{c} + \lambda\mathbf{d}$ (iv) $\mathbf{r} = 2\mathbf{d} + \mathbf{c} + \lambda(2\mathbf{c} + \mathbf{d})$
(v) $\mathbf{r} = 3\mathbf{c} + \lambda(\mathbf{d} - \mathbf{c})$ (vi) $\mathbf{r} = 2\mathbf{c} + \lambda(2\mathbf{c} + \mathbf{d})$. 2 Line through (i) $\{N, F, D\}$
(ii) $\{H, D, K\}$ (iii) $\{O, G\}$ (iv) $\{C, I\}$ (v) $\{D, C\}$. 3 (i) $\mathbf{r} = \mathbf{a} + \lambda\mathbf{b}$ (ii) $\mathbf{r} = \lambda(\mathbf{a} - \mathbf{b})$
(iii) $\mathbf{r} = \tfrac{1}{2}\mathbf{b} + \lambda\mathbf{a}$ (iv) $\mathbf{r} = (1 - \lambda)\mathbf{a} + \lambda\mathbf{b}$. 4 (i) Bisector of angle POQ
(ii) line through P parallel to $\overrightarrow{OQ}$ (iii) line through O parallel to $\overrightarrow{PQ}$ (iv) line PQ
(v) plane OPQ. 5 (i) (a) $k = 1$ (b) $k = \tfrac{1}{2}$ (c) $k = \tfrac{1}{3}$ (ii) $\overrightarrow{OD} = \mathbf{b} + \mathbf{c}, \overrightarrow{OE} = \mathbf{c}$.
7 $\overrightarrow{BA} = \mathbf{a} - \mathbf{b}, \overrightarrow{OD} = \mathbf{a} - \mathbf{b} + \mathbf{c}$.

Exercise 5.4 (p. 84)

1 $\mathbf{b} + \mathbf{d}, \tfrac{1}{2}\mathbf{b} + \mathbf{d}, \tfrac{1}{3}\mathbf{b} + \tfrac{2}{3}\mathbf{d}$. 2 Hint: prove $\overrightarrow{EF} = \overrightarrow{HG}$.
4 $\mathbf{q} - \mathbf{p}, -\mathbf{p}, -\mathbf{q}, \mathbf{p} - \mathbf{q}, 2\mathbf{p} - 2\mathbf{q}, \mathbf{p} - 2\mathbf{q}$. 5 $\tfrac{1}{2}\mathbf{a} - \tfrac{1}{2}\mathbf{b}, \tfrac{1}{2}\mathbf{a} + \tfrac{1}{2}\mathbf{b}, \tfrac{1}{2}\mathbf{b} - \tfrac{1}{2}\mathbf{a}, -\tfrac{1}{2}\mathbf{a} - \tfrac{1}{2}\mathbf{b}$.
6 $\tfrac{1}{2}\mathbf{b} + \tfrac{1}{2}\mathbf{c}, \tfrac{1}{2}\mathbf{c} + \tfrac{1}{2}\mathbf{a}, \tfrac{1}{2}\mathbf{a} + \tfrac{1}{2}\mathbf{b}$. 8 $\tfrac{1}{2}\mathbf{b} + \tfrac{1}{2}\mathbf{c}, \tfrac{1}{3}(\mathbf{a} + \mathbf{b} + \mathbf{c})$. 9 $\tfrac{1}{4}\mathbf{a} + \tfrac{1}{2}\mathbf{b}, \tfrac{1}{8}\mathbf{a} + \tfrac{1}{8}\mathbf{b} + \tfrac{3}{4}\mathbf{c}$.
10 8. 12 (ii) $\tfrac{1}{3}\overrightarrow{PQ} + \tfrac{2}{3}\overrightarrow{PS}, -\tfrac{2}{3}\overrightarrow{PQ} + \tfrac{2}{3}\overrightarrow{PS}, -\tfrac{1}{6}\overrightarrow{PQ} + \tfrac{1}{6}\overrightarrow{PS}$.

Exercise 5.5 (p. 87)

1 $\mathbf{b} + \mathbf{d}, \tfrac{1}{2}\mathbf{b} + \mathbf{d}, \tfrac{1}{3}\mathbf{b} + \tfrac{2}{3}\mathbf{d}$. 2 $\tfrac{3}{4}\mathbf{a} + \tfrac{3}{4}\mathbf{b}, 3\mathbf{a}, 3\mathbf{b}$. 3 $\tfrac{1}{2}\mathbf{c} - \tfrac{1}{2}\mathbf{b}, 2\mathbf{b}, \tfrac{3}{4}\mathbf{b} + \tfrac{1}{4}\mathbf{c}$.
4 $\tfrac{1}{3}\overrightarrow{AB} + \tfrac{2}{3}\overrightarrow{AC}$.

Miscellaneous Exercise 5 (p. 89)

1 (a) $\tfrac{1}{2}\mathbf{b} + \lambda(\mathbf{a} - \tfrac{1}{2}\mathbf{b})$ (b) $\tfrac{1}{2}\mathbf{a} + \mu(\mathbf{b} - \tfrac{1}{2}\mathbf{a}), \tfrac{1}{3}\mathbf{a} + \tfrac{1}{3}\mathbf{b}$. 2 (i) $\tfrac{1}{3}\mathbf{a} + \tfrac{2}{3}\mathbf{b}$
(ii) $\tfrac{1}{6}\mathbf{a} + \tfrac{1}{3}\mathbf{b}, \tfrac{2}{5}, -6$. 3 $2\mathbf{c} - \mathbf{b}, \tfrac{1}{3}\mathbf{a} + \tfrac{2}{3}\mathbf{b}, \tfrac{1}{5}\mathbf{a} + \tfrac{4}{5}\mathbf{c}$. 4 $\mathbf{b} - \mathbf{a}, \mathbf{b} - 2\mathbf{a}, 2\mathbf{a} - 2\mathbf{b}$.
5 $\tfrac{1}{2}\mathbf{a} + \tfrac{1}{2}\mathbf{b}, \tfrac{1}{8}\mathbf{a} + \tfrac{1}{8}\mathbf{b} + \tfrac{3}{4}\mathbf{c}$. 6 R is midpoint of CU, where U divides AB in the ratio $1:2$,
R divides AT in the ratio $2:1$, where T divides BC in the ratio $3:1$.
7 $\mathbf{a} + \lambda(\tfrac{1}{2}\mathbf{b} + \tfrac{1}{2}\mathbf{c} - \mathbf{a}), \mathbf{b} + \mu(\tfrac{4}{3}\mathbf{c} - \tfrac{1}{3}\mathbf{a} - \mathbf{b}), \tfrac{1}{7}(-\mathbf{a} + 4\mathbf{b} + 4\mathbf{c})$. 8 $\tfrac{1}{4}\mathbf{a} + \tfrac{1}{4}\mathbf{b} + \tfrac{1}{4}\mathbf{c}$.

Exercise 6.1 (p. 92)

1 $3x^2 + 2, x^3 + c, x^2 + x + c, c \in \mathbb{R}$. 2 (i) $2x$ (ii) x^2 (iii) 1 (iv) $3x^2$ (v) $3x^2$
(vi) 0 (vii) $4x^3$ (viii) $4x^3$ (ix) $\tfrac{3}{2}x^{\frac{1}{2}}$ (x) $2x + 2$ (xi) $x^{-\frac{1}{2}} + x^{-\frac{3}{2}}$ (xii) $\tfrac{1}{4}x^{-\frac{3}{4}} - \tfrac{3}{4}x^{-\frac{7}{4}}$.
3 (i) $\tfrac{1}{3}x^3 + c$ (ii) $\tfrac{1}{4}x^4 + c$ (iii) $\tfrac{2}{3}x^{\frac{3}{2}} + c$ (iv) $\tfrac{1}{2}x^2 - \tfrac{2}{3}x^{\frac{3}{2}} + c$ (v) $\tfrac{1}{3}x^3 + \tfrac{7}{2}x^2 + 7x + c$
(vi) $\tfrac{1}{3}x^3 + \tfrac{7}{2}x^2 + c$ (vii) $7x + c$ (viii) $\dfrac{x^4}{16} + cx + d$ (ix) $\tfrac{4}{7}x^{\frac{7}{4}} + \tfrac{4}{3}x^{\frac{3}{4}} + c, c \in \mathbb{R}$.

Exercise 6.3 (p. 94)

2 (i) $2x^3 + c$ (ii) $2x^2 - 3x + c$ (iii) $\tfrac{1}{5}x^5 + c$ (iv) $\tfrac{1}{2}\sin 2x + c$ (v) $\tfrac{1}{4}x^4 - x^2 + c$
(vi) $\tfrac{1}{7}x^7 + c$. 3 (i) $\tfrac{3}{4}x^2 + c$ (ii) $\tfrac{2}{x} + c$ (iii) $\dfrac{-5}{x} + x + c$ (iv) $x + \tfrac{1}{x} + c$

(v) $\frac{1}{3}x^3 + x^2 + x + c$ (vi) $\frac{1}{3}x^3 - \frac{1}{2}x^2 - 6x + c$.   **4**   (i) $x^3 + x^2 + x + c$

(ii) $2x^3 - \frac{11}{2}x^2 + 4x + c$ (iii) $x - \frac{1}{2}\cos 2x + c$ (iv) $\frac{1}{5}x^5 + 2x - \dfrac{1}{3x^3} + c$

(v) $\frac{1}{3}ax^3 + \frac{1}{2}bx^2 + cx + d$ (vi) $4x^{\frac{1}{2}} + 2x^{\frac{3}{2}} + c$.   **5**   (i) $\frac{1}{3}x^3 + x^2 + c$ (ii) $\frac{1}{3}t^3 + t^2 + c$

(iii) $-\frac{1}{2}\cos 2\theta + c$ (iv) $u^2 + \frac{2}{3}u^{\frac{3}{2}} + c$ (v) $\frac{1}{4}s^4 + 4s^3 + 24s^2 + 64s + c$

(vi) $\frac{1}{3}u^3 + 2u - \frac{1}{u} + c$.

Exercise 6.4 (p. 95)

1 $2x^2 + c, c = -14$.   **2**   (i) $2x^2 + 4$ (ii) $x^3 - 3x^2 + 3x - 1$ (iii) $x^3 + 6x^2 + 12x + 8$

(iv) $\sin 2x + \cos 2x$.   **3** $s = 6$.   **4**   (i) $44\frac{3}{4}$ (ii) $11\frac{1}{4}$.   **5**   (i) $s = ut - \frac{1}{2}gt^2 + c$

(ii) $h = \dfrac{u^2}{2g}$ (iii) time taken is $\dfrac{2u}{g}$.

Exercise 7.1 (p. 97)

1   (i) $1\,3\,2\,3\,7$ (ii) $2\,0\,1\,0 - 4$ (iii) $3 - 1\,1 - 1\,9$ (iv) $0\,4\,4\,4\,4$ (v) $1 - 2\,1 - 2\,0$

(vi) $2 - 4\,1 - 4\,0$ (vii) $1\,5 - 2\,5\,1$ (viii) $2 - 7 - 3 - 7 - 1\,1$ (ix) $5\,0 - 1\,0\,8$.

2   The constant term of p(x) is p(0).

Exercise 7.2 (p. 99)

1   (i) $x + 1$ (ii) $3x^2 + 2x + 4$ (iii) $-8x - 2$ (iv) $-3x^2 + 10x - 23$

(v) $5x^3 - 6x^2 - 11x - 3$ (vi) $41x^2 + 43x - 12$.   **2**   (i) $x^3 - x^2 + x - 6$

(ii) $x^5 - 2x^4 - 4x^3 - 2x^2 - 5x$ (iii) $4x^4 + 4x^3 + 5x^2 + 2x + 1$ (iv) $x^3 + x^2 - 8x - 12$

(v) $x^3 + 12x^2 + 48x + 64$ (vi) $x^5 - x^3 - 6x$.   **3**   (i) $3x^3 - x^2 + 6x - 2$

(ii) $6x^3 - 5x^2 - 2x + 1$ (iii) $12x^5 - 6x^4 - 4x^3 + 2x^2$ (iv) $25x^3 + 5x^2 - 17x - 6$

(v) $-8x^4 + 16x^3 - 4x^2 + x + 1$ (vi) $30x^5 + 3x^4 - 17x^3 - x^2 + x$

(vii) $3x^5 - 7x^4 + 11x^3 - 15x^2 + 19x - 5$ (viii) $3x^5 - 11x^4 + 16x^3 - 19x^2 + 10x - 4$.

4   (i) $3x^2 - 3x + 5$ (ii) $7x^2 - 6x + 11$ (iii) $2x^2 - 9x + 8$ (iv) $2x^4 - 3x^3 + 6x^2 - 3x + 4$

(v) $4x^4 - 12x^3 + 25x^2 - 24x + 16$ (vi) $x^4 + 2x^2 + 1$ (vii) $3x^4 - 12x^3 + 23x^2 - 24x + 15$.

5 $4x^5 - 5x^4 + 1$.   **6**   (i) 5 (ii) 7.   **7**   (i) $1 - 2x + 5x^2 - 6x^3$ (ii) $2 + 9x + 7x^2 - 4x^3$

(iii) $32 - 32x - 38x^2 + 41x^3$ (iv) $8x - 28x^2 + 34x^3$.

Exercise 7.3 (p. 100)

(i) $\dfrac{x-1}{x^2}$ (ii) $\dfrac{1 + 2x - x^2}{1 - x^2}$ (iii) $\dfrac{2x^2 + 2x + 1}{x + 1}$ (iv) $\dfrac{2x - 4}{3 - x}$ (v) $\dfrac{x^3 + 4x^2 + 2x - 1}{x + 3}$

(vi) $\dfrac{x^3 - x^2 + 3x - 1}{x^2 + 1}$ (vii) $\dfrac{2(x - 4)}{(x - 5)}, x \neq -3$ (viii) $\dfrac{2x^4 + 4x^3 + 16x^2 + 16x + 32}{x^5 + 2x^4 + 4x^3 - 8x^2 - 16x - 32}$.

Exercise 7.4 (p. 101)

1   (i) $x + 2, -9$ (ii) $x^2 - x + 1, 0$ (iii) $x + 2, 0$ (iv) $3x - 2, 2$ (v) $x^2 - 4x + 11, -28$

(vi) $2x^2 - 2x + 6, -6$ (vii) $x^2 - 2x - 3, 18$ (viii) $x^3 + 2x^2 + x + 2, 4$ (ix) $x^2 + x - 3, 0$

(x) $x^2 + \frac{1}{2}x - \frac{1}{4}, \frac{31}{4}$ (xi) $3x^3 - 7x^2 + 20x - 56, 163$ (xii) $\frac{1}{2}x^3 + \frac{3}{4}x^2 - \frac{3}{8}x + \frac{7}{16}, \frac{21}{16}$.

Exercise 7.5 (p. 103)

1   (i) -1 (ii) 3 (iii) 15 (iv) 0 (v) -1 (vi) 21.   **2**   (i) yes   (ii) yes   (iii) no

(iv) no   (v) yes   (vi) yes   (vii) no   (viii) yes.   **3**   (i) $(x - 1)(x + 1)(2x + 1)$

(ii) $(x + 1)(x + 1)(2x - 1)$ (iii) $(x + 1)(x + 1)(x + 1)$ (iv) $(x - 1)(x + 1)(x^2 + 1)$

(v) $(x - 1)(x^2 + x + 1)$ (vi) $(x - 1)(x - 1)(x + 1)$ (vii) $(x + 2)(x^2 - x + 1)$

(viii) $(x - 1)(x^2 + 1)$ (ix) $(2x - 1)(2x^2 + x + 2)$ (x) $(3x + 1)(2x^2 - 5x + 6)$

(xi) $(x - 1)(3x + 2)(x - 2)$

(xii) $(x + 1)(x - 2)(x - 3)$ (xiii) $(x - 1)(x - 4)(x + 5)$

(xiv) $(x - 1)(2x + 1)(2x - 3)$

(xv) $(2x-1)(3x+1)(x+3)$.   **4**   (i) $a = 6$
(ii) $a = -10$ (iii) $a = \frac{3}{4}$ (iv) $a = \frac{7}{2}$ (v) $a = \frac{23}{4}$.
5 (i) $a = 3, b = -3$ (ii) $a = -5, b = 8$ (iii) $a = -13, b = 6$.   **6** (i) n is odd
(ii) n is even   (iii) never true.   **7** (i) $(x-2)$ (ii) no linear factor (iii) $(x+3)$
(iv) $(2x-5)$.   **8** 95.   **9** $a = 14, 2(x+3)(x-1)(x-2)$.   **10** $a = 1, b = -37$.
11 6.   **12** $(x-3)(x+4)(x+5)$.   **13** $\sqrt{7}, \dfrac{\sqrt{5}-\sqrt{7}}{2}, \dfrac{-\sqrt{5}-\sqrt{7}}{2}$.

Exercise 7.6 (p. 105)

2 (i) 0 1 2 (ii) 1 1 −1 −1 (iii) 0 1 −1 (iv) $-1\frac{1}{2}$ 2. **3** $p(x) = 2x^3 - 6x^2 - 12x + 16$.
4 (a) $x^2 - 2x - 8$ (b) $x^3 + 2x^2 - 11x - 12$ (c) $x^4 - 4x^3 - 11x^2 + 30x$.

Miscellaneous Exercise 7 (p. 105)

1 $f(2) = f(-1) = 0, f(x) = (x-2)(x+1)(x^2 + 4x + 1), 2, -1, -2 + \sqrt{3}, -2 - \sqrt{3}$.
2 $a = -2, b = 2, c = 1$.   **3** $p = -1, q = 5$.
4 $a = 1, b = 1, (x+1)(x^2 - 3x + 3), 9 < 12$ so no other real roots.
5 quotient $(2x-1)$, remainder $(1 - 5x)$.   **7** $(2x-1)(x+1), 25x - 23$.

Exercise 8.1 (p. 108)

1 (i) John Smith's school; (ii) your paternal grandmother; (iii) the colour of Manchester United's strip. **2** your grandparents. **3** (i) 'the class containing the school' has no meaning; (iii) 'the strip of the colour' has no meaning. fg has a meaning when C is a subset of A. **4** (i) -1 (ii) 1 (iii) 13 (iv) 31 (v) 97 (vi) $2x^2 - 1$ (vii) $(2x-1)^2$
(viii) $2t^2 - 1$.

Exercise 8.2 (p. 110) Let $\mathbb{R}^+ \cup \{0\} = \mathbb{R}_0^+$.

1 (i) (a) $\mathbb{R}^+, \mathbb{R}^+$ (b) $\mathbb{R}, \mathbb{R}_0^+$ (ii) (a) $\mathbb{R}_0^+, \mathbb{R}_0^+$ (b) $\mathbb{R}, \mathbb{R}_0^+$ (iii) (a) $\mathbb{R}\backslash\{1, -1\}, \mathbb{R}\backslash\{3\}$
(iv) (a) $\{x: -2 \leqslant x \leqslant 0\}\backslash\{-1\}, \mathbb{R}_0^+$ (b) $\mathbb{R}\backslash\{x: -2 < x < 2\}, \{x: 0 < x \leqslant 2\}$.

Exercise 8.6 (p. 116)

1 (a) (i) $f(x-1)$, translation $+1$ along Ox (ii) $f(1-x)$, reflection in $x = \frac{1}{2}$
(iii) $f(3x)$, stretch along Ox S.F. $\frac{1}{3}$ (iv) $f(\frac{1}{2}x)$, stretch along Ox S.F.2
(v) $f(-2x)$, stretch along Ox S.F. $-\frac{1}{2}$ (vi) $f(\frac{1-x}{2})$, stretch along Ox S.F. 2 followed by reflection in $x = \frac{1}{2}$; (b) (i) $f(x) - 1$, translation -1 along Oy
(ii) $1 - f(x)$, reflection in $y = \frac{1}{2}$ (iii) $3f(x)$, stretch along Oy S.F. 3
(iv) $\frac{1}{2}f(x)$, stretch along Oy S.F. $\frac{1}{2}$ (v) $-2f(x)$, stretch along Oy S.F. -2
(vi) $\frac{1}{2} - \frac{1}{2}f(x)$, reflection in $y = \frac{1}{2}$ followed by stretch along Oy S.F. $\frac{1}{2}$.
2 (i) $g(x) = 3x, h(x) = \frac{1}{3}x$ (ii) $g(x) = -x, h(x) = x - 1$
(iii) $g(x) = \frac{1}{2}x, h(x) = -x$ (iv) $g(x) = 4 - x, h(x) = x$.

Exercise 8.7 (p. 118)

1 (i) even (ii) none (iii) odd (iv) even and periodic (v) odd and periodic
(vi) odd and periodic (vii) even (viii) odd (ix) even.   **2** (i) 4 (ii) $4\frac{7}{8}$ (iii) 4 (iv) -5.
3 (i) even (ii) none (iii) odd (iv) periodic, period 1 (v) even (vi) none (vii) even.
5 (a) not periodic (b) periodic, period π.   **6** 3π.   **10** $\pi, \pi, \pi, \{x: 0 < x < 2\}$.

Exercise 8.8 (p. 120)

1 (i) range $A = \{1, 0, -1, -2, -3, \ldots\}$, $f^{-1}(x) = 1 - x$ for $x \in A$
   (ii) range $B = \{0, 1, 4, 9, 16, \ldots\}$, $f^{-1}(x) = \sqrt{x}$ for $x \in B$
   (iii) range $C = \{1, \frac{1}{2}, \frac{1}{3}, \frac{1}{4}, \ldots\}$, $f^{-1}(x) = (1 - x)/x, x \in C$
   (iv) range $D = \{0, 1, 8, 27, 64, \ldots\}$, $f^{-1}(x) = \sqrt[3]{x}$ for $x \in D$.

2   (i) domain $\mathbb{R}$, range $\mathbb{R}$, inverse $f^{-1}(x) = 1 - x$

(ii) domain $\mathbb{R}$, range $\mathbb{R}^+ \cup \{0\}$, no inverse because $f(2) = f(-2)$

(iii) domain $\mathbb{R} \setminus \{-1\}$, range $\mathbb{R} \setminus \{0\}$, inverse $f^{-1}(x) = (1-x)/x$

(iv) domain $\mathbb{R}$, range $\mathbb{R}$, inverse $f^{-1}(x) = \sqrt[3]{x}$.

3 $a = 0$, range $\{b\}$, no inverse since $f(1) = b = f(2)$

$a \neq 0$, range $\mathbb{R}$, inverse $f^{-1}(x) = (x - b)/a$

4   (i) $f(1) = f(-1)$ so no inverse, restrict domain to $\mathbb{R}^+$, $f^{-1}(x) = \left(\dfrac{x+1}{2}\right)$

(ii) $f(2) = f(-2)$ so no inverse, restrict domain to $\{x : x > 1\}$, $f^{-1}(x) = \left(1 + \dfrac{1}{x}\right)$

(iii) $f(0) = f(\pi)$ so no inverse, restrict domain to $\left\{x : -\dfrac{\pi}{2} \leqslant x \leqslant \dfrac{\pi}{2}\right\}$, $f^{-1}(x) = \sin^{-1} x$

(iv) $f(0) = f(\pi)$ so no inverse, restrict domain to $\left\{x : 0 \leqslant x \leqslant \dfrac{\pi}{4}\right\}$, $f^{-1}(x) = \frac{1}{4}\cos^{-1} x$

(v) $f(1) = f(-1)$ so no inverse, restrict domain to $\mathbb{R}^+ \cup \{0\}$, $f^{-1}(x) = x$

(vi) $f(0) = f(\frac{1}{2})$ so no inverse, restrict domain to $\{x : 0 \leqslant x < 1\}$, $f^{-1}(x) = -x$.

Exercise 8.9 (p. 122)

1   (i) $f^{-1}(x) = \frac{1}{2}x$, domain $\mathbb{R}$ (ii) $f^{-1}(x) = x + 3$, domain $\mathbb{Z}$

(iii) $f^{-1}(x) = (x - 2)/3$, domain $\mathbb{R}$ (iv) $f^{-1}(x) = \sqrt{x} - 2$, domain $\{x : x > 4\}$

(v) $f^{-1}(x) = \sqrt[3]{x}$, domain $\mathbb{R}$ (vi) $f^{-1}(x) = x^2$, domain $\mathbb{R}^+$

(vii) $f^{-1}(x) = \sqrt{x}$ for $x \in \mathbb{R}^+$, $f^{-1}(x) = -\sqrt{(-x)}$ for $x \in \mathbb{R} \setminus \mathbb{R}^+$, domain $\mathbb{R}$

(viii) $f^{-1}(x) = 2 - x$, domain $\{x : -1 < x \leqslant 0\}$

(ix) $f^{-1}(x) = \sqrt{(1 - x^2)}$, domain $\{x : 0 \leqslant x \leqslant 1\}$.

2   Range of f is A where $A = \{x : x \geqslant 1\}$, $d = 2$, g^{-1} and h^{-1} have domain A, $g^{-1}(x) = 2 + \sqrt{(x - 1)}$, $h^{-1}(x) = 2 - \sqrt{(x - 1)}$.

3   For all x, $g(x) = eg(x) = hfg(x) = he(x) = h(x)$, so $g = h$.

4 $P(1)$ and $P(4)$ are each both necessary and sufficient. $P(2)$ and $P(3)$ are always true so they are necessary but not sufficient.

5   For all a in A, $gf(a) = a$ and so $g = f^{-1}$. For all b in B, since B is the range of f, there is some a in A with $b = f(a)$, then $fg(b) = fgf(a) = f(a) = b$.

6   Let $f^{-1}(x) = f^{-1}(y)$, with $x, y \in \mathbb{R}$. Then $x = ff^{-1}(x) = ff^{-1}(y) = y$, so f^{-1} is $1-1$.

7   Since gf is the identity function on the domain D, $gf(d) = d$ for every d in D, and so $f(d)$ lies in the domain of g, and the range of f is a subset of the domain of g. Let $f(a) = f(b)$ for $a, b \in D$, then $a = gf(a) = gf(b) = b$, and hence f is $1 - 1$. When $f(x) = \sqrt{x}$, $g(x) = x^2$, with the domains of f and g being $\mathbb{R}^+$ and $\mathbb{R}$ respectively, $gf(x) = (\sqrt{x})^2 = x$, so gf is the identity function on $\mathbb{R}^+$. The inverse of f is the function h with $h(x) = x^2$, with domain $\mathbb{R}^+$, and so $h \neq g$.

Miscellaneous Exercise 8 (p. 123)

1 $\dfrac{x+2}{x-1}$, $\mathbb{R} \setminus \{1\}$.   **2**   Both exist, $f^{-1}g = \cos^{-1}\tan$, domain $A = \left\{x : 0 \leqslant x \leqslant \dfrac{\pi}{4}\right\}$, range $B = \left\{x : 0 \leqslant x \leqslant \dfrac{\pi}{2}\right\}$, $g^{-1}f = \tan^{-1}\cos = (f^{-1}g)^{-1}$, domain B, range A; solution to $f(x) = g(x)$ is $x = 0.67$.   **3**   (i) $\{x : x \geqslant -\frac{1}{4}\}$, (ii) $\{x : x \leqslant -4\} \cup \{x : x > 0\}$.

4   (a) $gf(x) = \dfrac{2}{4x^2 - 1}$, domain $\mathbb{R} \setminus \{\frac{1}{2}, -\frac{1}{2}\}$ (b) $g^{-1}(x) = \dfrac{3x - 2}{4x}$.

5 $f(x) = 3(x - \frac{7}{6})^2 + \frac{11}{12} > 0$, $g(-2) < 0 < g(0)$, $h(0) < 0 < h(3)$, $g(x) > 0$ for $-1 < x < 5$, $h(x) > 0$ for $x < -2$ or $x > \frac{5}{2}$.   **6**   (i) $\{x : x \leqslant -\frac{3}{4}\}$, (ii) $4, -4$.

7 (a) even, odd and periodic period 2π, even (b) $\frac{1}{2}$.

8 (i) $y = x + 1$ (ii) $y = 3 - x$. **9** (c).

Exercise 9.2 (p. 126)

2 (i) $\dfrac{1}{a}$ (ii) $\dfrac{1}{a^3}$ (iii) $\dfrac{1}{a}$ (iv) $\dfrac{1}{a^4}$.

Exercise 9.3A (p. 127)

3 $2^{\frac{1}{2}} = 1\cdot41$, $2^{-\frac{1}{2}} = 0\cdot71$, $2^{\frac{3}{8}} = 1\cdot30$, $2^{-\frac{7}{8}} = 0\cdot55$; $2^x > 0$. **4** (i) $0\cdot1$ (ii) 100 (iii) x

(iv) x^9 (v) $0\cdot001$ (vi) 4 (vii) a^4 (viii) x^6 (ix) $\frac{64}{27}$ (x) 2^{12} (xi) a^7 (xii) $\dfrac{1}{2^{12}}$

(xiii) 2^{12} (xiv) 1 (xv) $\frac{3}{4}$ (xvi) $\dfrac{3^{10}}{9^4}$ (xvii) 1 (xviii) $a^4 b^6$ (xix) a^{12}/b^6 (xx) $1/a^4 b^6$

(xxi) $a^{12} b^8$.

Exercise 9.3B (p. 128)

1 (i) $2\cdot7 \times 10^1$ (ii) $2\cdot7 \times 10^2$ (iii) $2\cdot7 \times 10^{-1}$ (iv) $2\cdot7 \times 10^{-2}$ (v) $3\cdot456 \times 10^3$
(vi) $3\cdot4 \times 10^4$ (vii) $3\cdot456 \times 10^1$ (viii) $3\cdot456 \times 10^6$ (ix) $3\cdot456 \times 10^{-5}$
2 (i) $2\,700$ (ii) $27\,890$ (iii) $0\cdot001\,234$ (iv) $1\,200\,000\,000\,000\,000\,000\,000$
(v) $0\cdot000\,000\,000\,25$ (vi) $3\,450\,000$.

Exercise 9.4 (p. 129)

1 (i) 27 (ii) 3 (iii) 2 (iv) $2/3$ (v) $3/2$ (vi) 1 (vii) $1/3$ (viii) $\frac{1}{36}$ (ix) $\frac{1}{2}$ (x) 2 (xi) $\frac{3}{2}$
(xii) $\frac{3}{2}$. **2** (i) 4 (ii) $\frac{1}{8}$ (iii) 125 (iv) $5^{\frac{5}{6}}$ (v) 2 (vi) 12 (vii) $6\sqrt[3]{2}$ (viii) 3 (ix) 2
(x) $\frac{1}{3^n}$ (xi) 2. **4** (i) 3^3 (ii) $4^{\frac{3}{4}}$ (iii) $5^{\frac{3}{2}}$ (iv) $5^{\frac{5}{2}}$ (v) $a^{\frac{1}{2}}$ (vi) $x^{\frac{3}{5}}$ (vii) $a^{\frac{41}{20}}$ (viii) x^2
(ix) a^2 (x) $a^{\frac{1}{4}}$ (xi) 2^2 (xii) a^2 (xiii) $x^{-\frac{7}{12}}$ (xiv) $(\frac{8}{9})^n$ (xv) 2^4 (xvi) 2^{-3}.

5

x	-2	$-1\frac{1}{2}$	-1	$-\frac{1}{2}$	$-\frac{1}{4}$	0	$\frac{1}{4}$	$\frac{1}{2}$	$\frac{3}{4}$	1	$1\frac{1}{2}$	2
16^x	$0\cdot004$	$0\cdot016$	$0\cdot063$	$0\cdot25$	$0\cdot5$	1	2	4	8	16	64	256

(i) true (ii) true.

Exercise 9.6 (p. 132)

1 (i) 2 (ii) 3 (iii) 5 (iv) 1 (v) 0 (vi) -1 (vii) -2 (viii) $\frac{1}{2}$ (ix) $\frac{1}{3}$. **2** Reflection
in $y = x$ followed by reflection in $y = 0$, i.e. rotation $90°$ about O.

Exercise 9.7 (p. 133)

1 (i) 1 (ii) 2 (iii) 3 (iv) 3 (v) 4 (vi) 3 (vii) 10 (viii) $\frac{1}{2}$ (ix) $\frac{3}{2}$ (x) $\frac{5}{2}$ (xi) $\frac{5}{3}$
(xii) -4 (xiii) $\frac{1}{2}$ (xiv) $\frac{1}{2}$ (xv) 3 (xvi) $\frac{1}{4}$ (xvii) $\frac{2}{3}$ (xviii) 0 (xix) 10. **2** (i) $s^2 = t^2$
(ii) $\frac{1}{9} = 3^{-2}$ (iii) $y = x^z$. **3** (i) $\log_{10} 1\,000\,000 = 6$ (ii) $\log_5 125 = 3$
(iii) $\log_2 1024 = 10$ (iv) $\log_{16} \frac{1}{2} = -\frac{1}{4}$ (v) $\log_9 27 = \frac{3}{2}$ (vi) $\log_a b = c$.
4 $n = \dfrac{\log_{10} A - \log_{10} P}{\log_{10} (1 + \frac{x}{100})}$.

Exercise 9.8 (p. 134)

1 (i) $\log_a x + \log_a y - \log_a z$ (ii) $\log_a x + \log_a y + \log_a z$
(iii) $2\log_a x + 3\log_a y + 4\log_a z$ (iv) $\frac{1}{2}\log_a x + \frac{1}{2}\log_a z$ (v) $-\frac{1}{3}\log_a y$. **2** (i) $\log_a 2$
(ii) $\log_a\left(\dfrac{xy}{z}\right)$ (iii) $\log_a\left(\dfrac{y^3}{z}\right)$ (iv) $\log_a (3a)$ (v) $\log_a\left(\dfrac{a^5}{5}\right)$.

3 (i) 2   (ii) $-\frac{3}{2}$ (iii) $-\frac{1}{2}$ (iv) $\frac{5}{2}$ (v) 2
(vi) $-\frac{1}{6}$ (vii) 1   (viii) $\log_a b$ (ix) 0.
4 (i) 4   (ii) 27   (iii) 4   (iv) $\sqrt{2}$ (v) $\frac{125}{9}$
(vi) $\frac{864}{25}$.   **5** (i) $\log_3 7$ (ii) $\log_{10} 4$
(iii) $\log_{0.1} 7$ (iv) $1 - \log_5 3$ (v) $\log_2 24$.   **6** (i) -2 (ii) $-\frac{1}{2}$ (iii) 1.

Exercise 9.9 (p. 135)

1 (i) 1   (ii) $3\log_c b$.   **2** $\log_3 \sqrt{2}$.   **3** 2·322.

Miscellaneous Exercise 9 (p. 136)

1 $\log_5 2$, $\log_5 3$.   **2** (i) 1·58   (ii) 0·63   (iii) 2·32   (iv) 2·58   (v) 0·38.   **3** $\frac{3}{4}$.
4 $\{2, 16\}$.   **5** $\{4\}$.   **6** $y = 1000x^{-\frac{3}{4}}$.   **7** $x = -\frac{1}{2}$.   **8** $2\sqrt{2} - 2$.   **9** $e(1 - e^x)$.
10 4.   **11** $\frac{1}{2}\ln 3$.   **12** $\{1, 3\}$.   **13** $y = 6/\sqrt{x}$.   **14** $y = ex^{-3}$.
15 $\ln 2$.   **16** 8·6.   **17** (a) $\frac{2}{5}$ (b) 1·48.   **18** $x = 27 = y$ or $x = 9$, $y = 81$.
19 $x = 3$, $y = 9$ or $x = -4$, $y = 16$.   **20** $x = 3$, $y = 9$ or $x = 9$, $y = 3$.
21 (a) (i) 1·2041200   (ii) -0.9542426 (iii) 0·3597271, (b) (i) 3
(ii) 2,   (c) 13/5, 3/5,   (d) -0.30.

Exercise 10.1 (p. 139)

1 (i) $y = 0.29x + 3.4$ (ii) $y = -0.004x + 0.23$ (iii) $y = 133x - 319$.

Exercise 10.4 (p. 143)

1 $a = 1.3$, $b = 2.1$.   **2** $c = 10$, $d = 0.5$.   **3** $a = -23$, $b = 42$.   **4** $u = 1$, $f = 7$.
5 $n = 2$, $k = 0.0002$.   **6** $a = 22.9$, $b = 0.03$.   **7** $R = 8.3$.
8 $n = 3$, $a = 2.5$, $r = 2.5s^3$.   **9** $a = 25$, $b = 1.6$.

Miscellaneous Exercise 10 (p. 145)

1 $a = 7$, $b = 5$.   **2** $a = 2$, $x = 3.1$.   **3** $a = 10$, $K = 7.4$.   **4** $a = -0.5$, $b = 2.3$.
5 $n = 3$, $a = 50$.   **6** $a = 0.4$, $b = 1.5$.   **7** $f = 12$.
8 (a) $2y + 3x = 4$ (b) $\ln 5 + \ln x = y \ln 6$.   **9** $a = -12$, $b = 100$.
10 $a = 1.5$, $b = 1.1$.   **11** $a = 2$, $b = 3$, 202.   **12** $a = -5$, $b = 8$.
13 $a = 0.4$, $b = 2.7$, 0·9.   **14** $a = 0.5$, $b = 12$.

Exercise 11.4 (p. 154)

1 (i) 2, 1 max. and 1 min.   (ii) 3, 2 max. and 1 min. or 1 max. and 2 min.   (iii) $n - 1$, if n is odd the graph can have $\frac{1}{2}(n - 1)$ max. and $\frac{1}{2}(n - 1)$ min., if n is even the graph can have $\frac{1}{2}n$ max. and $\frac{1}{2}n - 1$ min. or $\frac{1}{2}n - 1$ max. and $\frac{1}{2}n$ min.   **3** Use $f(x) = :$ (i) $x(1 - x)(1 + x)$ (v) $x^3(1 - x)(1 + x)$ (vi) $x^2(x - 1)(x + 1)$ (vii) and   (viii) $f(x) > 0$ for all x.

Exercise 11.6 (p. 156)

2 (i) 1 way stretch parallel to Oy factor 2   (ii) translation -2 parallel to Oy (iii) translation $+3$ parallel to Oy (iv) reflection in Ox followed by translation $+3$ parallel to Oy (v) translation $+3$ parallel to Ox (vi) translation -2 parallel to Ox (vii) 1 way stretch parallel to Oy factor 2 followed by translation $+5$ parallel to Oy (viii) 1 way stretch parallel to Oy factor -1 followed by translation $+4$ parallel to Oy (ix) translation $+3$ parallel to Ox followed by 1 way stretch parallel to Oy factor 4 (x) translation -1 parallel to Ox followed by 1 way stretch parallel to Oy factor 4 (xi) translation -1 parallel to Ox followed by translation $+4$ parallel to Oy.

Exercise 12.1 (p. 162)

1

$$\binom{x_1}{y_1} = \binom{x_2}{y_2} \Leftrightarrow x_1\mathbf{i} + y_1\mathbf{j} = x_2\mathbf{i} + y_2\mathbf{j} \Leftrightarrow (x_1 - x_2)\mathbf{i} = (y_1 - y_2)\mathbf{j} \Leftrightarrow x_1 = x_2, \; y_1 = y_2$$

$$\binom{x_1}{y_1} + \binom{x_2}{y_2} = x_1\mathbf{i} + y_1\mathbf{j} + x_2\mathbf{i} + y_2\mathbf{j} = (x_1 + x_2)\mathbf{i} + (y_1 + y_2)\mathbf{j} = \binom{x_1 + x_2}{y_1 + y_2}$$

$$\lambda\binom{x}{y} = \lambda(x\mathbf{i} + y\mathbf{j}) = \lambda x\mathbf{i} + \lambda y\mathbf{j} = \binom{\lambda x}{\lambda y}.$$

2 (i) $\binom{3}{-3}$ (ii) $\binom{-4}{3}$ (iii) $\binom{3}{-11}$ (iv) $\binom{a-2b}{2a-b}$ (v) $\binom{7x}{-y}$ (vi) $\binom{ax+bu}{ay+bv}$.

Exercise 12.2 (p. 165)

1 (i) 5 (ii) 13 (iii) $\sqrt{2}$ (iv) 10 (v) 5 (vi) $\sqrt{5}$ (vii) 3. **2** (i) $\binom{-\frac{3}{5}}{-\frac{4}{5}}$

(ii) $\binom{\frac{5}{13}}{\frac{12}{13}}$ (iii) $\binom{\frac{1}{\sqrt{2}}}{\frac{1}{\sqrt{2}}}$ (iv) $\binom{-\frac{4}{5}}{\frac{3}{5}}$ (v) $\frac{3}{5}\mathbf{i} - \frac{4}{5}\mathbf{j}$ (vi) $\frac{1}{\sqrt{5}}\mathbf{i} + \frac{2}{\sqrt{5}}\mathbf{j}$ (vii) $\mathbf{j}$.

3 $\overrightarrow{AB} = \binom{3}{2}$, $\overrightarrow{CD} = \binom{-3}{-2}$, so $\overrightarrow{AB} = \overrightarrow{DC}$ and $ABCD$ is a parallelogram.

4 (i) $\mathbf{a} + \mathbf{b}$ (ii) $3\mathbf{a}$ (iii) $\frac{3}{11}\mathbf{a} + \frac{2}{11}\mathbf{b}$ (iv) $\frac{4}{11}\mathbf{a} - \frac{1}{11}\mathbf{b}$ (v) $\frac{4x+3y}{11}\mathbf{a} + \frac{2y-x}{11}\mathbf{b}$

(vi) $\frac{10}{11}\mathbf{a} + \frac{3}{11}\mathbf{b}$ (vii) $3\mathbf{a} + 2\mathbf{b}$. **5** (i) $-\frac{2}{5}\mathbf{a} + \frac{6}{5}\mathbf{b}$ (ii) $\frac{1}{5}\mathbf{a} + \frac{2}{5}\mathbf{b}$ (iii) $-\frac{2}{5}\mathbf{a} + \frac{1}{5}\mathbf{b}$

(iv) $-\frac{1}{5}\mathbf{a} + \frac{3}{5}\mathbf{b}$ (v) $\frac{3}{5}\mathbf{a} + \frac{1}{5}\mathbf{b}$ (vi) $\frac{x-2y}{5}\mathbf{a} + \frac{2x+y}{5}\mathbf{b}$ (vii) $-\frac{3}{5}\mathbf{a} + \frac{2}{5}\mathbf{b}$

(viii) $\frac{s-2t}{5}\mathbf{a} + \frac{2s+t}{5}\mathbf{b}$ **6** The point with position vector $\binom{x}{y}$ lies on the line joining the

points with position vectors $\binom{p}{q}$ and $\binom{s}{t}$ and divides the line in the ratio $\mu : \lambda$ if and only if

$\lambda\binom{p}{q} + \mu\binom{s}{t} = (\lambda + \mu)\binom{x}{y}$. The point (x, y) lies on the line joining (p, q) and (s, t) and

divides this line in the ratio $\mu : \lambda$ if and only if $\lambda p + \mu s = (\lambda + \mu)x$ and $\lambda q + \mu t = (\lambda + \mu)y$.

7 $\left(\frac{11}{2}, \frac{77}{18}\right)$. **8** $A\binom{1}{3}, B\binom{3}{-1}, C\binom{5}{7}, D\binom{4}{3}, E\binom{3}{5}, F\binom{2}{1}, G\binom{3}{3}$,

$3\overrightarrow{OG} = 2\overrightarrow{OD} + \overrightarrow{OA} = 2\overrightarrow{OE} + \overrightarrow{OB} = 2\overrightarrow{OF} + \overrightarrow{OC}$.

9 $\mathbf{u} = \binom{\frac{4}{5}}{\frac{3}{5}}, \; \mathbf{v} = \binom{\frac{3}{5}}{-\frac{4}{5}}, \; \mathbf{u} + \mathbf{v} = \binom{\frac{7}{5}}{-\frac{1}{5}}, \; \mathbf{u} - \mathbf{v} = \binom{\frac{1}{5}}{\frac{7}{5}}, \left(\frac{7}{5\sqrt{2}}, \frac{-1}{5\sqrt{2}}\right), \left(\frac{1}{5\sqrt{2}}, \frac{7}{5\sqrt{2}}\right).$

10 $m = 3, \; n = -2.$ **11** $-15/2.$

12 $|\overrightarrow{PQ}| = \sqrt{(2\lambda^2 + 2\mu^2)}, \; \overrightarrow{OR} = \frac{1}{2}(\lambda - \mu)\mathbf{i} + \frac{1}{2}(\lambda + \mu)\mathbf{j}.$

Exercise 12.3 (p. 169)

1 (b) (a) (a).

2 $3, 5\sqrt{2}, \sqrt{(29)}, 3\sqrt{(74)}, \frac{1}{3}\binom{1}{2}, \frac{1}{5\sqrt{2}}\binom{3}{-4}, \frac{1}{\sqrt{29}}\binom{4}{-2}, \frac{1}{3\sqrt{74}}\binom{-7}{16}.$

3 $\binom{-2}{5}{1}, \sqrt{30}.$ **4** (i) $\binom{-3}{1}{1}$ (ii) $\binom{0}{7}{-1}$ (iii) $\binom{14}{5}{-2}$ (iv) $\binom{9}{10}{0}.$

5 (i) $\begin{pmatrix}1\\2\\3\end{pmatrix}, \begin{pmatrix}1\\2\\3\end{pmatrix}$, yes (ii) $\begin{pmatrix}-2\\2\\-3\end{pmatrix}, \begin{pmatrix}-2\\1\\-3\end{pmatrix}$, no (iii) $\begin{pmatrix}2\\1\\-4\end{pmatrix}, \begin{pmatrix}-2\\-1\\4\end{pmatrix}$, yes.

6 $\begin{pmatrix}1\\2\\3\end{pmatrix}, \begin{pmatrix}-2\\0\\2\end{pmatrix}, \begin{pmatrix}-1\\1\\3\end{pmatrix}, \begin{pmatrix}-4\\4\\12\end{pmatrix}$, $2\overrightarrow{PQ}+3\overrightarrow{PR}=4\overrightarrow{PS}$, hence coplanar.

7 $(-\frac{7}{3}, -\frac{2}{3}, -\frac{5}{3})$.

Exercise 12.4 (p. 171)

1 (i) $x=2+5t, y=3+t, 5y=x+13$ (ii) $x=1-2t, y=-3+5t, 2y+5x+1=0$
(iii) $x=1-2t, y=t, 2y+x=1$.

2 (i) $r=\begin{pmatrix}4\\-3\end{pmatrix}+t\begin{pmatrix}-1\\8\end{pmatrix}$, $y+8x=29$ (ii) $r=2i+3j+t(3i+2j), 3y=2x+5$.

3 $r=\begin{pmatrix}\frac{5}{8}\\\frac{3}{4}\end{pmatrix}+t\begin{pmatrix}2\\1\end{pmatrix}$. **4** $\begin{pmatrix}-\frac{4}{5}\\\frac{3}{5}\end{pmatrix}$, $(-9,10), (15,-8)$. **5** $r=t\begin{pmatrix}1\\3\end{pmatrix}$.

6 (i) $(3,6)$ (ii) $r=\begin{pmatrix}2\\3\end{pmatrix}+t\begin{pmatrix}-1\\1\end{pmatrix}$, $r=\begin{pmatrix}-1\\2\end{pmatrix}+t\begin{pmatrix}1\\1\end{pmatrix}$ (iii) $\begin{pmatrix}1\\4\end{pmatrix}$.

Exercise 12.5 (p. 175)

1 (i) $x=2-3t, y=5+t, z=4-2t$, $\dfrac{x-2}{-3}=\dfrac{y-5}{1}=\dfrac{z-4}{-2}$

(ii) $x=2t, y=2+t, z=-1+4t$, $\dfrac{x}{2}=\dfrac{y-2}{1}=\dfrac{z+1}{4}$

(iii) $x=4-3t, y=1+12t, z=2-5t$, $\dfrac{x-4}{-3}=\dfrac{y-1}{12}=\dfrac{z-2}{-5}$

(iv) $x=2+s, y=-2+s, z=3+s, x-2=y+2=z-3$.

2 (i) $r=\begin{pmatrix}3\\-1\\4\end{pmatrix}+t\begin{pmatrix}-1\\3\\2\end{pmatrix}$ (ii) $r=\begin{pmatrix}1\\1\\-1\end{pmatrix}+t\begin{pmatrix}4\\3\\5\end{pmatrix}$ (iii) $r=\begin{pmatrix}2\\-3\\4\end{pmatrix}+t\begin{pmatrix}1\\0\\2\end{pmatrix}$

(iv) $r=\begin{pmatrix}2\\-4\\1\end{pmatrix}+t\begin{pmatrix}-1\\-1\\6\end{pmatrix}$ (v) $r=\begin{pmatrix}-7\\3\\-1\end{pmatrix}+t\begin{pmatrix}3\\-2\\2\end{pmatrix}$.

3 (i) $r=\begin{pmatrix}2\\-1\\3\end{pmatrix}+t\begin{pmatrix}1\\3\\-4\end{pmatrix}$ (ii) $r=\begin{pmatrix}0\\2\\0\end{pmatrix}+t\begin{pmatrix}1\\-3\\4\end{pmatrix}$ (iii) $r=\begin{pmatrix}4\\0\\0\end{pmatrix}+t\begin{pmatrix}-2\\1\\0\end{pmatrix}$

(iv) $r=\begin{pmatrix}3\\2\\0\end{pmatrix}+t\begin{pmatrix}0\\-1\\1\end{pmatrix}$. **4** (i) $r=\begin{pmatrix}0\\3\\-2\end{pmatrix}+x\begin{pmatrix}1\\2\\-4\end{pmatrix}$ (ii) $r=\begin{pmatrix}-7\\0\\-1\end{pmatrix}+y\begin{pmatrix}3\\1\\2\end{pmatrix}$

(iii) $r=\begin{pmatrix}-4\\0\\0\end{pmatrix}+z\begin{pmatrix}3\\1\\1\end{pmatrix}$ (iv) $r=\begin{pmatrix}6\\0\\2\end{pmatrix}+y\begin{pmatrix}2\\1\\0\end{pmatrix}$ (v) $r=\begin{pmatrix}0\\3\\2\end{pmatrix}+x\begin{pmatrix}1\\-1\\1\end{pmatrix}$

(vi) $r=\begin{pmatrix}0\\2\\\frac{4}{5}\end{pmatrix}+x\begin{pmatrix}1\\\frac{3}{2}\\-\frac{1}{5}\end{pmatrix}$. **5** (i) $\begin{pmatrix}4\\2\\3\end{pmatrix}$ (ii) $\begin{pmatrix}2\\\frac{3}{2}\\1\end{pmatrix}$

(iii) $\begin{pmatrix}-\frac{7}{2}\\-\frac{5}{2}\\\frac{3}{2}\end{pmatrix}$ (iv) $\begin{pmatrix}2\\1\\-3\end{pmatrix}$ (v) $\begin{pmatrix}2\\-1\\-2\end{pmatrix}$ (vi) $\begin{pmatrix}3\\2\\1\end{pmatrix}$.

6 (i) $\dfrac{x-2}{-3} = \dfrac{y-4}{-14} = \dfrac{z-3}{9}$ (ii) $3x = -2y = z$ (iii) $\dfrac{x-3}{-1} = \dfrac{y-5}{2}, z = 7$

(iv) $\dfrac{x-5}{3} = \dfrac{y-7}{3} = \dfrac{z+3}{-8}$ (v) $x = 3, y = \dfrac{z-1}{-2}$.   **7** No.

8 $t = 0, t = 3, t = -4$, $AB:AC = 3:4$.   **9** $(0, 1, -9)$.   **10** (i) no (ii) no.
11 $\mathbf{r} = \mathbf{i} - \mathbf{j} + 3\mathbf{k} + t(3\mathbf{j} - \mathbf{k})$, $\mathbf{i} + \mathbf{j} + \tfrac{7}{3}\mathbf{k}$.   **12** (ii) is a line and (i) is a plane. The point
$(6, 3, 2)$ lies on both loci and is the point of intersection of the line and the plane.

Exercise 12.6A (p. 179)

1 $\mathbf{a}.\mathbf{b} = ab\cos\theta = b(a\cos\theta) = a(b\cos\theta)$.
2 $1, 25, 4, 5/2, \sqrt{3}, 0, 5/2 + \sqrt{3}$, all in km^2.
3 $-\tfrac{1}{2}15\sqrt{3}, -10, 0, -\tfrac{1}{2}15\sqrt{3}, -10 - \tfrac{1}{2}15\sqrt{3}$.   **5** 17, 17.   **7** 7.

Exercise 12.6B (p. 184)

1 Approximately, in radians, (i) 1·38 (ii) 2·47 (iii) 0·28 (iv) 1·03 (v) 1·41.

2 0·79.   **4** 7.   **5** $\dfrac{1}{\sqrt{14}}(2\mathbf{i} - \mathbf{j} - 3\mathbf{k})$, $4/\sqrt{14}$.   **6** (i) no (ii) yes $(6, -7, -8)$

(iii) no.   **7** $3, (\tfrac{2}{3}, \tfrac{2}{3}, \tfrac{1}{3})$.   **8** (i) 5·34, $(4, -\tfrac{1}{2}, \tfrac{7}{2})$ (ii) 3·94, $(1, -\tfrac{7}{2}, \tfrac{3}{2})$.
9 $(2, 6, 8), 4\sqrt{(247)}$.   **11** $(1\tfrac{9}{19}, 2\tfrac{13}{19}, 1\tfrac{4}{19})$.   **12** $1:6, \mathbf{r} = \mathbf{a} + t(\mathbf{a} + 6\mathbf{b})$, $\begin{pmatrix} -12 \\ -6 \\ 6 \end{pmatrix}$.

13 $3, (4, -1, 2)$.   **14** $\mathbf{r} = \begin{pmatrix} 3 + 5t \\ 2 - 7t \\ 1 + t \end{pmatrix}$, $(13, -12, 3), 10\sqrt{3}$.

15 $\overrightarrow{PQ} = \begin{pmatrix} 3q - 2p - 2 \\ 2p + 4q - 1 \\ 7q + 1 \end{pmatrix}$, $k = -4/3, 4\sqrt{3}/3$.   **16** $1/\sqrt{15}$.

Exercise 12.7 (p. 188)

1 (i) $y = 0$ (ii) $2x + 3y + 4z = 0$ (iii) $2x + 3z = y$ (iv) $x = y$ (v) $5x + 3y = 2z$.
2 (i) $\mathbf{i} + 2\mathbf{j}$ (ii) $\mathbf{i} + \mathbf{j} + \mathbf{k}$ (iii) $3\mathbf{i} - 4\mathbf{j} + 2\mathbf{k}$.   **3** $x + 3z = 2y$.
4 $2\mathbf{i} + \mathbf{j} - 3\mathbf{k}, -2\mathbf{i} + 3\mathbf{j} + \mathbf{k}, 3x = 6y = -2z, -3x = 2y = 6z, 1\cdot86$.

Exercise 12.8 (p. 193)

1 (i) $x + z = 4$ (ii) $2x - y + 3z = 10$ (iii) $3x - 2y + z = -18$.

2 (i) $\mathbf{r}.\begin{pmatrix} 2/3 \\ 1/3 \\ 2/3 \end{pmatrix} = 2$ (ii) $\mathbf{r}.\begin{pmatrix} 3/\sqrt{10} \\ 2/\sqrt{10} \\ 0 \end{pmatrix} = 4/\sqrt{10}$ (iii) $\mathbf{r}.\begin{pmatrix} 1/\sqrt{3} \\ -1/\sqrt{3} \\ 1/\sqrt{3} \end{pmatrix} = 1/\sqrt{3}$

(iv) $\mathbf{r}.\begin{pmatrix} -4/\sqrt{42} \\ 1/\sqrt{42} \\ 5/\sqrt{42} \end{pmatrix} = -7/\sqrt{42}$.   **4** (i) $\mathbf{r}.\begin{pmatrix} 1 \\ -1 \\ 0 \end{pmatrix} = 1, x - y = 1$

(ii) $\mathbf{r}.\begin{pmatrix} 2 \\ -1 \\ 3 \end{pmatrix} = -2, 2x - y + 3z = -2$ (iii) $\mathbf{r}.\begin{pmatrix} 1 \\ -1 \\ 2 \end{pmatrix} = 9, x - y + 2z = 9$

(iv) $\mathbf{r}.\begin{pmatrix} 4 \\ 2 \\ 3 \end{pmatrix} = 10, 4x + 2y + 3z = 10$ (v) $\mathbf{r}.\begin{pmatrix} 3 \\ 9 \\ 5 \end{pmatrix} = -4, 3x + 9y + 5z = -4$

(vi) $\mathbf{r}.\begin{pmatrix} 2 \\ 1 \\ 1 \end{pmatrix} = 5, 2x + y + z = 5$ (vii) $\mathbf{r}.\begin{pmatrix} 2 \\ 1 \\ 0 \end{pmatrix} = 1, 2x + y = 1$.
5 (i) $(2, 0, 1)$ (ii) $(-1, 4, -2)$.   **6** (i) 5/3 (ii) 4/7 (iii) 7/5.

Exercise 12.9 (p. 195)

1   (i) $x+y+z=5$, $\mathbf{r}.\begin{pmatrix}1\\1\\1\end{pmatrix}=5$ (ii) $2x+5y+3z=-8$, $\mathbf{r}.\begin{pmatrix}2\\5\\3\end{pmatrix}=-8$

(iii) $x-2y=3$, $\mathbf{r}.\begin{pmatrix}1\\-2\\0\end{pmatrix}=3$.   2   (i) $\mathbf{r}=s\mathbf{j}+t\mathbf{k}$ (ii) $\mathbf{r}=s\mathbf{j}+t(\mathbf{i}-\mathbf{k})$

(iii) $\mathbf{r}=3\mathbf{k}+s(\mathbf{i}+2\mathbf{j})+t(\mathbf{j}+\mathbf{k})$ (iv) $\mathbf{r}=-4\mathbf{j}+s\mathbf{i}+t(3\mathbf{j}+\mathbf{k})$

(v) $\mathbf{r}=-3\mathbf{i}+s(2\mathbf{i}+\mathbf{k})+t(\mathbf{j}+\mathbf{k})$.   3 $\mathbf{r}.\begin{pmatrix}2\\6\\5\end{pmatrix}=8$, $2x+6y+5z=8$.

4   $\mathbf{r}=\mathbf{k}+s\mathbf{a}+t\mathbf{b}$, $\mathbf{r}.\mathbf{c}=\mathbf{k}.\mathbf{c}$, for all s, t.

Exercise 12.11 (p. 199)

1   (i) $6/\sqrt{26}$, opposite side   (ii) $2/\sqrt{29}$, same side.

2   (i) $\mathbf{r}=\begin{pmatrix}1\\2\\-3\end{pmatrix}+t\begin{pmatrix}3\\-1\\2\end{pmatrix}$, $\dfrac{x-1}{3}=\dfrac{y-2}{-1}=\dfrac{z+3}{2}$, $70{\cdot}6°$

(ii) $\mathbf{r}=\begin{pmatrix}5\\-3\\2\end{pmatrix}+t\begin{pmatrix}7\\-6\\7\end{pmatrix}$, $\dfrac{x-5}{7}=\dfrac{y+3}{-6}=\dfrac{z-2}{7}$, $33{\cdot}1°$.

3   (i) $27{\cdot}2°$, $\mathbf{r}=\begin{pmatrix}-2\\0\\8\end{pmatrix}+t\begin{pmatrix}3\\2\\5\end{pmatrix}$ (ii) $64{\cdot}8°$, $\mathbf{r}=\begin{pmatrix}-1\\1\\0\end{pmatrix}+t\begin{pmatrix}27\\-7\\23\end{pmatrix}$.

4   $4x=2y+3z+5$.   5 $\dfrac{x}{2}=\dfrac{y}{2}=z$, $4x-3y-2z=0$, $\frac{1}{2}\pi$.

Miscellaneous Exercise 12 (p. 200)

1   $\dfrac{2\pi}{3}$.   2 $64{\cdot}6°$, $198{\cdot}7$.   4 $p=-2$, $q=2$.   5 $1, 1, \frac{1}{2}, \dfrac{\sqrt{7}}{3}, \dfrac{2}{\sqrt{7}}$.

6   $\dfrac{1}{11}(a+6b+4c)$.   7 $\frac{1}{2}(a+b)$, $\frac{1}{3}(b+2c)$, $1:3$.   9 $\mathbf{r}.\begin{pmatrix}2/3\\2/3\\1/3\end{pmatrix}=3$.   10 $\begin{pmatrix}9\\4\\7\end{pmatrix}$.

11   $\mathbf{i}+7\mathbf{j}$.   12   (ii) $(1,-1,2)$, $70{\cdot}5°$.   13 $\frac{1}{17}(-6,-4,4)$, $\frac{1}{17}(40,-13,47)$.

14   $-2\mathbf{i}+2\mathbf{j}+3\mathbf{k}$.   15 $\sqrt{6}$, $\sqrt{2}$, $\frac{\pi}{6}$.   16   (a) -3 . (b) $4/3$ (c) 10, -0.4.

17   $\sqrt{2}$, $-\sqrt{2}$.   18 6, $(\frac{2}{3},-\frac{2}{3},\frac{1}{3})$.   19 $\frac{3}{7}(6\mathbf{i}+3\mathbf{j}+2\mathbf{k})$.

20   $\begin{pmatrix}-1\\-3\\-3\end{pmatrix}+t\begin{pmatrix}2\\1\\3\end{pmatrix}=\mathbf{r}$, $(1,-2,0)$, $\sqrt{5}$.   21 $\mathbf{r}=t\begin{pmatrix}5\\-1\\-3\end{pmatrix}$.   22   (i) $(1,-7,-6)$

(ii) $(-\frac{1}{3},\frac{4}{3},\frac{10}{3})$.   23 $x-14=y-5=4-2z$, $2/3$, $x=2y+2z$.   24 $\mathbf{r}.(\mathbf{i}-\mathbf{j})=1$.

25   $\dfrac{1}{\sqrt{2}}(\mathbf{i}-\mathbf{j})$.   26 $(-1-k,k,1+k)$, $-2/3$.

27   $2x-3y+6z=70$.   28 $(0,-3,0)$, $(3,-1,7)$.

29   $(3\mathbf{i}+5\mathbf{j}+4\mathbf{k})\dfrac{1}{5\sqrt{2}}$, $3x+5y+4z=30$, $3\sqrt{2}$.

30   (i) line, (ii) plane, (iii) line; line (iii) lies in plane (ii), line (i) is at right angles to plane (ii) and meets it and line (iii) at $(2,1,3)$.   32 $\dfrac{\pi}{6}$.   33 $\begin{pmatrix}1\\2\\1\end{pmatrix}$.

34 $x - 3y + 4z = 2$, $\dfrac{1}{\sqrt{26}}(1, -3, 4)$, $\dfrac{1}{\sqrt{26}}(\mathbf{i} - 3\mathbf{j} + 4\mathbf{k})$, $\dfrac{2}{\sqrt{26}}$, $\dfrac{2}{\sqrt{26}}$.

35 $(1, 2, -3)$, $6x = 3y - 2z = 18$, $\frac{38}{7}$. **36** (i) $-\mathbf{i} + \mathbf{j} + 3\mathbf{k}$, (ii) $3\mathbf{j} - \mathbf{k}$, (iii) $55 \cdot 1°$

(iv) $34 \cdot 9°$. **37** $\lambda = \mu = \frac{2}{3}$, $19 \cdot 5°$. **38** $\begin{pmatrix} -2 \\ 1 \\ 2 \end{pmatrix}$, $2x = y + 2z + 2$, $\dfrac{\sqrt{74}}{11}$, $\frac{2}{3}$.

39 (i) $x = 3 + t$, $y = -1 - t$, $z = 2t$ (ii) $(2, 0, -2)$ (iii) $(1, 1, -4)$

(iv) $(\frac{7}{3}, \frac{1}{3}, -2)$ (v) $\mathbf{r} = \begin{pmatrix} 3 \\ 0 \\ -1 \end{pmatrix} + t \begin{pmatrix} 2 \\ -1 \\ 3 \end{pmatrix}$.

40 $\lambda = -1$, $\mu = 2$, $\mathbf{r} \cdot \begin{pmatrix} -1 \\ 2 \\ 1 \end{pmatrix} = 2$, $\mathbf{r} = \begin{pmatrix} 1 \\ 0 \\ -1 \end{pmatrix} + t \begin{pmatrix} -1 \\ 2 \\ 1 \end{pmatrix}$, $\dfrac{4}{\sqrt{6}}$.

42 $\dfrac{\pi}{6}$, $\mathbf{r} = \begin{pmatrix} 1 \\ 0 \\ -1 \end{pmatrix} + t \begin{pmatrix} 1 \\ 1 \\ 1 \end{pmatrix}$, $(2, 1, 0)$. **43** S is line OA, where $\overrightarrow{OA} = \mathbf{a}$,

(i) $\mathbf{n}$ is normal to Z (ii) O is not in Z, $t = \dfrac{k}{\mathbf{a} \cdot \mathbf{n}}$ if $\mathbf{a} \cdot \mathbf{n} \neq 0$, S is parallel to Z if $\mathbf{a} \cdot \mathbf{n} = 0$.

45 (c) $\dfrac{1}{\sqrt{10}}$ (d) 300. **46** (i) $\dfrac{\pi}{6}$, $\begin{pmatrix} 2 + q - 2p \\ -3 + p \\ 5 + q - p \end{pmatrix}$, $p = 1$, $q = -2$.

47 $\mathbf{r} = \begin{pmatrix} -3 \\ 5 \\ 0 \end{pmatrix} + s \begin{pmatrix} 1 \\ -1 \\ -1 \end{pmatrix} + t \begin{pmatrix} 2 \\ 1 \\ -1 \end{pmatrix}$.

Exercise 13.1 (p. 210)

1 (i) $a < b$ (ii) $c > b$ (iii) $x \not> y$ (iv) $y \leqslant z$ (v) $-1 < x < 5$. **2** (i) $x < 2$, 0
(ii) $y > 4$, 5 (iii) $-4 < z < 2$, 1 (iv) $w < 5$ or $w > 9$, 4. **3** The subset of real
numbers: (i) less than 4 (ii) less than 7 (iii) less than or equal to -3 (iv) greater than
or equal to -2 and less than 3 (v) either less than or equal to -2 or greater than 2.
4 (i) $\{x : x > -2\}$ (ii) $\{x : x \geqslant 3\}$ (iii) $\{x : x < \frac{3}{2}\}$ (iv) $\{x : x > \frac{1}{20}\}$
(v) $\{x : -2 \leqslant x \leqslant 1\}$. **5** (i) $\{x : 5 < x < 7\}$ (ii) $\{x : -2 \leqslant x \leqslant -1\}$
(iii) $\{x : \frac{9}{2} < x \leqslant 6\}$ (iv) $\{x : -1 < x < 1\}$.

Exercise 13.2 (p. 211)

1 (i) $-3 < x < 3$ (ii) $-1 < x < 7$ (iii) $-2 \leqslant x \leqslant \frac{8}{3}$ (iv) $x \leqslant -5$ or $x \geqslant 5$
(v) $x \leqslant -5$ or $x \geqslant 1$. **2** (i) $\{x : |x| < 2\}$ (ii) $\{x : |x| \geqslant 7\}$ (iii) $\{x : |x - 1| < 2\}$
(iv) $\{x : |x + 1| \geqslant 3\}$ (v) $\{x : |x| < 5\}$ (vi) $\{x : |x - 6| > 2\}$.

Exercise 13.3 (p. 213)

1 (i) $\{x : x < 0\} \cup \{x : x > \frac{1}{5}\}$ (ii) $\{x : x \geqslant 6\}$ (iii) $\{x : -\frac{1}{2} < x < 0\}$
(iv) $\{x : x < 0\} \cup \{x : x \geqslant 1\}$ (v) $\{x : -1 < x < 0\}$ (vi) $\{x : 0 < x \leqslant \frac{1}{2}\}$
(vii) $\{x : x < 0\} \cup \{x : x > \frac{1}{2}\}$. **2** (i) $\{x : -3 < x < 2\}$ (ii) $\{x : 1 < x \leqslant \frac{9}{7}\}$
(iii) $\{x : -5 < x < -2\}$ (iv) $\{x : \frac{1}{2} < x \leqslant 1\}$. **3** $\{x : |x| > 3\}$.
4 $\{x : |x| < 2\}$. **5** $\{x : x < -2\} \cup \{x : x > \frac{2}{3}\}$.

Exercise 13.4 (p. 216)

1 (i) $\{x : -2 < x < 1\} \cup \{x : x > 3\}$ (ii) $\{x : x < -2\} \cup \{x : 1 < x < 3\}$
(iii) $\{x : -4 \leqslant x \leqslant 3\}$ (iv) $\mathbb{R}$. **2** $\{x : 2 < x < 3\} \cup \{x : x > 9\}$.

3 $\{p: -3 < p < 0\}$.   **4** $\{x: -2 < x < \frac{1}{2}\}$ **5** $\{x: -4 < x < \frac{1}{2}\} \cup \{x: x > 5\}$.
6 $\{x: x < -3\} \cup \{x: -1 < x < 2\} \cup \{x: x > 4\}$.

Miscellaneous Exercise 13 (p. 218)

1 (i) $\{x: x < \frac{11}{5}\}$ (ii) $\mathbb{R}^+$ (iii) $\{x: x < 4\}$ (iv) $\mathbb{R}^+$ (v) $\{x: 0 < x < \frac{4}{5}\}$
(vi) $\{x: x < -3\} \cup \{x: x > 5\}$ (vii) $\{x: -2 < x < 3\}$ (viii) $\{x: x > \frac{4}{3}\} \cup \{x: x \leqslant 1\}$
(ix) $\{x: x > \frac{4}{3}\} \cup \{x: x < 1\}$.   **2** (i) $\{x: x < -1\} \cup \{x: x > 5\}$
(ii) $\{x: -5 \leqslant x \leqslant 1\}$ (iii) $\{x: x < 0\}$.   **3** $\{x: x < 1\} \cup \{x: x > 3\}$.
4 $\{x: -2\sqrt{2} < x < 2\sqrt{2}\}$.   **5** $\{x: x < -1\} \cup \{x: x > 2\}$
6 $\{x: -2 < x < -1\} \cup \{x: x > 2\}$.   **7** $\{x: \frac{17}{6} < x < \frac{13}{4}\}$.   **8** $\{x: \frac{5}{3} < x < 3\}$.
9 $\mathbb{R}^+$.   **10** (i) $x^2 - 1 < 0$ (ii) $(x - a)(x - b) < 0$ (iii) $x^2 > 4x$.
11 (a) $\{x: x \geqslant 6\}$ (b) $\{x: x < 1\} \cup \{x: x \geqslant 6\}$.   **12** $-\frac{1}{2}, 3$.
13 $a = 5 - c, \{c: \frac{1}{2} < c < 4\frac{1}{2}\}$.   **15** $\{x: -1 < x < 3\}$.
16 $\{\theta: -\frac{5}{6}\pi < \theta < -\frac{\pi}{6}\}$.   **17** $\{x: |x| < 4\}$.
18 (a) $\{x: -3 < x < -1\} \cup \{x: 1 < x < 2\}$ (b) $\{x: |x| < \sqrt{(\frac{3}{2})}\}$.
19 $\{\theta: -\frac{\pi}{4} < \theta < \frac{\pi}{4}\}$.   **20** $\{x: -1 < x < -\frac{1}{2}\}$.
21 $y = x - 4$, (a) $\{2\}$ (b) $\{x: x < 0\}$ (c) $\{x: x < 3\} \cup \{x: x > 4\}$.

Exercise 14.1 (p. 221)

1 1·4.

Exercise 14.2 (p. 222)

1 1·379.   **2** 0·32.   **3** (a) 1·828 (b) $2\sqrt{2} - 1$, error is 0·0004 to 1 S.F.
4 4·56, 0·44 to 2 D.P.

Exercise 14.3 (p. 224)

1 Answer between 1·3769 and 1·3789.   **2** 1·38.   **3** 2·646, -2·646, 13 steps
needed.   **4** 12 iterations.   **5** 9·9.   **6** 2·72, 20 calculations, 2·72, 10 calculations.
7 f(1·286) $= -0$·873, f(1·392) $= -0$·303, f(1·427) $= -0$·094.

Exercise 14.4 (p. 226)

1 1·44203, 1·44224, 2 steps.   **2** (i) -1·784 (ii) 0·1835 (iii) 1·236.
3 (ii) $c = 1$·25 (iii) $c = 1$·4156 (iv) $c = 1$·3379.
5 no root between 2 and 3, -4·164, wrong.

Exercise 14.5 (p. 229)

1 (i) 1·54, 1·39 (ii) 0·5, 0·33 (iii) -3·83, -3·828 (iv) -1·5, -1·28
(v) 2·925, 2·924.   **2** 1·532, -1·879, 0·347.   **3** 0·8514.   **4** 2·03054.
5 -2·61803, -0·38197.

Miscellaneous Exercise 14 (p. 229)

1 $\alpha \approx -0$·727, $\beta \approx 0$·8, $f'(0) = 0$ gives division by zero, start $\gamma = 4, \gamma \approx 3$·875.
2 f(0) $= 1$, f(1) $= -0$·45, f(0·5) $= 0$·37, f(0·75) $= -0$·01, f(0·625) $= 0$·18,
f(0·6875) $= 0$·08, so the answer is 0·7 to 1 D.P.   **3** $x_{n+1} = 1·5x_n - 0·1x_n^3$.   **4** 0·453.
5 (i) 0, 3, 2·05, 2·13 (ii) 0, 1, -0·72, 1·51, 2·12.   **6** 3·73.   **7** 0·5.   **8** 0·9051.

9 (i) 2·236 (ii) 3, 2·33, 2·238, 2·236.   **10** $p_{n+1} = \frac{1}{3}\left(2p_n + \frac{k}{p_n^2}\right)$.

11 $p_{m+1} = \frac{1}{n}\left((n-1)p_m + \frac{k}{p_m^{n-1}}\right)$.   **12** 1·31, α is the root, approximately 1·166.
13 3, 1·43, larger.   **14** 1·52.

Exercise 15.1 (p. 235)

1 (i) $7+10i$ (ii) $7-7i$ (iii) $7-15i$ (iv) $1-3i$ (v) $11+4i$ (vi) $-2i$.
2 (i) $2+4i$ (ii) $28+12i$ (iii) $-7+12i$. **3** (i) $5+14i$ (ii) $-25i$ (iii) $26-7i$
(iv) 2 (v) $-5+12i$ (vi) $-15+6i$ (vii) $19+17i$ (viii) $4-22i$ (ix) $6+27i$ (x) 1.
4 (i) $\dfrac{8}{13}-\dfrac{i}{13}$ (ii) $\dfrac{27}{25}+\dfrac{11}{25}i$ (iii) $\dfrac{-20}{29}+\dfrac{8}{29}i$ (iv) $\tfrac12+\tfrac12 i$ (v) $\dfrac{9}{41}+\dfrac{40}{41}i$
(vi) $\dfrac{78}{676}+\dfrac{52}{676}i$ (vii) $\dfrac{72}{289}+\dfrac{154}{289}i$. **5(a)** (i) $(3,2)+(5,1)=(8,3)$
(ii) $(4,-2)+(0,6)=(4,4)$ (iii) $(3,4)-(8,-2)=(-5,6)$
(iv) $(-4,-2)-(7,0)=(-11,-2)$ (v) $3(2,-5)=(6,-15)$
(vi) $2(0,3)-3(1,1)=(-3,3)$ (vii) $(5,2)(3,-4)=(23,-14)$
(viii) $\dfrac{(1,-2)}{(2,-1)}=\left(\dfrac{4}{5},\dfrac{-3}{5}\right)$ **(b)** (i) $(0,7)$ (ii) $(-7,11)$ (iii) $(-3,5)$
(iv) $(-13,21)$ (v) $(-2,1)$ (vi) $(-1,1)$ (vii) $(2,5)$ (viii) $(2\cdot3,-0\cdot9)$
(ix) $(-4,72)$ (x) $(a+c,b+d)$ (xi) $(ac-bd,ad+bc)$ (xii) $\left(\dfrac{ac+bd}{c^2+d^2},\dfrac{-ad+bc}{c^2+d^2}\right)$.

6 $-1\cdot2+2\cdot4i$. **7** $x=1, y=-\tfrac12$. **8** $x=\dfrac{2}{13}, y=\dfrac{3}{13}$. **9** i.

Exercise 15.2 (p. 238)

1 (i) $-1, -3$ (ii) $1,\tfrac52$ (iii) $3+\sqrt3, 3-\sqrt3$ (iv) -3
(v) $\dfrac{-5+\sqrt{37}}{6}, \dfrac{-5-\sqrt{37}}{6}$ (vi) $\dfrac{7+\sqrt{17}}{8}, \dfrac{7-\sqrt{17}}{8}$. **2** (i) $2+i, 2-i$
(ii) $3+i, 3-i$ (iii) $4+i, 4-i$ (iv) $-6-2i, -6+2i$ (v) $-\dfrac16+\dfrac{\sqrt{11}}{6}i, -\dfrac16-\dfrac{\sqrt{11}}{6}i$
(vi) $\dfrac12+\dfrac{\sqrt3}{2}i, \dfrac12-\dfrac{\sqrt3}{2}i$. **3** (i) $(x-1)(3x-1)$ (ii) $(x+2)(2x+1)$
(iii) $(x+1)(x+2)x$ (iv) $(x-2)(x+2)x$. **4** (i) $2x^2+3x+2$ (ii) $x^2+8x+17$
(iii) $(x-4)(x-5)$ (iv) $3x^2-x+6$ (v) $(x-1)(x^2+1)$ (vi) $(x^2+5)(x^2+2)$
(vii) $x^2(x-3)(x+2)$ (viii) $(x-2)(x+2)^2$. **6** (i) $-i$ (ii) 1 (iii) i (iv) $-i$
(v) -1 (vi) i. **7** (i) -4 (ii) -5 (iii) -49 (iv) -2. **8** (i) $i\sqrt5, -i\sqrt5$
(ii) $5i, -5i$ (iii) $2i\sqrt2, -2i\sqrt2$ (iv) $3i\sqrt3, -3i\sqrt3$.
9 (i) $\dfrac52+\dfrac{\sqrt7}{2}i, \dfrac52-\dfrac{\sqrt7}{2}i, 5, 8$ (ii) $\dfrac{-3}{4}+\dfrac{\sqrt{23}}{4}i, \dfrac{-3}{4}-\dfrac{\sqrt{23}}{4}i, \dfrac{-3}{2}, 2$
(iii) $\dfrac16+\dfrac{\sqrt{59}}{6}i, \dfrac16-\dfrac{\sqrt{59}}{6}i, \dfrac13, \dfrac53$.

Exercise 15.3A (p. 240)

2 (i), (ii) & (iii) rotation $180°$ about O (iv), (v) & (vi) reflection in $\mathbb{R}$-axis
(vii), (viii) & (ix) rotation $90°$ about O (x), (xi) & (xii) rotation $270°$ about O.
3 $A=d, B=b, C=a, D=c$. **4** (i) $5, 0\cdot64$ (ii) $2\sqrt2, \dfrac{\pi}{4}$ (iii) $13, 1\cdot18$
(iv) $10, 2\cdot21$ (v) $\sqrt{10}, 3\cdot46$. **5** $2-i, -2+i$.

Exercise 15.3B (p. 242)

3 rotation $90°$ about O. **4** $\dfrac{\pi}{2}, a$. **5** rotation $-90°$ about O.

6 $5, \sqrt2, 5\sqrt2, 0\cdot64, 0\cdot79, 1\cdot43$, rotation $\dfrac{\pi}{4}$ about O, enlargement S.F. $\sqrt2$.

Exercise 15.4 (p. 246)

1   (i) $\left(\sqrt{2},\dfrac{\pi}{4}\right)$ (ii) $(5, 0\cdot64)$ (iii) $(13, -1\cdot18)$ (iv) $(13, 2\cdot75)$ (v) $\left(4\sqrt{2}, -\dfrac{\pi}{4}\right)$

(vi) $(10, -2\cdot21)$ (vii) $\left(2,\dfrac{\pi}{6}\right)$ (viii) $\left(2,\dfrac{2\pi}{3}\right)$ (ix) $\left(4, -\dfrac{\pi}{6}\right)$ (x) $(25, 1\cdot29)$

(xi) $(5, -0\cdot93)$.   2   (i) $\sqrt{2}+i\sqrt{2}$ (ii) $2\sqrt{3}+2i$ (iii) $-i$ (iv) $4-4i\sqrt{3}$

(v) $\dfrac{-3\sqrt{3}}{2}-\dfrac{3}{2}i$ (vi) $12i$ (vii) $\dfrac{-1}{\sqrt{2}}+\dfrac{1}{\sqrt{2}}i$ (viii) $1-i$ (ix) $1\cdot93+0\cdot52i$.

3   (i) $-5+10i$ (ii) $-14+34i$ (iii) $-2+14i$ (iv) $-2+6i$ (v) $68-67i$

(vi) $11-7i$.   4   (a) (i) $\left(6,\dfrac{\pi}{2}\right)(\tfrac{1}{3}, 0)$ (ii) $\left(10,\dfrac{\pi}{2}\right)\left(\dfrac{5}{2},\dfrac{\pi}{6}\right)$ (iii) $\left(5,\dfrac{7\pi}{12}\right)\left(\dfrac{1}{5},\dfrac{5\pi}{12}\right)$

(iv) $\left(7,\dfrac{5\pi}{12}\right)\left(\dfrac{1}{7},\dfrac{-11\pi}{12}\right)$ (v) $\left(6,\dfrac{5\pi}{12}\right)\left(\dfrac{2}{3},\dfrac{-\pi}{12}\right)$ (vi) $(2,\pi)\left(2,\dfrac{-5\pi}{7}\right)$

5   (i) $\left(2,\dfrac{\pi}{2}\right)$ (ii) $\left(4,\dfrac{\pi}{2}\right)$ (iii) $\left(1,\dfrac{2\pi}{3}\right)$ (iv) $\left(\dfrac{1}{\sqrt{2}},\dfrac{\pi}{2}\right)$ (v) $\left(1,\dfrac{5\pi}{12}\right)$

(vi) $\left(1,\dfrac{\pi}{2}\right)$ (vii) $\left(\dfrac{1}{\sqrt{2}},\dfrac{-11\pi}{12}\right)$ (viii) $\left(1,\dfrac{-\pi}{2}\right)$.

6   $\dfrac{z_1}{z_2}=\tfrac{1}{2}-\tfrac{1}{2}i,\dfrac{z_2}{z_1}=1+i,\ z_1-z_2=1-2i,\ z_2-z_1=-1+2i,\ z_1+z_2=3+4i,$

$z_1z_2=-1+7i$.   8 $\dfrac{1}{2}\left(\cos\dfrac{-\pi}{3}+i\sin\dfrac{-\pi}{3}\right)$.

9   (i) $1,\dfrac{\pi}{3}$ (ii) $|z_1z_2|=|z_1||z_2|,\ \arg(z_1z_2)=\arg(z_1)+\arg(z_2)$

(iii) $a=0\cdot63, b=3\cdot1$.   10 $\sqrt{50}, 5, -2\cdot4$.   11 $-\cos\theta$.   12   (i) $\left(4,\dfrac{\pi}{3}\right)$

(ii) $\left(2, -\dfrac{\pi}{6}\right)$ (iii) $(64, \pi)$ (iv) $\left(32,\dfrac{-5\pi}{6}\right)$.   13 $-22-4i, 34, 680$.

Exercise 15.5 (p. 249)

1   $\overrightarrow{OB}=w+z,\ \sqrt{5}, 5, \sqrt{50}$.   2 $z_1=1+2i,\ z_2=2+4i,\ z_3=3+6i$.

Exercise 15.6A (p. 250)

1   (i) $2-3i$ (ii) $3+4i$ (iii) 4 (iv) $-3i$ (v) $\left(2,\dfrac{-\pi}{4}\right)$ (vi) $\left(3,\dfrac{3\pi}{4}\right)$.

Exercise 15.6B (p. 252)

1   (i) $3-i, 1$.   2 $x=1+2i, 1-2i, 1+i\sqrt{23}, 1-i\sqrt{23}$.   3 $2-i, -4$.

4   $2-3i, 2$.   5   (i) $x=2, y=1, \dfrac{1}{\sqrt{2}}+\dfrac{i}{\sqrt{2}}, \dfrac{-1}{\sqrt{2}}-\dfrac{i}{\sqrt{2}}$ (ii) $1-i, 2$.

6   $a=2, b=5$.   7   (i) $1+i, 3, -1$ (ii) $\dfrac{-1}{2}+\dfrac{\sqrt{3}}{2}i, \dfrac{-1}{2}-\dfrac{\sqrt{3}}{2}i$.

Exercise 15.7 (p. 256)

1   5.   3   (i) mediator of A and B (ii) half line from A parallel to $1+i$

$\{(x, y): x+5y+9=0\}, \{(x, y): y-x=1, x\geqslant 2\}$.   4 $|z-2-i|=\sqrt{5}$.   6   (i) $2\sqrt{3},\dfrac{\pi}{6}$

(ii) $y+\sqrt{3}x=2\sqrt{3}, y\geqslant\sqrt{3}$.

Miscellaneous Exercise 15 (p. 256)

1 $-\frac{1}{2}+\frac{7}{2}i.$ **2** $\frac{4}{5}-\frac{3}{5}i.$ **3** $z=-1+2i, w=1-i.$ **4** $32+47i, 32-47i, 61, 53.$

5 $1+i, 2.$ **6** $2-i, -2+i.$ **7** $x^2-2r\cos\theta x+r^2=0, \dfrac{-p}{\sqrt{q}}.$

8 $p=-5-4i, q=1+7i, a=-3, b=-1.$

9 $-\frac{1}{2}, i, -i, 2+i, 2-i, p=1, q=4, -1+i, -1-i, 1+i, 1-i.$

10 (i) $4x^2-9x+18=0$ (ii) (a) $k>-\frac{5}{4}$ (b) $k=-\frac{5}{4}$ (c) $-\frac{5}{3}<k<-\frac{5}{4}.$

11 $x^2+2x+9=0.$ **12** $\left(\sqrt{2}, \dfrac{-\pi}{12}\right).$ **13** (i) (a) $\left(2, \dfrac{2\pi}{3}\right)$ (b) $\left(1, \dfrac{\pi}{2}\right)$

(ii) $a=-3, b=4$ or $a=3, b=-4$ (iii) $\alpha-\beta+\gamma.$ **14** (i) $-1-i, \dfrac{3\pi}{4}$

(ii) $2-i, 2, k=-10.$ **15** $z_1=\left(1, \dfrac{2\pi}{3}\right) z_2=\left(1, \dfrac{-2\pi}{3}\right) z_3=(1, 0).$ **16** $\dfrac{\pi}{4}, -\dfrac{\pi}{4}.$

17 $(\alpha_2-\alpha_1)+(\beta_2-\beta_1)i, k(\cos\theta+i\sin\theta), \overrightarrow{AB}=\sqrt{3}-i, \overrightarrow{AC}=2\sqrt{3}+2i, z_3=\left(2, \dfrac{\pi}{3}\right),$

$D=6\sqrt{3}, 4\sqrt{3}.$ **18** $\left(2, \dfrac{\pi}{3}\right)\left(2, -\dfrac{\pi}{3}\right), z^2-2z+4=0, a=-2, b=12.$

19 $(2\cos 2\theta, 5\theta).$ **21** $\left(2, \dfrac{\pi}{6}\right), \left(2, \dfrac{-\pi}{6}\right), \dfrac{1}{2}+\dfrac{\sqrt{3}}{2}i.$

23 (a) $(10, 90°), (5, 126\cdot9°), (2, -36\cdot9°)$ (b) $x-y=1, x^2+y^2=1.$

24 (i) $2(1+\sqrt{2})$ (ii) $1+(2+\sqrt{3})i.$ **25** (i) U lies on a circle centre A radius 3

(ii) UAV is a right angle

(iii) WUA is a straight line with $WU=UA, |AV|=\sqrt{18}.$ **26** (i) $3\cdot54-2\cdot55i$

(ii) $3+\sqrt{3}i, 3-\sqrt{3}i.$ **27** $a=4, b=-5, 5.$ **28** $1+2i, \sqrt{50}, \alpha=-2, \beta=-1.$

29 $\frac{1}{2}(\sqrt{3}+3i), \frac{1}{2}(\sqrt{3}-3i), \frac{1}{2}(\sqrt{3}-6+3i), \frac{1}{2}(\sqrt{3}-6-3i),$

$z^2+(6-\sqrt{3})z+12-3\sqrt{3}=0.$ **30** $\dfrac{4}{3}+\dfrac{2\sqrt{2}}{3}i, \dfrac{2}{3}+\dfrac{4\sqrt{2}}{3}i.$

31 $\cot\frac{1}{2}\theta.$ **32** (i) $a=\dfrac{63}{25}, b=\dfrac{16}{25}, r=\dfrac{13}{5}, \cos\theta=\dfrac{63}{65}, \sin\theta=\dfrac{16}{65}$ (ii) $\dfrac{z_2}{z_1}=\dfrac{w_2}{w_1}.$

33 $k=2, 56°, -124°.$ **34** (a) $\dfrac{1}{13}+\dfrac{5}{13}i, 1\cdot37, 2\cdot75, \dfrac{2}{13}$ (b) $|z|^2:1.$

35 $y^2+(x+5)^2=9.$ **36** $4\sin^2\theta, \dfrac{1}{4\sin^2\theta}, -\theta, y=-\frac{1}{2}.$

37 (i) $1+\sqrt{5}i, 1-\sqrt{5}i$ (ii) $1+i.$ **38** (i) (a) $p=\dfrac{7}{5}, q=\dfrac{-4}{5}$

(b) $p=2-i, q=2+i.$ **39** $\frac{5}{2}, -1\frac{1}{2}+2i.$

40 (i) $x=1, y=2$ or $x=-1, y=-2.$

41 $a=\sqrt{2}, b=1$ or $a=-\sqrt{2}, b=-1.$

42 $z^2-2z+4, \alpha=\left(2, \dfrac{-\pi}{3}\right), \alpha^2=\left(4, \dfrac{-2\pi}{3}\right), \alpha^3=(8, \pi), \alpha, \alpha^*, -2, 3+\sqrt{3}i, \left(1, \dfrac{\pi}{6}\right),$

$\sqrt{3}-2+3i.$ **43** $8, 0\cdot8.$ **44** (b) $|z-2|=2$ (c) $-1+\sqrt{3}i, -1-\sqrt{3}i$

(d) $\left(2, \dfrac{11\pi}{12}\right)\left(2, \dfrac{-5\pi}{12}\right).$

Index

Pure Mathematics for Advanced Level is available either as a single volume or in two parts.
  Part A: Chapters 1–15
  Part B: Chapters 16–28
  Complete Volume: Chapters 1–28
Page numbers in bold indicate references to Part A: page numbers in italic indicate references to Part B.